D1548479

THE PROBLEM OF LOSS AND MOURNING: PSYCHOANALYTIC PERSPECTIVES

THE PROBLEM OF LOSS AND MOURNING:
Psychoanalytic Perspectives

DAVID R. DIETRICH, PH.D.
Department of Fsychiatry
Wayne State University School of Medicine

and

PETER C. SHABAD, PH.D.
Institute of Psychiatry
Northwestern University Medical School

Editors

INTERNATIONAL UNIVERSITIES PRESS, INC.
Madison   Connecticut

Library of Congress Cataloging in Publication Data

The Problem of loss and mourning: psychoanalytic perspectives / David R. Dietrich and Peter Shabad, editors.
     p.   cm.
    Includes bibliographies and indexes.
    ISBN 0-8236-4349-2
    1. Loss (Psychology) 2. Bereavement—Psychological aspects.
3. Grief—Psychological aspects. 4. Psychoanalysis. [1. Attitude
to Death. 2. Grief.] I. Dietrich, David R. II. Shabad, Peter.
    [DNLM: BF 575.G7 P962]
    RC455.4.L67P76   1989
    155.9′3—dc20
    DNLM/DLC
    for Library of Congress   89-2128
                                                CIP

Manufactured in the United States of America

To Nancy and Rachel

D.D.

Dedicated to the memory of Theodore Shabad

P.S.

Contents

Part V
LOSS, MOURNING, AND THE HOLOCAUST

EPILOGUE

Contributors

HENRY B. BILLER, PH.D.
Professor of Psychology, University of Rhode Island

MORTON CHETHIK, M.S.W.
Clinical Associate Professor of Child Psychoanalysis and
Director, Divorce Clinic, Department of Psychiatry,
University of Michigan Faculty
Michigan Psychoanalytic Institute

YAEL DANIELI, PH.D.
Co-Founder and Director, Group Project for Holocaust
Survivors and their Children, New York
Senior Representative to the United Nations Headquarters
of the World Federation for Mental Health

DAVID R. DIETRICH, PH.D.
Clinical Assistant Professor of Psychology in Psychiatry
(Adjunct), Wayne State University School of Medicine
Adjunct Professor and Psychotherapy Supervisor, University
of Detroit, Clinical Psychology Doctoral Program
Faculty, Supervisor, and Director of Clinical Research, De-
troit Psychiatric Institute
Associate Member, Michigan Psychoanalytic Society

ERNA FURMAN, B.A. HON.
  Assistant Clinical Professor, Department of Psychiatry, Case
    Western Reserve School of Medicine
  Faculty, The Cleveland Center for Research in Child Devel-
    opment and the Hanna Perkins Therapeutic Nursery
    School and Kindergarten
  Instructor, Cleveland Psychoanalytic Institute

ROBERT A. FURMAN, M.D.
  Assistant Clinical Professor of Child Psychiatry, Case Western
    Reserve University School of Medicine
  Director, The Cleveland Center for Research in Child Devel-
    opment and the Hanna Perkins Therapeutic Nursery
    School and Kindergarten
  Training and Supervising Analyst in Adult and Child Anal-
    ysis, Cleveland Psychoanalytic Institute

JEROME GRUNES, M.D.
  Assistant Professor of Psychiatry, Northwestern University
    Medical School
  Senior Psychiatric Consultant, The Older Adult Program,
    Northwestern Memorial Hospital
  Member, Chicago Psychoanalytic Society

JUDITH S. KESTENBERG, M.D.
  Clinical Professor of Psychiatry, Division of Psychoanalytic
    Education, New York University
  Project Director, Jerome Riker International Study of Orga-
    nized Persecution of Children, Sands Point, New York
  Founder, Group for the Psychoanalytic Study of the Effect of
    the Holocaust on the Second Generation
  Training and Supervising Analyst in Adult and Child Anal-
    ysis, The Psychoanalytic Institute, New York University
    Medical Center

DAVID W. KRUEGER, M.D.
  Clinical Associate Professor of Psychiatry, Baylor College of
    Medicine

Director, Eating Disorders Treatment Program, Spring
Shadows Glen Hospital, Houston
Member, Houston–Galveston Psychoanalytic Society

NANCY MANN KULISH, PH.D.
Clinical Assistant Professor of Psychology in Psychiatry
(Adjunct), Wayne State University School of Medicine
Adjunct Professor and Psychotherapy Supervisor, University
of Detroit, Clinical Psychology Doctoral Program
Director of Psychology, Detroit Psychiatric Institute
Associate Member, Michigan Psychoanalytic Society

REBECCA LOHR, M.S.W.
Chief Social Worker and Lecturer, Child and Adolescent
Psychiatry, Department of Psychiatry, University of Mich-
igan

MARGARETE MITSCHERLICH-NIELSEN, M.D.
Training Analyst, Sigmund Freud Institute, Frankfurt
Member, German Psychoanalytic Association and Interna-
tional Psychoanalytic Association

WILLIAM G. NIEDERLAND, M.D.
Clinical Professor Emeritus of Psychiatry, State University of
New York, Downstate Medical Center
Consultant Psychiatrist, Hackensack Medical Center, Hack-
ensack, New Jersey
Member, New York Psychoanalytic Society
Member, Psychoanalytic Association of New York

FRED PINE, PH.D.
Professor of Psychiatry (Psychology), Albert Einstein College
of Medicine/Montefiore Medical Center
Visiting Professor, New York University Postdoctoral Pro-
gram in Psychoanalysis
Past President, Division of Psychoanalysis, American Psycho-
logical Association
Research Member, New York Psychoanalytic Society

GEORGE H. POLLOCK, M.D., PH.D.
  Professor of Psychiatry, Northwestern University Medical School
  President, Center for Psychosocial Studies, Chicago
  Past President, American Psychoanalytic Association
  Training and Supervising Analyst, Institute for Psychoanalysis, Chicago

MARGERY SALTER, PH.D.
  Clinical Psychologist, Associates for Adolescent and Family Psychotherapy

PETER C. SHABAD, PH.D.
  Postdoctoral Fellow, Institute of Psychiatry, Northwestern University Medical School
  Clinical Associate, University of Illinois–Chicago
  Associate Attending, Professional Staff, Michael Reese Hospital and Medical Center
  Instructor, Division of Psychology, Northwestern University Medical School

MILTON VIEDERMAN, M.D.
  Professor of Clinical Psychiatry, Cornell University Medical College
  Training and Supervising Analyst, Columbia University Psychoanalytic Center for Training and Research

VAMIK VOLKAN, M.D.
  Professor of Psychiatry, University of Virginia Medical Center
  Medical Director, Blue Ridge Hospital
  Training and Supervising Analyst, Washington Psychoanalytic Institute

WENDY WASSON, PH.D.
  Psychological Coordinator, The Older Adult Program, and Associate of Clinical Psychiatry, Northwestern Memorial Hospital

ROBERT ZUCKERMAN, PSY.D.
   Clinical Assistant Professor of Psychiatry, Eastern Virginia
      Medical School
   Clinical Associate Member, Virginia Psychoanalytic Society

Preface

This book is a carefully organized selection of contributions, all original, by many of the foremost psychoanalysts and innovative psychoanalytic clinicians and researchers working in the area of loss and mourning. One of our principal aims in this work is to bring together new, substantive contributions that shed light on some important and heretofore unexplored clinical, theoretical, and research areas. Another purpose of the work is to significantly extend and clarify some areas of our present psychoanalytic knowledge of loss, object loss, mourning processes, and their vicissitudes. There were some topics we would have liked to include, which for various reasons we could not. The present book is not a handbook nor is it intended to be a comprehensive volume or handbook. In addition, we hope this book will assist the analyst and therapist in their important daily clinical practice with and supervisory work of those patients who have suffered the inevitable pain of loss, grieving, and mourning.

A major advantage of assembling a wide range of original papers written from multiple perspectives (clinical, developmental, theoretical, conceptual, research) is that the final result, or gestalt, is more richly varied and more far-ranging than a work deriving from a single author.

We offer this book to the reader who is interested in the

fascinating, painful, and labyrinthine problems of loss and mourning: to the psychoanalyst, psychotherapist, supervisor, clinical researcher, and scholar—in the hope it will contribute to their important work.

David Dietrich
Huntington Woods, Michigan

Peter Shabad
Lincolnwood, Illinois

Acknowledgments

I wish to acknowledge and thank my patients, and those therapists I have supervised, who have taught me much about the complex and enduring effects of loss; the individuals who participated in my loss research; my friends, colleagues, and teachers at the Michigan Psychoanalytic Society and Institute for a clinically and intellectually rich atmosphere conducive to the exchange of ideas in psychoanalysis; and the members of my object loss seminar, which I taught from 1985 to 1986 at the Detroit Psychiatric Institute, whose questions helped clarify some of my ideas contained in this book.

My years at Washington University in doctoral training, at the Detroit Psychiatric Institute in postdoctoral training and as a faculty member and supervisor, and at the Michigan Psychoanalytic Institute in psychoanalytic training have stimulated my interest and work on loss, trauma, and mourning. Over the years, teachers, supervisors and others who have been particularly influential have included Marvin Margolis, M.D, Ph.D., Martin Mayman, Ph.D., Mayer Subrin, M.D., Saul Rosenzweig, Ph.D., Nathan Segel, M.D., Henry Krystal, M.D., Melvin Bornstein, M.D., and Channing Lipson, M.D. I am grateful for what they have taught me. I wish to thank those who read all or parts of my chapter, and appreciate their valuable suggestions for its improvement: Nathan Segel, M.D., Nancy Dietrich, Ph.D. candidate, and Peter Shabad, Ph.D.

Special thanks go out to each of the individual contributors to this book whose sustained interest, diligent work in the preparation of their chapters, and cooperation are genuinely appreciated. Their fine efforts have made this contribution possible. My heartfelt thanks.

I am especially grateful to my wife, Nancy, a psychologist, who functioned in many capacities as my additional "coeditor" in bringing this book to fruition. I deeply value her encouragement, support, and bearing with me during the mammoth amount of time, editing, and writing this project required. throughout the entire project. Thanks go to Mr. Martin Azarian, President of International Universities Press, and to Dr. Margaret Emery, Editor-In-Chief, for their valued interest and helpful suggestions.

Thanks to Penelope Morris for the fine and careful job of typing she has done with my manuscript.

I also wish to thank my coeditor and friend, Dr. Peter Shabad, for all of the hard work and energy he put into this project.

A large portion of thanks go to my mother, Marian Dietrich, and my father, Francis Dietrich, for helping foster in me an early interest in the study of and healing of people, as well as in the pleasures of learning.

And I thank my daughter, Rachel, who taught me much about early childhood, development, and love.

D.D.

I would first like to thank my coeditor, David Dietrich, for his thoughtful suggestions regarding my chapter. I am glad that our collaboration has borne fruit.

I would also like to thank George Feden for providing valued friendship and professional support when it was most needed.

I am grateful to my brother, Steven, for introducing me to and sharing with me his pleasures and interests throughout our life together; his guiding influence has been integral to the forming of my identity.

Thanks go to my mother, Leslie Shabad, for her nourishing love, wise words, and psychologically minded ethic she instilled in me from an early age.

I am also grateful to my father, Theodore Shabad, who, before his untimely death, helped guide me with generous affection and love, calm wisdom, and, above all, a profound example of how to deeply appreciate the precious moments of one's life.

I am greatly indebted to my wife, Cindy Shabad, for her thoughtful comments, invaluable moral support, and steadfast perseverance in bearing with me during the course of this labor.

And finally, I would like to acknowledge my sons, Alexander and Benjamin, who in their own endearing ways lend me needed humility and perspective about what really is important in life.

P.S.

I fell down
On the ship's deck and wept. Why? Why did they
Have to die! I couldn't understand. I asked
Unanswerable questions a child asks
When a parent dies—for nothing. Only slowly
Did I make myself believe—or hope—they
Might all be swept up in their fragments
Together
And made whole again
By some compassionate hand.
But my hand was too small
To do the gathering.
I have only known this feeling since
When I look out across the sea of death,
This pull inside against a littleness—myself—
Waiting for an upward gesture.

from *Gilgamesh*
HERBERT MASON

It is the image in the mind that links us to our
lost treasures; but it is the loss that shapes
the image, gathers the flowers, weaves the garland.

from *My Mother's House*
COLETTE

. . . memory nourishes the heart, and grief abates.

from *Letters*
MARCEL PROUST

Although we know that after such a loss the acute state
of mourning will subside, we also know we shall remain inconsolable
and will never find a substitute. No matter what may fill
the gap, even if it is filled completely, it nevertheless
remains something else. And actually this is how it
should be. It is the only way of perpetuating that love
which we do not want to relinquish.

from a 1929 letter to Dr. Binswanger
SIGMUND FREUD

Introduction: The Scope of the Problem of Loss and Mourning

DAVID R. DIETRICH, PH.D.
PETER C. SHABAD, PH.D.

Loss and its complex psychological sequelae assume a greater importance in psychoanalysis, psychotherapy, psychopathology, diagnostic evaluation, and for normal development than is generally realized. With Freud's discovery of psychoanalysis, however, for the first time it was possible to clinically and theoretically understand loss and its vicissitudes such as mourning, associated unconscious fantasies, conflict and defense, and various forms of restitution, in a systematic fashion within a radically new, powerful, and cohesive framework.

In recent years, within psychoanalysis, psychology, and psychiatry, there has been an upsurge of interest in various types of loss and mourning. This interest has been reflected in a growing literature on object loss and mourning processes and their variants, topics which are now often addressed not only from a childhood developmental perspective but as occurring throughout the life span as well. Many of the following areas have received significant scholarly attention: loss of a parent through death and divorce; loss and mourning as part of the aging process; other "loss" experiences, including the dynamic, interdependent mother–infant relationship and separation from the mother, and, increasingly, from the father; mourning and its complex relationship to mass death, including the Holocaust; loss and mourning of a spouse and loss and mourning associated with internal and external body parts. These are but a few of the areas which have received significant attention. Furthermore, as Rochlin (1965) observed: "Much attention has been paid to the pain which losses or failures produce but their obverse—the restitution and creativity they generated—has been accorded too little notice" (p. 127). This statement, we would add, is less true today than it was over twenty years ago, as many of the chapters in the present volume demonstrate so well.

E. Furman (1974) has noted that different psychoanalytic writers define loss explicitly or implicitly, and, consequently, view those phenomena which precipitate mourning in quite different terms. Certain authors, such as Solnit and Stark (1961) and Rochlin (1961), include and extend Freud's (1917) concepts of object loss and loss of abstractions in their definitions of loss, while others, such as Wolfenstein (1969) and Nagera (1970), exclude the concept of loss of abstractions in their definition. E. Furman (1974) offers an excellent summary discussion of what she and the Cleveland research group understood as constituting mourning as distinct from other reactions to a wide assortment of types of loss experience, including the loss of a love object; loss of body functions; loss of idealized aspects of the self; loss of abstractions such as an ideal; loss of inanimate objects, and so on. She views mourning as, and restricts it to, "a response solely to the loss of a love object through death" (p. 245). Wetmore (1963), on the other hand, broadened its definition: "Since I am talking not only of sadness, mourning, or the reaction to past loss, but of a unique emotional response experienced, perhaps, only in the psychoanalytic process, I have chosen, for the time being, the term 'effective grief'" (p. 97).

We feel that loss has limitless internal and external meanings. We mention but a few of them: loss by death, or temporary or permanent separation of mother, father, child, sibling, or friend; loss of bodily functions (such as the ability to walk, to use the senses); loss of psychological or mental functions (due to disease or psychosis); loss of internal body parts and organs via surgery, and loss of external body parts; loss due to physical illness or injury; loss due to aging; loss of important self and object representations; loss of one's geographic heritage and home; loss of hopes, dreams, and ideals; loss of one's cherished work; loss of a world leader, or a president, of writers, artists, scientists, composers, or other creative people.

A Selective Historical Overview of the Psychoanalytic Literature on Loss and Mourning

Our purpose in this Introduction is not to comprehensively discuss Freud's considerable work on loss, object loss, and mourning, but rather to selectively refer to and highlight relevant facets of Freud's body of work, and the contributions of others.

Loss and Mourning in Freud's Work

Pollock (1961) presents a careful historical account of Freud's various evolving contributions on mourning and aspects of loss. Useful literature reviews have been provided by Neubauer (1960), Pollock (1961), Krupp (1965), Siggins (1966), Miller (1971), Bowlby (1973), and E. Furman (1974), the Bowlby contribution focusing upon separation reactions. Max Schur's (1972) study of Freud and his death, in which he also comments upon some of Freud's publications concerning death, loss, and mourning, is another especially valuable and noteworthy contribution.

It is useful to reflect upon the fact that Freud wrote the first draft of his monumental *Mourning and Melancholia* (1917) just over seventy years ago. Although Freud's primary emphasis in this work does not specifically focus on mourning ("we will now try to throw some light on the nature of melancholia by comparing it with the normal affect of mourning" [p. 243]), he nevertheless does explore a number of important issues and opens wide the problem of mourning and loss for future psychoanalytic study.

Not restricting loss to the death or loss of a loved one, Freud (1917) describes mourning as "the reaction to the loss of a loved person, or to the loss of some abstraction which has taken the place of one, such as one's country, liberty, an ideal, and so on" (p. 243).

In 1895, Freud discussed loss and mourning in Draft G of the Fliess papers on "Melancholia," including earlier versions of ideas that later appeared in more elaborated form in *Mourning and Melancholia*. Freud wrote: "The affect corresponding to melancholia is that of mourning—that is, longing for something lost. Thus in melancholia it must be a question of a loss—a loss in *instinctual* life" (p. 200). And later, also in part II of Draft G, he adds: "It would not be far wrong, therefore, to start from the idea that *melancholia consists in mourning over loss of libido*" (p. 201).

In a later Fliess paper, Draft K, entitled "The Neuroses of Defense: A Christmas Fairy Tale" written prior to January 1, 1896, Freud states: "There are four types of these and many forms. . . . They are pathological aberrations of normal psychical affective states: of *conflict* (hysterical), of *self-reproach* (obsessional neurosis), of *mortification* (paranoia), of *mourning* (acute hallucinatory amentia). They differ from these affects in that they do not lead to anything being settled but to a permanent damage to the ego" (p. 220).

Finally, let us turn to another Fliess paper, Draft N, dated May 31, 1897, titled "Impulses, Fantasies and Symptoms." Here, Freud states that hostile impulses directed against one's parents, in other words, wishing they would die, are an integral constituent of neuroses. Such impulses, Freud goes on to say, are repressed at times of the parent's illness or death. Freud suggests:' "On such occasions it is a manifestation of mourning to reproach oneself for their death (what is known as melancholia) or to punish oneself in a hysterical fashion (through the medium of the idea of retribution) with the same states [of illness] that they have had" (p. 255). He adds that it seems this death wish is directed against fathers in sons, and is directed against mothers in daughters. Some of the ideas developed here are elaborated after an interval of twenty years in *Mourning and Melancholia*.

In "Thoughts For the Times on War and Death" (1915) which, as James Strachey, in an editorial comment, mentions was written in March or April, 1915, just after his initial draft of *Mourning and Melancholia*, Freud explores, among other themes, the phenomenon of belief in immortality within the unconscious. "Hence the psycho-analytic school could venture on the assertion that at bottom no one believes in his own death, or, to put the same thing in another way, that in the unconscious every one of us is convinced of his own immortality" (p. 289).

Later in the paper, Freud asks a most pertinent and important question: "What, we ask, is the attitude of our unconscious towards the problem of death? The answer must be; almost exactly the same as that of primaeval man. In this respect, as in many others, the man of prehistoric times survives unchanged in our unconscious. Our unconscious, then, does not believe in its own death; it behaves as if it were immortal" (p. 296).

Freud (1917) synopsizes as follows: "To sum up: our unconscious is just as inaccessible to the idea of our own death, just as murderously inclined towards strangers, just as divided (that is, ambivalent) towards those we love, as was primaeval man. But how far we have moved from this primal state in our conventional and cultural attitude towards death!" (p. 299).

Freud's "On Transience" (1916) was written in November of 1915, during the second year of World War I. In writing of a young poet and friend who had accompanied him on a summer's walk, Freud (1916) observes:

> What spoilt their enjoyment of beauty must have been a revolt in their minds against mourning. The idea that all this beauty was transient was giving these two sensitive minds a foretaste of mourning over its decease; and, since the mind instinctively recoils from anything that is painful, they felt their enjoyment of beauty interfered with by thoughts of its transience [p. 306].

We shall include one more selection from Freud's (1917) *Mourning and Melancholia*, a selection of some length wherein

Freud evocatively and succinctly describes the work of mourning. Freud's description of mourning has served as a cornerstone for all later psychoanalytic discoveries:

> In what, now, does the work which mourning performs consist? I do not think there is anything far-fetched in presenting it in the following way. Reality-testing has shown that the loved object no longer exists, and it proceeds to demand that all libido shall be withdrawn from its attachments to that object. This demand arouses understandable opposition—it is a matter of general observation that people never willingly abandon a libidinal position, not even, indeed, when a substitute is already beckoning to them. This opposition can be so intense that a turning away from reality takes place and a clinging to the object through the medium of a hallucinatory wishful psychosis. Normally, respect for reality gains the day. Nevertheless, its orders cannot be obeyed at once. They are carried out bit by bit, at great expense of time and cathectic energy, and in the meantime the existence of the lost object is psychically prolonged. Each single one of the memories and expectations in which the libido is bound to the object is brought up and hypercathected, and detachment of the libido is accomplished in respect of it. Why this compromise by which the command of reality is carried out piecemeal should be so extraordinarily painful is not at all easy to explain in terms of economics. It is remarkable that this painful unpleasure is taken as a matter of course by us. The fact is, however, that when the work of mourning is completed the ego becomes free and uninhibited again [pp. 244–245].

Interestingly, according to Rochlin (1965), Freud's (1920) observation about his grandson, who was left in Freud's care briefly, is the first study of object loss in a child by a psychoanalyst.

Other Psychoanalytic Contributions to Loss and Mourning

For the sake of clarity, we shall organize these key contributions to the literature according to three broad themes: (1) losses during childhood and their sequelae; (2) definitions of the mourning process and mourning processes; and (3) pathological grief processes. Some of the contributions overlap categories, and categories we have elected to use to organize this literature review are approximate ones.

Marmor (1979) made an interesting point in observing how Rank's (1924) conception of birth trauma (while questionable itself) actually anticipated by over twenty years the studies of separation from the mother done by Spitz (1946) and Mahler (1969), and, we would add, Bowlby (1960). Also, Rank's general theoretical emphasis on separation as a powerful determinant of character anticipated other later psychoanalytic work as well.

Bonaparte (1928) wrote an early autobiographical paper which addressed aspects of identification with the lost, dead parent.

H. Deutsch's (1937) classic paper "Absence of Grief" described four individuals who experienced the death of a parent during childhood or adolescence and their lack of appropriate emotions following bereavement. Later, as adults, they exhibited identification, idealization, depression, and denial. Levy (1937) described "primary affect hunger" in children who experienced early separations from their mothers and who were characterized by an inability to establish object attachments. Bender and Schilder (1937) reported that children's suicide attempts were based upon reunion fantasies with dead parents, while Peck (1939) noted certain adult suicide attempts derived from reunion wishes toward a dead spouse. Zilboorg (1937) described a case of a young woman who committed suicide on the anniversary of her mother's death which had occurred during her childhood.

Klein (1935, 1940) made important and original, albeit controversial, contributions to mourning. She held that infants mourn and that "this early mourning is revived whenever grief is experienced in later life" (1940, p. 344). She maintained that "the absence of the mother arouses in the child anxiety lest it should be handed over to bad objects, external and internalized, either because of her *death* or because of her return in the guise of a 'bad' mother" (1935, p. 266). In speaking of mourning, Klein wrote: "In normal mourning, as well as in abnormal mourning and in manic-depressive states, the infantile depressive position is reactivated." She adds, however, that in normal mourning "the early depressive position, which had become revived through the loss of the loved object, becomes modified again, and is overcome by methods similar to those used by the ego in childhood" (p. 369).

Burlingham and A. Freud (1942, 1944) and A. Freud and Burlingham (1943) reported on children in the Hampstead nurseries who, because of World War II, were separated from or had lost their father or mother. These children demonstrated intense distress, fantasies of reunion and identification with the parent, and regression and decathexis from the representation of the longed-for parent.

In 1946, Spitz (1946, 1965) published his influential paper on "Anaclitic Depression" in which he examined some effects of maternal loss upon the developing infant. Mahler (1950, 1961) has contributed to the early literature on death and, more generally, has richly added to our developmental understanding of the complex array of effects resulting from object loss.

Rochlin (1953, 1959, 1961, 1965) has made several very important contributions in the area of object loss in children, and stresses narcissism, identification, and attempts at restitution in response to such loss. He writes: "Unlike other conflicts, those entailed in losses and transience apparently are not resolved; instead, defenses are raised against them" (p. 60). Jacobson (1957, 1965) described fantasies of restitution and reunion with the lost parent, and the process of identification in mourning, while Hilgard, Newman, and Fisk (1960) studied the multiple influences surrounding the death of a parent which contributed to the development of adult ego strength.

Bowlby made numerous important contributions to the area of loss, separation, and mourning (1960, 1961, 1963, 1980). He has consistently argued that infants and very young children go through periods of mourning. In comparing the responses of children to bereavement to those of adults, he maintains "since the evidence makes it clear that at a descriptive level, the responses are similar in the two age groups, I believe it to be wiser methodologically to assume that the underlying processes are similar" (1960, p. 27). However, certain of Bowlby's views, such as his very early timetable for mourning and his contention that mourning is the same in children and adults, have come under critical scrutiny for a variety of reasons by many psychoanalytic researchers (A. Freud, 1960; Schur, 1960; Spitz, 1960; Wolfenstein, 1966; Miller, 1971; Dietrich, 1983).

Robert Furman (1964, 1968, 1970, 1973) and Erna Furman (1970, 1974, 1986) have also written many excellent and influential papers and a book (Furman, 1974) which have substantively contributed to our current analytic knowledge and understanding of childhood bereavement and mourning. E. Furman (1974) noted forthrightly: "Now, after some years of concentrated study, the members of our group realize more than ever that bereavement in childhood is a vast, complicated, and extremely painful subject; that our experience and insight are limited and our conclusions tentative" (p. 9). She adds that "when a child's parent dies, he faces an incomparable stress which threatens the further development of his personality" (Furman, 1974, p. 11). Fleming (1963, 1972), Fleming and Altschul (1963), and Altschul (1968) have made important contributions to clarifying our understanding of the role of developmental aspects of object loss, specifically, loss of a parent by death, how psychoanalysis can reactivate mourning, how various developmental arrests typically result from such loss (specifically in the area of object relations), and technical difficulties which arise in the psychoanalytic treatment of such patients.

Wolfenstein (1966, 1969, 1973) published a series of most evocative papers examining many clinically significant features of individuals whose parents died during the patient's childhood, including their defensive splitting of the ego, long-term pathological consequences of a lack of mourning, denial of the traumatic parental death experience, and of fantasies, conscious and unconscious, of the parent's return.

Regarding the mourning process, Abraham's classic 1924 paper "A Short Study of the Development of the Libido, Viewed in the Light of Mental Disorders," suggests that identification comprises part of the mourning process and further clarifies the concept of introjection of the object and other aspects of object loss. Concepts, fears, and representations of death were explored in a number of important papers by Chadwick (1929), Bromberg and Schilder (1933), Zilboorg (1943), and Wahl (1958), as well as others.

Of all psychoanalytic writers concerned with problems associated with loss and mourning over the past twenty-five years, Pollock's many contributions (1961, 1962, 1968, 1970, 1971a,b, 1972, 1975, 1978) have been among the most influential and important. He writes:

> The mourning process occurs in the lives of all and is not the same as bereavement, which . . . I see as the specific sub-class of the mourning process occurring after a meaningful person has died. I do not absolutely link the mourning process with object loss, although object loss has been most characteristically associated with mourning and I myself have studied object loss as the example *par excellence* to investigate the mourning process. The subject of the external and internal meaning of the object and its loss is one that psychoanalysis has and will continue to study [1978, p. 262].

Pollock says earlier in the same paper: "I believe each phase or stage of the mourning process has varied affect states and that three outcomes of a mourning process are possible: successful completion with a creative outcome; an arrest at various stages of the process; and a pathological or deviated process that is closely, though not exclusively, related to melancholia, the depressive disorders and their potentially lethal outcome" (p. 258). Later, he emphasizes that "there are, however, some instances where the mature mourning process may not be able to be fully concluded, e.g., maternal mourning for the death of her child, or when the mourning process cannot be completed because of the immaturity of the psychic apparatus at the time of the loss" (Pollock, 1978, p. 265).

Eissler (1955) wrote an important, and perhaps too often overlooked book, examining Freud's thanatology and issues of the dying patient, among other interesting problems. Loewald (1962), Wetmore (1963), Kliman (1965), Nagera (1970), Parkes (1972), Weisman (1972), Stolorow and Lachmann (1975), Hägglund (1976), Berman (1978), Horowitz, Wilner, Marmar, and Krupnick (1980), and Krystal (1987) as well as many others have also made noteworthy contributions to the area of loss and mourning. Volkan's (1971, 1981) important writings have clarified different aspects of identification in grief reactions and object loss, and, in particular, linking objects. Fairbairn (1936) commented upon some of the various effects the death of an important figure evoked in his analytic patients. Physical illness and somatic symptoms occurring in response to bereavement were discussed in early papers by Cobb, Bauer, and Whiting (1939), McDermott and Cobb (1939), and Lindemann (1945). Rosenzweig (1943) and Rosenzweig and Bray (1943) examined the pathogenic and unconscious effects of sibling death upon schizophrenia and aspects of creativity.

Classic, detailed descriptions of acute grief reactions were reported by Lindemann (1944), who observed that acute grief is a syndrome with specific psychologic and somatic symptomatology; it may appear after a bereavement, or be delayed and suppressed, and by appropriate techniques it can be resolved with a normal grief reaction. Benedek (1946) examined bereavement processes and reunion during World War II, and Sterba (1946) described some reactions to the death of President Roosevelt. Bibring (1953), in his discussion of depression, emphasized the wish for reunion with the lost love object and the feeling that one should have prevented the death. Lipson (1963), Scott (1964), Niederland (1965), and Pinderhughes (1971) have also made useful contributions to various aspects of denial in mourning, mourning, the search for the lost parent, and social and somatic sequelae of loss, respectively.

Kohut's (1971) work can also be viewed as focusing upon selective facets of loss: namely, loss experienced via empathic failures.

The Mitscherlichs, in their important work, *The Inability to Mourn* ([1975], originally published in German in 1967), demonstrated how an entire nation, in this case the German people, can fail to mourn and instead resort to denial, repression, suppression, and substitute activities.

Organization of the Book

The book is divided into five sections: Theoretical and Applied Psychoanalytic Perspectives; Developmental Perspectives; Clinical Contributions; Empirical Studies on Loss and Their Implications: Research Perspectives; and Loss, Mourning, and the Holocaust.

In chapter 1, "The Mourning Process, the Creative Process, and the Creation," Dr. George Pollock examines the relationship between mourning and creativity as a form of liberation and how this is often related to early loss, with special reference to the case of the composer Gustav Mahler. In those less gifted, a creative outcome to the mourning process may eventuate in the ability to experience joy or satisfaction or newer sublimations. In certain others, great creativity may stem from efforts toward completion of mourning work. Dr. Pollock adds that the mourning process can be of major significance in the creative process where there is not object loss via death. He elucidates in a compelling fashion how the multiple sibling losses in Mahler's life influenced his personality, musical compositions, and the selection of texts. Dr. Pollock points out that the sibling losses do not account for his genius, but rather the expression of his genius. Pollock shows that Mahler's consultation with Freud in 1910, a few months before Mahler died, allowed him to expend libido toward his wife, and gave him hope.

In chapter 2, "Trauma, Loss, Restoration, and Creativity," Dr. William Niederland begins by carefully examining the concept, range, and definition of trauma. He discusses prenatal and perinatal trauma and trauma in infancy, childhood, and adulthood. Dr. Niederland then delineates, via applied analytic insights, the process of loss, restoration, and creativity within the lives of such individuals as Moses, Cervantes, Joyce, Monet, Kipling, and Kant, to name but a few. When a defect exists in fantasy or reality, adaptive and creative strivings are set in motion with an aim toward restoration of completeness in those of talent.

Dr. Nancy Kulish offers an analytic study of Peter Pan, its creator, James Barrie, and the role of mourning in adolescence and childhood, in chapter 3, "Mourning a Lost Childhood: The Problem of Peter Pan." Through an analysis of the myth of Peter Pan and the "happy childhood," Dr. Kulish focuses upon the wide-ranging impact of James Barrie's sibling loss experience when he was seven years old. Fantasies of rebirth, time standing still, death being reversed, and identification are discussed. She includes two interesting clinical vignettes which illustrate the way in which overt, childlike appearances, linked with fantasies of a happy childhood, gratified unconscious infantile aims, and covered deep losses and disappointments. Finally, Dr. Kulish discusses how mourning became an important part of the therapeutic work in these cases.

In "Vicissitudes of Psychic Loss of a Physically Present Parent" (chapter 4), Dr. Peter Shabad discusses an often neglected variety of loss experience, contrasting physical loss with psychic loss. He notes that grief and mourning are typically viewed as reactions to physical loss. However, when loss is defined only in terms of physical loss, we do not do justice to the phenomenology of the loss experience. Drawing upon the work of Greenacre, Kris, and Khan on chronic trauma, Dr. Shabad discusses the concept of "traumatic theme" and its relationship to psychic loss. He stresses how this type of loss experience does not readily lend itself to an adaptive mourning process, in part because there is no objective reference point for the child to use in validating his or her experience. Dr. Shabad then discusses how the difficulty in mourning psychic loss engenders a form of characterological defense resembling identification with the aggressor. Diagnostic and treatment implications of psychic loss are discussed as well.

Part II of the book, "Developmental Perspectives," consists of contributions by Erna Furman and Drs. Robert Furman, Fred Pine, Jerome Grunes, and Wendy Wasson. In their chapter "Some Effects of the One-Parent Family on Personality Development" (chapter 5), Erna Furman and Dr. Robert Furman discuss, from a clinical and developmental perspective, a large group of children who have experienced loss of a parent by death, divorce, or other reasons. The Furmans' important clinical findings show how many individuals growing up in one-parent families begin to exhibit manifestations of psychological problems in the earliest stage of phallic-narcissistic development. The play of such children, for example, often lacks zest and they are extremely vulnerable to criticism. They display unattenuated aggression that interferes with the capacity for neutralization. The Furmans delineate how these youngsters have great difficulty in successfully progressing to the oedipal phase proper and achieving oedipal phase dominance. Analysis, and at times treatment via the remaining parent, can resolve their difficulty. Erna and Robert Furman explain how the loss of the parent critically affects superego structuralization and adolescent development as well. They include a moving clinical vignette to illustrate their discussion.

In chapter 6, "The Place of Object Loss in Normal Development," Dr. Fred Pine focuses upon nonadventitious losses, those inherent in the developmental process of adolescence, childhood, and adulthood, and demonstrates how these normal developmental losses can set the structural preparedness for non-normal, adventitious losses. Dr. Pine clearly shows that when such losses occur according to their normal timetable, they are linked by adaptive reactions including object replacement or object retention that function to temper the various effects of such loss experiences.

In chapter 7, "The Significance of Loss and Mourning in the Older Adult: Clinical and Research Findings," Drs. Jerome Grunes and Wendy Wasson describe the "stressors" of later life and their relationship to early trauma and loss. They report on aspects of their research conducted at Northwestern University Medical School, and include several vignettes to illustrate their discussion. Drs. Grunes and Wasson found that certain fantasies about ourselves appear to be important for psychological well-being, and that these fantasies are open to attack by stressors later in life.

Part III, "Clinical Contributions," is comprised of chapters by Dr. Milton Viederman, Dr. David Krueger, Rebecca Lohr and Morton Chethik, and Drs. Robert Zuckerman and Vamik Volkan. Drawing upon his thorough understanding of the psychoanalytic process in "Personality Change Through Life Experience: Two Creative Types of Response to Object Loss," chapter 8, Dr. Viederman presents a schematic outline of the first case consultation and process of change by way of his discussion of the clinical material. Also, he analyzes two dreams from the second case. He delineates how in situations of crisis, actual interactions with an object can result in significant shifts in self and object representations, and how wished for, fantasied change in the object relationship can also result in such changes. The chapter also includes a discussion of the regressive model of pathological grief response, undoing of identifications within the context of object loss, and the psychobiology of bereavement.

Dr. David Krueger examines and illuminates an aspect of parent loss by drawing upon some of the findings of self psychology in his chapter "The 'Parent Loss' of Empathic Failures and the Model Symbolic Restitution of Eating Disorders" (chapter 9). Dr. Krueger shows how preoedipal losses profoundly affect aspects of narcissistic development, suggesting that some empathic failures result in effects similar to those caused by the actual loss of a parent. He discusses the development of body self, developmental deficits, and overly intrusive parents and presents findings from the treatment of over 300 eating disordered patients. He also includes three clinical vignettes, including one from the middle phase of an analysis, along with a discussion of the family system.

In "Parental Loss Through Divorce: Dimensions of the Loss Experience," chapter 10, Rebecca Lohr and Morton Chethik focus upon aspects of children's loss experience via parental divorce, including the important loss of the parental unit itself. This experience includes the child's sense of loss of familial continuity, and the child's denial of the reality of the divorce as expressed, in part, in the child's wish and fantasy for parental reconciliation. They also discuss loss of the parental object (typically the noncustodial parent, the father). In their comprehensive clinical case material, Lohr and Chethik include, in their description of the course of the child's treatment, clinical work with the mother and father, and the child's status upon termination from treatment.

In chapter 11, "Complicated Mourning Over a Body Defect: The Making of a 'Living Linking Object,'" Drs. Robert Zuckerman and Vamik Volkan present a detailed treatment case of a woman with a unique living linking object. The patient was in psychoanalytic psychotherapy and used her son as a fantasied reservoir for her deformed spine (due to kyphosis). In their analysis of the clinical material, Drs. Zuckerman and Volkan show how mourning over this deformity was postponed, in part, to allow the patient the fantasy of complete control over her male child/spine with its condensed and associated unconscious meanings. In the course of the treatment the therapist, in the transference, also became a fantasied reservoir for the patient's damaged spine. The authors note that they have become more sensitive in their diagnostic and treatment work to the frequency of patients exhibiting living linking objects and to what Volkan has referred to as generational continuity, where unassimilated self and object representations are passed on to the child.

Part IV of the book is devoted to an examination of relevant empirical research findings, too often missing in psychoanalytic volumes, and is entitled "Empirical Studies on Loss and Their Implications: Research Perspectives." Dr. David Dietrich, in chapter 12, "Early Childhood Parent Death, Psychic Trauma and Organization, and Object Relations," makes an empirical psychoanalytic and theoretical contribution to the literature on parent loss and object relations. Dr. Dietrich discusses the lost immortal parent complex which can be seen clinically in these patients, and posits a developmental line of mourning. He ends his chapter with a study demonstrating the powerful effects childhood parent death continues to exert on aspects of object relations and object representations; namely, individuals who have lost a parent by death exhibit a lower quality of object relations, lower object warmth and psychological mindedness, and higher superego harshness and depression as compared with nonloss individuals. Also, Dr. Dietrich includes a scale for assessing object relations and representations from projective and clinical material. Problems which often arise in the psychoanalytic psychotherapy of such patients are also discussed.

Chapter 13, "Father Loss, Cognitive and Personality Functioning," by Drs. Henry Biller and Margery Salter, comprehensively reviews most of the relevant psychological research concerned with cognitive and personality features as they relate to father loss. This is a literature which is often overlooked in psychoanalytic approaches to the area. Chapter 13 focuses upon a very wide range of developmental consequences of varieties of father loss, noting that psychoanalysts have stimulated more research on parent–infant relationships than have any other group of scientists or clinicians. Father absence and masculine development, the father and cognitive functioning, social adjustment and moral development, interpersonal relationships, psychopathology, the father and female personality development, and research implications are some of the areas the authors carefully discuss. Drs. Biller and Salter bring to light differential effects of types of father loss, the strengths and limitations of current research, and areas where further research is clearly needed.

Part V is entitled "Loss, Mourning, and the Holocaust," and contains chapters by Drs. Judith Kestenberg, Margarete Mitscherlich-Nielsen, and Yael Danieli. Dr. Judith Kestenberg begins this section (chapter 14) with her contribution, "Coping with Losses and Survival." Dr. Kestenberg writes a moving chapter and brings to bear her considerable clinical experience with survivors of the Holocaust and discusses some of the consequences of not saying good-bye and of being left alone. She discusses the losses of children whose parents were killed in the Holocaust and the last words said at the parting between the child and his or her parents. Dr. Kestenberg also examines the significance of the role of specific memories, such as the man who could recall his mother's soup cooking. The issue of being given the right (through love) to feel entitled to survive, and links to the past via transitional and substitute objects are dealt with, as is survival in overwhelming circumstances. Dr. Kestenberg raises the question of whether one can mourn in the face of impending death, and ends with a discussion of survival after liberation.

In "The Inability to Mourn—Today," chapter 15, Dr. Margarete Mitscherlich-Nielsen offers an analysis of whether, in Germany today, mourning over the Nazi past and the Holocaust is possible for the majority of Germans or only possible for individuals, Dr. Mitscherlich-Nielsen points out how the younger generation in Germany has repressed and denied, but not worked through, their collective past; they experience themselves as without guilt. This contribution examines the repetitive unconscious tendencies toward mass conformity that links Nazi Germany with the consumerist society of West Germany today. She further discusses the place of memory work, education, and atonement in collective mourning, as well as the role of psychoanalysis in facilitating the work of mourning. She describes the manner in which guilt and shame are warded off, and the relation between gender and the ability to mourn.

Finally, in "Mourning in Survivors and Children of Survivors of the Nazi Holocaust: The Role of Group and Community Modalities," chapter 16, Dr. Yael Danieli points out the limitations of mourning the Holocaust in individual therapeutic modalities. She describes the conspiracy of silence both during and after the war, the manner in which psychotherapists participate in it, and how it makes mourning very difficult. She describes the Group Project for Holocaust Survivors and their Children, a collective therapeutic modality that breaks the conspiracy of silence. She notes that re-creating a family was one way individuals compensated for their terrible losses, and that having children was often seen as a symbol of victory over the Nazis. Dr. Danieli also examines the function of guilt in such individuals and the need to reaffirm their Jewish identity. Dr. Danieli calls the Holocaust the fourth narcissistic blow, the "ethical blow" to mankind.

In the Epilogue, entitled "Reflections on Loss, Mourning, and the Unconscious Process of Regeneration," the editors conclude by discussing the themes of adaptive and constructive reactions to loss, as they have emerged from the various contributions in the book.

References

Abraham, K. (1924), A short study of the development of the libido, viewed in the light of the mental disorders. In: *Selected Papers on Psycho-Analysis*. New York: Basic Books, 1960, pp. 418–501.

Altschul, S. (1968), Denial and ego arrest. *J. Amer. Psychoanal. Assn.*, 16: 301–318.

Bender, L., & Schilder, P. (1937), Suicidal preoccupations and attempts in children. *Amer. J. Orthopsychiat.*, 7: 225–234.

Benedek, T. (1946), *Insight and Personality Adjustment: A Study of the Psychological Effects of War*. New York: Ronald Press.

Berman, L. (1978), Sibling loss as an organizer of unconscious guilt: A case study. *Psychoanal. Quart.*, 47:568–587.

Bibring, E. (1953), The mechanism of depression. In: *Affective Disorders*, ed. P. Greenacre. New York: International Universities Press, pp. 13–48.

Bonaparte, M. (1928), L'identification d'une fille à sa mère morte. *Revue Française Psychanalytique*, 2:541–565.

Bowlby, J. (1960), Grief and mourning in infancy and early childhood. *The Psychoanalytic Study of the Child*, 15:9–52. New York: International Universities Press.

———(1961), Processes of mourning. *Internat. J. Psycho-Anal.*, 42:317–340.

———(1963), Pathological mourning and childhood. *J. Amer. Psychoanal. Assn.*, 11:500–541.

———(1973), *Attachment and Loss*, Vol. 2. New York: Basic Books.

———(1980), *Attachment and Loss*, Vol. 3. New York: Basic Books.

Bromberg, W., & Schilder, P. (1933), Death and dying; A comparative study of the attitudes and mental reactions toward death and dying. *Psychoanal. Rev.*, 20:133–135.

Burlingham, D., & Freud, A. (1942), *Young Children in War-Time*. London: Allen & Unwin.

———(1944), *Infants Without Families*. London: Allen & Unwin.

Chadwick, M. (1929), Notes upon the fear of death. *Internat. J. Psycho-Anal.*, 10:321–334.

Cobb, S., Bauer, W., & Whiting, I. (1939), Environmental factors in rheumatoid arthritis. *J. Amer. Med. Assn.*, 113:668–670.

Deutsch, H. (1937), Absence of grief. *Psychoanal. Quart.*, 6:12–22.

Dietrich, D. (1983), Bowlby and childhood mourning: A critical evaluation twenty years later. Paper presented to the Annual Meeting of the American Psychological Association, Division of Psychoanalysis, Los Angeles, August.

Eissler, K. (1955), *The Psychiatrist and the Dying Patient*. New York: International Universities Press.

Fairbairn, W. (1936), The effect of the King's death upon patients under analysis. *Internat. J. Psycho-Anal.*, 17:278–284.

Fleming, J. (1963), The evolution of a research project in psychoanalysis. In: *Counterpoint: Libidinal Object Constancy. A Tribute to René A. Spitz on His 75th Birthday*, ed. H. Gaskill. New York: International Universities Press, pp. 75–105.

———(1972), Early object deprivation and transference phenomena: The working alliance. *Psychoanal. Quart.*, 41:23–39.

———Altschul, S. (1963), Activation of mourning and growth by psychoanalysis. *Internat. J. Psycho-Anal.*, 44:419–431.

Freud, A. (1960), Discussion of Dr. John Bowlby's paper. *The Psychoanalytic Study of the Child*, 15:53–62. New York: International Universities Press.

———Burlingham, D. (1943), *War and Children*. New York: International Universities Press.

Freud, S. (1895), Extracts from the Fliess papers, Draft G. *Standard Edition*, 1: 200–206, London: Hogarth Press, 1966.

———(1896), Extracts from the Fliess papers, Draft K: The neuroses of defense. *Standard Edition*, 1:220–229. London: Hogarth Press, 1966.

———(1897), Extracts from the Fliess papers, Draft N: Notes III. *Standard Edition*, 1:254–257. London: Hogarth Press, 1966.

————(1915), Thoughts for the times on war and death. *Standard Edition*, 14: 273–300. London: Hogarth Press, 1961.

————(1916), On transience. *Standard Edition*, 14:303–307. London: Hogarth Press, 1961.

————(1917), Mourning and melancholia. *Standard Edition*, 14:237–258. London: Hogarth Press, 1961.

————(1920), Beyond the pleasure principle. *Standard Edition*, 18:3–64. London: Hogarth Press, 1957.

Furman, E. (1970), Research on bereaved children. *Arch. Found. Thanatol.*, 2: 75–77.

————(1974), *A Child's Parent Dies*. New Haven, CT: Yale University Press.

————(1986), On trauma: When is the death of a parent traumatic? *The Psychoanalytic Study of the Child*, 14:191–208. New York: International Universities Press.

Furman, R. (1964), Death and the young child: Some preliminary considerations. *The Psychoanalytic Study of the child*, 19:377–397. New York: International Universities Press.

————(1968), Additional remarks on mourning and the young child. *Bull. Philadelphia Assn. Psychoanal.*, 18:51–64.

————(1970), The child's reaction to death in the family. In: *Loss and Grief: Psychological Management in Medical Practice*, ed. B. Schoenberg, A. Carr, D. Peretz, & A. Kutscher. New York: Columbia University Press, pp. 70–86.

————(1973), A child's capacity for mourning. In: *The Child in His Family: The Impact of Disease and Death*, ed. E. J. Anthony & C. Koupernik. (Yearbook of the International Association for Child Psychiatry & Allied Professions, Vol. 2). New York: John Wiley, pp. 225–231.

Hägglund, T. (1976), *Dying: A Psychoanalytical Study with Special Reference to Individual Creativity and Defensive Organization*. Helsinki: Psychiatric Clinic, Helsinki University Central Hospital (Monograph 6).

Hilgard, J., Newman, M., & Fisk, F. (1960), Strength of adult ego following childhood bereavement. *Amer. J. Orthopsychiat.*, 30:788–798.

Horowitz, M., Wilner, N., Marmar, C., & Krupnick, J. (1980), Pathological grief and the activation of latent self images. *Amer. J. Psychiat.*, 137: 1157–1162.

Jacobson, E. (1957), On normal and pathological moods. *The Psychoanalytic Study of the Child*, 12:73–113. New York: International Universities Press.

————(1965), The return of the lost parent. In: *Drive, Affects, Behavior*, Vol. 2, ed. M. Schur. New York: International Universities Press, pp.193–211.

Klein, M. (1935), A contribution to the psychogenesis of manic-depressive states. *Internat. J. Psycho-Anal.*, 16:145–174.

————(1940), Mourning and its relation to manic-depressive states. *Internat. J. Psycho-Anal.*, 21:125–153.

Kliman, G. (1965), Oedipal themes in children's reactions to the assassination. In: *Children and the Death of a President*, eds. M. Wolfenstein & G. Kliman. Garden City, NY: Doubleday, pp. 107–134.

Kohut, H. (1971), *The Analysis of the Self*. New York: International Universities Press.

Krupp, G. (1965), Identification as a defense against anxiety in coping with loss. *Internat. J. Psycho-Anal.*, 46:303–314.

Krystal, H. (1987), The impact of massive psychic trauma and the capacity to grieve effectively. In: *Treating the Elderly with Psychotherapy*, eds. J. Sadavoy & M. Leszcz. Madison, CT: International Universities Press, pp.95–156.

Levy, D. (1937), Primary affect hunger. *Amer. J. Psychiat.*, 94:643–652.

Lindemann, E. (1944), Symptomatology and management of acute grief. *Amer. J. Psychiat.*, 101:141–148.

———(1945), Psychiatric factors in the treatment of ulcerative colitis. *Arch. Neurol. Psychiat.*, 53:322–324.

Lipson, C. (1963), Denial and mourning. *Internat. J. Psycho-Anal.*, 44:104–107.

Loewald, H. (1962), Internalization, separation, mourning, and the superego. *Psychoanal. Quart.*, 31:483–504.

Mahler, M. (1950), Helping children to accept death. *Child Study*, 27(4): 98–99; 119–120.

———(1961), On sadness and grief in infancy and childhood: Loss and restoration of the symbiotic love object. *The Psychoanalytic Study of the Child*, 16:332–351. New York: International Universities Press.

———(1969), *On Human Symbiosis and the Vicissitudes of Individuation*. New York: International Universities Press.

Marmor, J. (1979), Short-term dynamic psychotherapy. *Amer. J. Psychiat.*, 136: 149–155.

McDermott, N., & Cobb, S. (1939), A psychiatric survey of fifty cases of bronchial asthma. *Psychosom. Med.*, 1:203–244.

Miller, J. (1971), Children's reactions to the death of a parent: A review of psychoanalytic literature. *J. Amer. Psychoanal. Assn.*, 19:697–719.

Mitscherlich, A., & Mitscherlich, M. (1975), *The Inability to Mourn*. New York: Grove Press.

Nagera, H. (1970), Children's reactions to the death of important objects: A developmental approach. *The Psychoanalytic Study of the Child*, 25:360–400. New York: International Universities Press.

Neubauer, P. (1960), The one-parent child and his oedipal development. *The Psychoanalytic Study of the Child*, 15:286–309. New York: International Universities Press.

Niederland, W. (1965), An analytic inquiry into the life and work of Heinrich Schliemann. In: *Drives, Affects, Behavior*, Vol. 2, ed. M. Schur. New York: International Universities Press, pp. 369–396.

Parkes, C. (1972), *Bereavement: Studies of Grief in Adult Life*. New York: International Universities Press.

Peck, M. (1939), Notes on identification in a case of depression reactive to the death of a love object. *Psychoanal. Quart.*, 8:1–17.

Pinderhughes, C. (1971), Somatic, psychic, and social sequelae of loss. *J. Amer. Psychoanal. Assn.*, 19:670–696.

Pollock, G. (1961), Mourning and adaptation. *Internat. J. Psycho-Anal.*, 42: 341–361.

———(1962), Childhood parent and sibling loss in adult patients: A comparative study. *Arch. Gen. Psychiat.*, 7:295–305.

———(1968), The possible significance of childhood object loss in the Josef Breuer–Bertha Pappenheim (Anna O.)–Sigmund Freud relationship. *J. Amer. Psychoanal. Assn.*, 16:711–739.

———(1970), Anniversary reactions, trauma and mourning. *Psychoanal. Quart.*, 39:347–371.

———(1971a), On time and anniversaries. In: *The Unconscious Today*, ed. M. Kanzer. New York: International Universities Press, pp. 233–257.

———(1971b), Temporal anniversary manifestations: Hour, day, holiday. *Psychoanal. Quart.*, 40:123–131.

———(1972), Bertha Pappenheim's pathological mourning: Possible effects of childhood sibling loss. *J. Amer. Psychoanal. Assn.*, 21:328–332.

———(1975), On mourning, immortality and utopia. *J. Amer. Psychoanal. Assn.*, 23:334–362.

———(1978), Process and affect: Mourning and grief. *Internat. J. Psycho-Anal.*, 59:255–276.

Rank, O. (1924), *The Trauma of Birth*. New York: Robert Brunner, 1952.

Rochlin, G. (1953), Loss and restitution. *The Psychoanalytic Study of the Child*, 8: 288–309. New York: International Universities Press.

———(1959), The loss complex: A contribution to the etiology of depression. *J. Amer. Psychoanal. Assn.*, 7: 299–316.

———(1961), The dread of abandonment: A contribution to the loss complex and to depression. *The Psychoanalytic Study of the Child*, 16:451–470. New York: International Universities Press.

———(1965), *Griefs and Discontents*. Boston: Little, Brown.

Rosenzweig, S. (1943), Sibling death as a psychological experience with special reference to schizophrenia. *Psychoanal. Rev.*, 30:177–186.

———Bray, D. (1943), Sibling death in the anamneses of schizophrenic patients. *Arch. Neurol. & Psychiat.*, 49:71–92.

Schur, M. (1960), Discussion of Dr. John Bowlby's paper. *The Psychoanalytic Study of the Child*, 15:63–84. New York: International Universities Press.

———(1972), *Freud: Living and Dying*. New York: International Universities Press.

Scott, C. (1964), Mania and mourning. *Internat. J. Psycho-Anal.*, 45:373–377.

Siggins, L. (1966), Mourning: A critical survey of the literature. *Internat. J. Psycho-Anal.*, 47:14–25.

Solnit, A., & Stark, M. (1961), Mourning and the birth of a defective child. *The Psychoanalytic Study of the Child*, 16:523–537. New York: International Universities Press.

Spitz, R. (1946), Anaclitic depression: An inquiry into the genesis of psychiatric conditions in early childhood. II.*The Psychoanalytic Study of the Child*, 2:313–342. New York: International Universities Press.

———(1960), Discussion of Dr. John Bowlby's paper. *The Psychoanalytic Study of the Child*, 15:85–94. New York: International Universities Press.

———(1965), *The First Year of Life: A Psychoanalytic Study of Normal and Deviant Development of Object Relations*. New York: International Universities Press.

Sterba, R. (1946), Report on some emotional reactions to President Roosevelt's death. *Psychoanal. Rev.*, 33:393–398.

Stolorow, R., & Lachmann, F. (1975), Early object loss and denial: Developmental considerations. *Psychoanal. Quart.*, 44:596–611.

Volkan, V. (1971), A study of a patient's "re-grief work" through dreams, psychological tests, and psychoanalysis. *Psychiat. Quart.*, 45:255–273.

————(1981), *Linking Objects and Linking Phenomena: A Study of the Forms, Symptoms, Metapsychology, and Therapy of Complicated Mourning*. New York: International Universities Press.

Wahl, C. (1958), The fear of death. In: *The Meaning of Death*, ed. H. Feifel. New York: McGraw-Hill, 1959, pp. 16–29.

Weisman, A. (1972), *On Dying and Denying: The Practical Significance of Mortality*. New York: Behavioral Publications.

Wetmore, R. (1963), The role of grief in psycho-analysis. *Internat. J. Psycho-Anal.*, 44:97–103.

Wolfenstein, M. (1966), How is mourning possible? *The Psychoanalytic Study of Child*, 21:93–123 New York: International Universities Press.

————(1969), Loss, rage and repetition. *The Psychoanalytic Study of the Child*, 24:432–462. New York: International Universities Press.

————(1973), The image of the lost parent. *The Psychoanalytic Study of the Child*, 28:433–456. New Haven, CT: Yale University Press.

Zilboorg, G. (1937), Considerations on suicide with particular reference to that of the young. *Amer. J. Orthopsychiat.*, 7:15–31.

————(1943), Fear of death. *Psychoanal. Quart.*, 12:465–475.

Part I

Theoretical
and Applied
Psychoanalytic
Perspectives

1

The Mourning Process,
the Creative Process,
and the Creation

GEORGE H. POLLOCK, M.D., PH.D.

Introduction

My research on the mourning–liberation process has been ongoing for over thirty years (Pollock, 1961, 1962, 1968, 1970, 1971a, 1971b, 1971c, 1972a, 1975a, 1975b, 1975c, 1976, 1977, 1978, 1982, 1985, 1986a). It has covered many areas of this most important universal transformational adaptive process regarding loss and change. My work reveals that this process has biologic roots, has existed as long as man has been on earth, has been and is found in all cultures and religions, and has evolved in order to allow individuals and societies to adjust to transitions and progressions. The focus of this chapter is on the relationship of mourning to creativity—a form of liberation—and how this may be related to loss in childhood and adolescence. Such losses, also occurring in adulthood and older age, can result in creative outcomes. Losses due to death result in bereavement reactions. However, it is my belief that these reactions are a subclass of the mourning–liberation process which

27

may include other "losses" (e.g., divorce, abandonment, migra-
tion, change). In my research on the mourning–liberation
process and loss, I have focused on specific losses through the
death of a parent or parents during childhood or adolescence,
the loss of siblings during childhood or adolescence, the loss of
a child, and the loss of a spouse.

My thesis is that the successful completion of the mourning
process results in creative outcome. Where the creator has the
spark of genius or talent that is not related to mourning per se,
this end result can be a great work of art, music, sculpture,
literature, poetry, philosophy, or science. Indeed, the creative
product may reflect the mourning process in theme, style,
form, content, and it may itself stand as a memorial. In the less
gifted, and we have seen this in many clinical situations, a
creative outcome may be manifested in a new real relationship,
the ability to feel joy, satisfaction, a sense of accomplishment, or
newer sublimations that reflect a successful resolution of the
mourning process. In some individuals, great creativity may
not be the outcome of the successfully completed mourning
process but may be indicative of attempts at completing the
mourning work. These creative attempts may be conceptualized as restitution, reparation, discharge, or sublimation.
Though they may not always be successful in terms of mourning work solutions, the intrinsic aesthetic or scientific merit of
the work still may be great despite the failure of mourning
completion.

Let me illustrate my thesis by examining the resolution of a
piece of mourning work by the founder of psychoanalysis,
Sigmund Freud. Freud's father, Jakob, died on October 23,
1896. Although Jones (1953) notes that Freud first fully
analyzed one of his dreams in July 1895, his "casual analyses
became a regular procedure with a definite purpose" (p. 323)
in July 1897. In thanking Fliess for the condolences he sent
Freud after Jakob's death, Freud wrote:

> By one of the dark ways behind the official consciousness my
> father's death has affected me profoundly. I treasure him highly
> and had understood him exactly. With his peculiar mixture of
> deep wisdom and fantastic lightness he had meant very much in

my life. He had passed his time when he died, but inside me the occasion of his death has reawakened all my early feelings. Now I feel uprooted [Jones, 1953, p. 324].

Jones reminds us that Freud told us it was this experience, his father's death and his mourning for him, that led Freud (1900) to write *The Interpretation of Dreams* in 1898. The writing of this classic went hand in hand with the first year or two of his self-analysis. "In the Preface to the Second Edition, written in 1908, Freud said he only recognized the connexion with his father's death after finishing the book. 'It revealed itself to me as a piece of my self-analysis, as my reaction to my father's death; that is, to the most important event, the most poignant loss, in a man's life'" (Jones, 1953, p. 324). Freud's father's death was the stimulus for the transformation of Freud's scientific interest and research into the mechanism of dreams and of mental life, as well as for the composing of his monumental book. In the February after his father's death, Freud questioned the seduction hypothesis and there were the first hints of his discovery of the Oedipus complex.

On October 15, 1897, almost a year after his father's death, Freud announced two elements of the Oedipus complex, the love for one parent and jealous hostility to the other, in a letter to Fliess. These insights came directly from his self-analysis (Jones, 1953, p. 356). "The after-effects of his father's death had been slowly working in those months between it and the decisive reaction to the event [the writing of *The Interpretation of Dreams*]" (Jones, 1953, p. 356). It is my suggestion that we see here in dramatic fashion a superb illustration of my hypothesis that the successful completion of the mourning process results in a creative outcome—in Freud's life, a creation that has influenced all of our lives. I have elsewhere written about such creative outcome as related to the mourning process in the lives of Lenin (Pollock, 1975a), De Quincey, James Barrie, Käthe Kollwitz, Jack Kerouac (Pollock, 1978), Bolivar (Pollock, 1986b), and Dahlberg (Pollock, in preparation), and am investigating the relationship of the mourning process in other writers, poets, artists, scientists, composers, philosophers, religious leaders, political and historically significant royal figures, in individuals whose accomplishments are not so widely known, and in patients who in the course of their analytic mourning work have the energy and motivation to lead productive, happy, and fulfilling lives. Although I have studied the biographies of creative individuals where there was an object loss through death, my research focus has been on the mourning process and not just on the object loss. It is my belief that the mourning process may be a critical factor in the creative process even without object loss through death. This hypothesis will require additional investigation.

Psychoanalysts have studied well-known individuals who have had childhood losses through death and reported their findings, but the focus usually is on either object loss or a preoccupation with death. Rentchnick has written in *The Orphans Lead the World* (1975) that after studying over 350 biographies of political and religious leaders in history, a common denominator emerges, namely that "all the great leaders in history have been orphans, abandoned children, illegitimate children, or children who have rejected their father" (p. 50). I can confirm this correlation, though perhaps not agreeing that "all" such leaders are orphans. I have found similar mourning/object loss correlations in many writers and other gifted individuals. William Niederland, Bernard Meyer, Phyllis Greenacre, and others have discussed the relationship of creativity to object loss and grief in particular writers, scientists, explorers, and artists. Tor-Björn Hägglund, a colleague from Helsinki, has actively pursued research on mourning and has published a most interesting monograph. Hägglund (1976) concluded that "creativity is a continuation of mourning work"; however, when "creativity replaces mourning work, it is manifested in compulsory repetition" (p. 134).

Gay (1976) believes we can distinguish between three kinds of causal factors in works of art: the impact of the surrounding culture of the artist; his craft; and his personal psychological configuration. For different artists—and I use the word *artist* in the broad sense and not as dealing only with visual spatial representations—one or another of the "causes" noted by Gay may be the predominant feature. With regard to the first cause, we may ask how we can assess the relative dominance of cultural impact or personal urgency, since both are present. One might additionally ask how one can compare the external and internal significances of cultural determinants in an individual creator. Conversely, one may query what impact the personal elements have on shaping the culture. For example, the personality of a Stalin, Hitler, Churchill, or Roosevelt can and I believe did have an impact on the political–sociocultural state of the world during a critical period of history. Furthermore, can we discern in the creative product, through an analysis of the content, which elements are represented? We may not be talking about causes and effects but about antecedent elements that are woven together in unique ways to result in conditions, responses, reflections, and creations. To try to isolate the antecedent elements may be impossible or at least difficult. Analogously it would be like a qualitative–quantitative chemical analysis—we might determine which elements are present and in what amounts, but the unique configuration resulting in reactivity may not be so easily ascertained. The psychological reflections, definitions and reworkings, additions and reflections, involvements and choices that went on in the creator's mind in the preparation and production of the creative work are usually unavailable to us. Thus our speculations, even buttressed by seemingly appropriate correlations and significant repetitions, are at best approximations. This we should state, repeat, and emphasize.

We need also to separate explicitly the questioning of the psychoanalytic historian from the appreciation of the critic. As Gay (1976) notes: "The historian does not render critics redundant; his most exhaustive and most satisfactory causal explanation remains mute on the aesthetic properties, let alone aesthetic value, of a landscape or a symphony" (p. 3). Gay deals with art, not as an aesthetic object, but as a "piece of history." Too often this important distinction is overlooked. We lose sight of the aesthetic value of a creation in our pursuit of understanding the psychological factors in the creator that may have played a role in its genesis. Both can be and are useful, but we must with humility address both considerations. Why a story, painting, musical composition, poem, appeals to us can be as useful a contribution as is the approximate understanding of the creator's psychology or psychopathology. To be sure, we have not as yet fully addressed the question of aesthetics from a psychoanalytic vantage point. Perhaps we should begin thinking about this as an area for further study. In addition, to investigate the genetic determinants of the creator, it may be useful to also explore the historical factors associated with the particular creative work. This is to be contrasted with the search for the psychological meaning of the artistic achievement for its creator. At times we may easily detect the self-revelations in the creative product, at times what is formally expressed is less easily or at times impossible to discern and outside the domain of psychoanalytic study.

When we look at craft we are at a disadvantage unless we are truly students of the discipline in which the artist works. We need to know more about technique, style, sensitivity, and so again with humility decline to conjecture about that which we know only superficially.

With regard to personality and psychological configuration, we recognize that multiple determinants and outcomes can be puzzling. Different psychoanalysts may focus upon one or another aspect of the same event or the same manifestations. Insofar as they ask different questions, use different theoretical approaches, look for different etiological antecedents, different features will assume a saliency that at times borders on exclusivity. Analogies or models may be treated as actualities. Fancy can become fact and caution is not in evidence. The theoretical approach and the question addressed may, if not put into appropriate perspective, appear to be the sole variable responsible for whatever is the subject of the report. It is true that some factors are more important, more serious, more meaningful than others. But such distinctions can be made more explicitly as well as the reasons for the choice and evaluation.

An artistic work undoubtedly represents some aspect, narrow or broad, shallow or deep, simple or complex, of its creator. But as is well known, understanding the creator, the meaning of the work, is speculative and probabilistic, unlike the data and explanations we can offer about individuals with whom we have had direct contact. This notwithstanding, I do not advocate abandoning the investigation of artists and their creations as I believe artists do give articulation to their personal perceptions, understandings, ideas, and values in their products. We may attempt to give meaning to these works but we have the responsibility to present evidence, not just subjective impression, which has some significance. Perhaps repetitive patterns of response or style, correlations of thematic content with life events—past or present, observing similarities and connections—all of these should push the answerable questioning further and make the formulations more convincing. We should discriminate between instances where all we can do is speculate or broadly approximate from those where meaning and significance can be traced in fine detail. Purpose and motivation can usually only at best be inferred. These should not be avoided in discussions. They should be labeled as conjectures based on evidence more significant than chance explanations.

I have attempted to use the above guidelines in my own research on mourning and creativity, although in this presentation my focus has been an emphasis of one facet of a complex situation.

I wish to acknowledge the contributions of Melanie Klein, Hanna Segal, and Ella Freeman Sharpe to our deeper understanding of the relationship of deeper psychological processes to creativity. Klein's theories are well known. Her suggestion that reparative drives restoring loved internal and external objects form the basis of creativity and sublimation is a cornerstone of her theories (Klein and Riviere, 1953). Restoration preserves the lost object and gives it eternal life. She noted in 1929 that drawing and painting could be used to restore and repair a psychological injury. In 1935, reparation was seen as a central concept in relation to the depressive position. In 1940, reparation was emphasized as being of specific special significance in overcoming states of mourning. She writes that:

> In acute mourning suffering can become productive. We know that painful experiences of all kinds sometimes stimulate sublimations, or even bring out quite new gifts in some people, who may take to painting, writing or other productive activities under

the stress of frustrations and hardships. Others become more productive in a different way—more capable of appreciating people and things, more tolerant in their relationships to others—they become wiser [Klein, 1940, p. 143].

Hanna Segal (1952), in her paper "A Psychoanalytic Approach to Aesthetics," builds on the work of Klein, especially that dealing with loss and infantile depression and its relationship to later reparation and restoration through sublimation and creativity.

Utilizing the works of Proust, Segal (1952) calls our attention to the statement that "the artist is compelled to create by his need to recover his lost past. But a purely intellectual memory of the past even when it is available, is emotionally valueless and dead" (Proust, quoted in Segal, 1952, p. 199). Through chance associations filled with vivid emotions remembrances of the past occur and then the experience of loss and the mourning process is activated. Yet Proust observes that the past remains elusive because such memories are transient. Segal quotes Proust: "I had to recapture from the shade that which I had felt, to reconvert it into its psychic equivalent. But the way to do it, the only one I could see, what was it—but to create a work of art" (Proust, quoted in Segal, 1952, p. 199). Through his memory work, Proust's past is revived and includes his parents, his beloved grandmother, and his Albertine. Proust comments that it is only the lost past and the lost or dead object that can be made into a work of art. To Segal, "it is only when the loss has been acknowledged and the mourning experienced that re-creation can take place" (1952, p. 199). I would question whether the piece of art is only a re-creation. My view is that it is a new creation deriving its energy and perhaps inspiration and direction from the past, but still a successor creation and not just a replacement creation. Furthermore, I have evidence that suggests that at times the creative product is not the end result of the mourning process, but represents an attempt at mourning work through creativity. At times the mourning is pathological with a suicidal outcome, and yet the creative works have an aesthetic validity nonetheless (e.g., Virginia Woolf, Anne Sexton, Sylvia Plath, John Berryman). Segal does suggest that writing for Proust could be seen as mourning work. As his past objects are gradually given up, "they are reinstated in the ego, and re-created in the book." Furthermore, she believes that

> [In the unconscious of all artists] all creation is really a re-creation of a once loved and once whole, but now lost and ruined object, a ruined internal world and self. It is when the world within us is destroyed, when it is dead and loveless, when our loved ones are in fragments, and when we ourselves in helpless despair—it is then that we must re-create our world anew, reassemble the pieces, infuse life into dead fragments, re-create life [Segal, 1952, p. 199].

Linking the wish and capacity to create to the successful working through of the depressive position, Segal conversely sees inhibitions of artistic expression as indicative of an inability to acknowledge and overcome this early depressive anxiety. When I think of Segal's explanations as nonabsolutes I can confirm some of her assertions. But I have found creativity at times where little mourning process was evidenced or where it was grossly distorted or arrested. I also maintain that the mourning process is distinct from the infantile depressive position. Actually Segal discusses how an assimilated or re-nounced object or its equivalent becomes a symbol which is differentiated from the lost, recovered, or changed object, is a creation of the self—a creation that has personal meaning but also in the talented it has aesthetic significance to others. In Segal's view, "all aesthetic pleasure includes an unconscious re-living of the artist's experience of creation" (1952, p. 204). I would also add the conscious and unconscious response to the artistic product itself. If the artist touches a universal affective theme, each of our individual responses, coming from our own specific sources, having unique meanings, could still have a commonality that is stimulated by the product itself. Perhaps in order for us to enjoy, appreciate, or be moved by the creative product we ourselves must have undergone our own mourning processes and so can empathize with that process and its outcome in the artist. "All artists aim at immortality; their objects must not only be brought back to life, but also the life has to be eternal. And of all human activities art comes nearest to achieving immortality; a great work of art is likely to escape destruction and oblivion" (Segal, 1952, p. 207).

The Case of Gustav Mahler[1]

In earlier works, I have described the adaptive aspect of the mourning process and suggested that this adaptation, so unique in man, could be seen in higher forms of animal life and, in later studies, anniversary phenomena were described as manifestations of abnormal or incompleted mourning processes (Pollock, 1961, 1962, 1968, 1971a, 1971d, 1972a, 1972b, 1973).

Through a study of Gustav Mahler and his music, I shall attempt to illustrate my thesis that the creative product is utilized in the service of mourning and is also an outcome of this process. Although it is impossible in a relatively brief presentation to give a complete biography and discussion of the works of such a prolific composer as Mahler, I shall attempt to present an account of the pertinent biographical facts of this individual, and some of his selected musical creations as they relate to his attempts at mourning resolution. In Mahler's life we will see how his multiple childhood sibling losses played a role in shaping his personality, in his musical compositions, and in his selection of the texts he chose for his music. Again, I wish to emphasize my belief that the multiple childhood traumas do not account for his genius; however, they did give direction to the expression of this genius. The thematic perseveration of music and texts as they relate to death, resurrection, and mourning are especially noteworthy. Of particular interest also is Mahler's extensive consultation with Freud in Leyden a few months before Mahler's untimely death in 1911. I am particularly indebted to the published works of Donald Mitchell (1955, 1958), Theodore Reik (1953), and Alma Mahler (1969; see also Werfel, 1958) for many details I have used in this presentation.

[1]A portion of this material was first presented at the Regional Conference of the Chicago Psychoanalytic Society on March 30, 1974.

Gustav Mahler was born in Kalischt in Bohemia (near the Moravian border) on July 7, 1860. In December 1860, the family moved to the town of Iglau (Jihlava), which was not far from Kalischt, and it was here that Mahler spent most of his childhood and early adolescence. Of his father, Bernhard, who was known to have a violent temper, Mahler wrote in a letter:

> My father (whose mother previously supported the family as a pedler of drapery) had the most diverse phases of making a livelihood behind him and, with his usual energy had more and more worked himself up [the social scale]. At first he had been a waggoner, and while he was driving his horse and cart, had studied and read all sorts of books—he had even lernt a bit of French, which earned him the nickname of a "waggon scholar." Later he was employed in various factories, and subsequently he became a private coach [Hauslehrer]. On the strength of the little estate in Kalischt, he eventually married my mother—the daughter of a soap manufacturer from Leddetsche—who did not love him, hardly knew him prior to the wedding, and would have preferred to marry another man of whom she was fond. But her parents and my father knew how to bend her will and to assert his. They were as ill-matched as fire and water. He was obstinacy itself, she all gentleness. And without this alliance, neither I nor my third [Symphony] would exist . . . [cited in Mitchell, 1958, p. 5].

Bernhard Mahler was also born at Kalischt, on August 2, 1827. Mahler's mother, Marie, was born on March 3, 1837, of a Jewish family having higher social status than that of his father. Mitchell suggests that Bernhard Mahler chose her in order to acquire "culture in the shape of a refined wife of a good family. The prize would have flattered his vanity, soothed his feelings of inferiority, and swelled his self-esteem" (Mitchell, 1958, p. 6). Marie Frank, being handicapped from birth, had a delicate constitution, and suffered from a "weak heart." Since the man she loved was not interested in her, she was resigned to an unhappy marriage, which it was. Bernhard Mahler treated his wife roughly, at times violently, and the young Gustav saw the suffering his mother had to endure as a result of his father's brutality. Gustav Mahler's wife, Alma, indicated that she "never heard Mahler say an affectionate word of his father, but his love for his mother had the intensity of a fixation, then and always" (Mahler, 1969, p. 8).

Bernhard and Marie Mahler had fourteen children in twenty-one years. Of their three daughters and eleven sons, most died at an early age. De la Grange (1973) has provided the following chronology:

1. Isidor—born March 22, 1858, died accidentally in Kalischt in 1859.
2. Gustav, the composer—born July 7, 1860, died May 18, 1911.
3. Ernst—born 1861, died April 13, 1875, of pericarditis. . . .
4. Leopoldine—born May 18, 1863, died in Vienna September 27, 1889, of a tumor of the brain or meningitis. Married Ludwig Quittner; two children, Anna and Heinrich.
5. Karl—born August 1864, died in Iglau December 28, 1865. . . .
6. Rudolf—born August 17, 1865, died in Iglau February 21, 1866.
7. Louis or Alois (later Hans Christian), born October 6, 1867, died in 192? . . . .
8. Justine—born December 16, 1868, died in 1938. She married in 1902 the famous violinist Arnold Rosé, by whom she had two children, Alfred and Alma.
9. Arnold—born December 19, 1869, died of scarlet fever about December 14, 1871. . . .
10. Friedrich—born April 23, 1871, died of scarlet fever about December 14, 1871. . . .
11. Alfred—born April 22, 1872, died in Iglau of "*Lungenwassersucht*" (pulmonary congestive heart failure) on May 6, 1873.
12. Otto—born June 18, 1873. He had just begun a career as a theater orchestra conductor when he committed suicide in Vienna on February 6, 1895.
13. Emma—born October 19, 1875. Married in 1898 Eduard Rosé the violoncellist, brother of the violinist;

lived in Boston, Vienna, and Weimar; she died May 15,
1933. Two children, Ernst and Wolfgang.
14. Konrad—born April 17, 1879, died of diphtheria on
   January 9, 1881 [de la Grange, 1973, pp. 11–12].

Ernst's death was a particularly meaningful experience for
Gustav Mahler. "He loved his brother Ernst and suffered with
him all through his illness up to the end. For months he scarcely
left his bedside and never tired of telling him stories. To all else
he was blind (Mahler, 1969, p. 7). And in later years, "Mahler
reproached himself, as though he were partly to blame for [his
sister Leopoldine's] unhappiness" (Mahler, 1969, p. 9).

His sister Justine joined Gustav Mahler's household after the
deaths of their parents. She had peculiar fantasies as a child.
Alma Mahler mentions that "while still a child, she stuck candles
all around the edge of her cot. Then she lay down and lit the
candles and firmly believed she was dead" (Mahler, 1969, p. 9).
Since orthodox Jewish practice after death includes placing
candles around the body of the deceased, one wonders if this
morbid act did not relate to the number of dead siblings she
had seen in such a position.

Justine and Emma married musicians, who were brothers, as
noted by de la Grange (1973). Justine married Arnold Rosé
(1863–1946), a leading member of the Vienna Philharmonic
Orchestra, and a friend and close colleague of Mahler. He left
for England in 1938, I assume after his wife's death, and died
in London in 1946. Emma married Eduard Rosé, Arnold's
brother, and a distinguished cellist. He was deported by the
Nazis to Theresienstadt in the fall of 1942 and died there of
starvation at age 84 in January 1943.

As I hope to demonstrate more clearly later in this chapter,
the impact of many sibling deaths during Mahler's childhood
also left lifelong psychological scars. He was second, but became
first when his brother Isadore died. Perhaps the great involvement with his dying brother, Ernst, reflected a displacement of
his guilt over survival with overcompensatory defenses.

Theodor Reik (1953), writing in another connection, provides us with some evidence to support the idea that Mahler
suffered from guilt over his childhood sibling deaths and, I

would point out, over his successes as a conductor. Reik indicates that the last concert of the 1894 season was to be dedicated to Hans von Bülow who had just died. Richard Strauss was to direct the concert, but he became ill at the last moment and Mahler took his place. The young musician wrote then to his sister Justine: "It is strange that someone always has to become ill to make it possible for me to conduct a symphony" (cited in Reik, 1953, p. 346). Reik indicates that he felt Mahler believed that such a replacement opportunity was not due to chance but was "fatefull or preordained"; that is, "as if the illness of his predecessor were the only possible way that his wish to conduct a symphony concert could be fulfilled" (Reik, 1953, p. 346). My interpretation of this fantasy of Mahler relates to his childhood replacement experience. When the first sibling-son dies, then he, the second in line, takes over the first position. The preferred conductor becomes ill or dies and then his place is taken by Mahler. Reik considered this chain of events as possibly indicating a concealed belief that the thoughts of the successful rival (Mahler) were responsible for the removal of his predecessor. This may be so, but Mahler's genius extended to two musical areas—conducting and composing. In his conducting, which he viewed as interfering with his composing, competition for position could and did occur, and I believe this competition was connected with his sibling relationships. But in his musical composing, the creative urge was less involved with successful competition with a rival.

Reik cited several instances in Mahler's career where he advanced as a conductor after someone before him became ill. Hans von Bülow was forced to quit as conductor of the Hamburg Orchestra after a serious illness, leaving Mahler as substitute conductor until after Bülow's death, when Mahler became the permanent leader. Prior to Hamburg, Mahler owed his early position as conductor in Olmütz to the death of the conductor there. Since 1886, Mahler had functioned as the second conductor in Leipzig. In February 1887, the first conductor became ill and Mahler took over for several months. When the primary conductor recovered, Mahler left as he felt he could not get this position. Then Alexander Erkel, the director of the Royal Opera in Budapest, became ill and Mahler was appointed director in his place. After the Hamburg post, Wilhelm Jahn, the director of the Vienna opera for seventeen years, became ill. Wanting to ease his burden, he engaged Mahler as assistant director. Jahn became further incapacitated through an eye disease and was unable to read a score; Mahler became his successor and led the Royal Theater to a phase of great artistic achievement.

The same pattern was repeated with Hans Richter, conductor of the Vienna Philharmonic Orchestra, who became ill and whose place Mahler took while he was also director of the Vienna opera. Mahler never hesitated to take a place vacated by a rival's illness. There was no evidence of conscious guilt feelings in these situations, but Reik believes, and I agree with his formulation, that Mahler feared for his own replacement. He frequently quoted, "Vita fugax" ("Life is transient"). He seemed to fear that his own end was not far away. This is understandable when we remember the number of his siblings who died early and almost regularly.

In 1907, Mahler left Vienna for New York where he was conductor at the Metropolitan Opera. The concertmaster, whom Mahler admired, told Mahler that he planned on being a conductor after he fulfilled his obligations as violinist to the orchestra. Reik noted that Mahler remarked, "Well, I have to become ill in order to give you the opportunity" (1953, p. 349). Mahler feared retribution by becoming the victim of those competitive and destructive wishes of others against him. However, we must also consider that Mahler may have felt from early childhood that his days would be very few. When Mahler was a little boy, he was asked what he wanted to be. He replied, "A martyr." Mitchell (1958) interprets this reply as the overwhelming expression of his identification with his mother's martyrdom. I would see it additionally as an identification with his dead siblings and his fear that he was doomed as they were.

To return to Mahler's two brothers, Otto and Alois, for a moment: "Alois [who] later called himself Hans, because it sounded less Jewish, ran into debt, forged notes and finally had to flee to America" (Mahler, 1969, p. 10). Otto showed great musical talent, and Gustav acted as his mentor helping him in every way possible. Otto failed at the jobs Gustav obtained for him and in February 1895, Otto killed himself, leaving a note behind saying that life no longer pleased him and so he handed back his ticket. In Otto's desk were found two symphonies, a number of songs with orchestration, three books of lieder, and a nearly completed third symphony (Mitchell, 1958).

Mahler's musical abilities appeared early. Around the age of five, on a visit to his maternal grandparents, he could not be found. He was finally discovered in the attic playing on an old piano. From that period on, his parents, especially his father, were convinced that he was destined to be a musician and they encouraged him in this goal. Mahler himself claimed that from the age of four onward he was both making music and composing, even before he could play scales. Between the ages of four and six, he supposedly could sing over two hundred folksongs, learned from servants. It is also claimed that at age four he could correctly play on an accordion all of the march tunes used in the neighboring barracks (Engel, 1970). Mahler started piano lessons at five. He learned rapidly and at age eight had a pupil of his own, aged seven. On October 13, 1870, the ten-year-old Gustav Mahler made his piano debut at a concert in Iglau before a large audience. The weekly newspaper wrote, "The great success the future virtuoso achieved with his audience did him honor; one could only wish that for his excellent playing he had had an equally good instrument at his service" (Mitchell, 1958, p. 19). The young Mahler was now in demand. He played piano, accompanied choirs, and played at local patriotic occasions such as the celebration of the silver wedding of the Emperor and Empress on April 24, 1879.

In 1871, when Mahler was eleven, he spent the winter term at the Gymnasium in Prague. This did not work out well, and he returned to Iglau, at whose gymnasium he remained until he left for Vienna in 1875, where he enrolled at the Conservatory at the age of fifteen. Because of poverty, his days at the Conservatory were not easy. In addition to his courses at the Conservatory, Mahler continued to study for his school-leaving examinations, which he passed in 1877, after which he enrolled at the University of Vienna, studying philosophy, history, and the history of music.

He progressed rapidly at the Conservatory, and at the end of his first year, on June 23, 1876, he was unanimously awarded first place in the piano playing competition. He also won first prize in the composition competition on July 1, 1876, for the first movement of a piano quartet. In addition, he received the highest grades in his three courses—piano playing, harmony, and composition. At the close of the next year, on June 21, 1877, he again won the first prize in the piano competition.

Mahler completed his work at the Conservatory in 1878. He was granted his matriculation and also was honored by being awarded a Diploma, for which the requirements were very stringent. In 1879, Mahler continued with his studies at the University of Vienna, spending much time with Hugo Wolf, the composer, who had tutored the children of Josef Breuer from 1873 to 1883. The relationship with Wolf, its ambivalence, and final dissolution, though interesting, will not be discussed further here. At this time, Mahler developed his friendship with Anton Bruckner, although they were separated by a wide age gulf (Mahler was seventeen and Bruckner was fifty-three). Mahler's devotion to Bruckner and his music was lifelong.

Mitchell notes that after he became a great conductor and composer, Mahler's piano playing, which played so prominent a role in his childhood, youth, and student days, "died so complete a death in later years, but for spasmodic domestic returns to the keyboard; and in his maturity as a composer, the instrument had no role at all" (1958, p. 83). Mahler was known to privately play his compositions on the piano and to also play for purely recreational purposes in the company of congenial musicians such as Bruno Walter, with whom he played piano duets in private.

It is interesting to note that in his last years at the Conservatory, Mahler's pattern of moves from house to house was an "endless succession of removals from one lodging to another, in search of cheap, yet decent and quiet 'diggings,' where he could work at his music in peace. Between . . . September 1876 and May 1879 . . . there are recorded no fewer than twenty-one addresses where he occupied rooms" (Mitchell, 1958, p. 83). One can wonder about the meaning of these many moves and Mahler's later moves from city to city.

I now turn to two early works composed by Mahler as I

believe they illustrate themes connected with Mahler's mourning. The first, an opera composed in 1877–1878, is entitled "Herzog Ernst von Schwaben." The second, a cantata for soprano, contralto, and tenor soloists, mixed chorus, and large orchestra, "Das klagende Lied" ("Song of Woe") was composed from 1878–1880. Mahler finished "Das klagende Lied" in 1880, at which time he undertook his first engagement as a conductor at Bad Hall in upper Austria. His career as a composer actually antedates the beginning of his career as a conductor.

By March 1878, Mahler had completed the text of "Das klagende Lied," having laid aside "Herzog Ernst von Schwaben" in the same year. Mahler clearly associated the memory of his much loved younger brother, Ernst, who died in 1874, to the "Herzog Ernst von Schwaben" work. Mitchell feels the connection lies in the similarity of the names. In fact, he believes that the name is influential "in such matters as the choice of opera libretto or text for a song" (1958, p. 130). I feel one must go further and ask, what does this mean? Does it serve the purpose of remembering the dead brother? Does it represent an attempt at immortalizing the dead brother? Or, does it represent a continuation of the mourning process for the dead brother?

"In the summer of 1901, Mahler composed the music for some songs by the German poet Friedrich Rückert, amongst them the first three poems known as "Kindertotenlieder" ("Songs on the Death of Infants"). Rückert had lost two children, Ernst and Luise, and wrote as many as four hundred forty-eight songs expressing his grief" (Reik, 1953, p. 315). Mahler was not married at the time of the composition of these three songs,[2] and had no child. Reik asks why Mahler chose those songs. He asserts that something in the wording and atmosphere of the "Kindertotenlieder" must have appealed to Mahler and suggests that an intense mourning was reawakened by memories of terrible loss and of the past when the children were still alive.

The Rückert poems speak of the death of two children. Reik

[2]In fact, he had not even known Alma when he wrote the *Kindertotenlieder* cycle (Taylor, personal communication, 1987).

asserted that it was the unconscious remembrance of the past that made Mahler compose these sad songs. At the time of the composition of the "Kindertotenlieder," Mahler said that "he felt sorry for himself while he composed them and felt sorry for the world which would hear them" (Reik, 1953, p. 317). Reik, I believe, correctly connected the Rückert poems with conscious or unconscious memory traces of revived grief and sorrow for two lost children from his childhood, Isadore, who preceded Gustav, and Ernst, who was one year younger than Gustav, and who died in 1874. But Reik attributed the grief and mourning to Mahler's parents. Undoubtedly their bereavement affected Mahler and his surviving siblings. I would add, however, that the more significant mourning was that of Gustav Mahler himself. I would suggest that Gustav felt survivor guilt toward both of these dead siblings. The dead child of Rückert was named Ernst, as was Mahler's own dead brother. So when Mahler felt sorry for himself while composing the "Kindertotenlieder," he was still expressing his mourning for his brothers, especially for Ernst, whom he knew, loved, and cared for. The feelings which were not fully expressed, and the words which he could not say, came out in the music to the Rückert songs. Reik has pointed out that:

> Children whose siblings have died and who witness the mourning and grief of their parents feel vivid emotions akin to envy and jealousy toward their dead brother or sister, as if they wished they themselves had died or that their parents would mourn for them in such a deeply felt manner. It is easy to recognize in this reaction the feelings of rivalry and competition with the sibling when he was alive. More intense than this tendency is perhaps the wish to be loved and mourned by the parents as much as the child who has died. Here is yet another process of unconscious identification, that with the dead brother [Reik, 1953, pp. 318–319].

When Mahler's beloved daughter died five years later in 1907, he connected the dirge composition with the possibility of a prophetic anticipation. Could it not instead be that his guilt was such that he felt he had to have done to his child what was done to both his immediately older and younger siblings? The music and the texts were still aspects of Mahler's mourning work for his childhood losses.[3] Mahler expected tragedy to be constantly with him, and unfortunately this was the true state of affairs. He himself died at age fifty-one of the same illness as his mother, who died at fifty-two. By moving about, working hard, destroying his early works as a possible means of destroying the past, Mahler may have tried to avert his felt destiny, but to no avail.

When a fellow student at the Conservatory, Hans Rott (1859–1881), whom he had beaten in the composition competition, died in 1881, Mahler wrote:

> What music has lost in him cannot be estimated. Such is the height to which his genius already soars in this first symphony, which he wrote as a twenty-year-old youth and which makes him—I am not exaggerating—the founder of the new symphony as I see it. To be sure, what he wanted is not yet quite achieved. It is as if somebody raised his arm for the farthest possible throw and, still clumsy, falls far short of the target. But I know where he aims. Indeed, he is so near to my innocent self that he and I seem to me like two fruits from the same tree which the same soil has produced and the same air nourished. He could have meant infinitely much to me and perhaps the two of us would [have] well-nigh exhausted the content of this new time which was breaking out for music [cited in Mitchell, 1958, p. 95].

Do we read here the mourning for what was and what would never be? Is this mourning for a sibling with whom Mahler feels like "two fruits from the same tree which the same soil has produced and the same air nourished" or for himself?

When we turn to "Das klagende Lied," we are confronted with data that may give us a clue as to why Mahler chose the fairytale for this cantata and how he changed it to suit his

[3]We cannot ignore the fact that Gustav Mahler may have been treated as a replacement child for the dead older sibling and that Ernst (born in 1861) was in utero while Gustav was himself an infant. This may have resulted in a further "mother loss"—the mother grieving for Isadore and the very quickly pregnant mother while Gustav was less than one year old.

needs. The text of this work has been traced by Mitchell to a tale of Grimm and to one by Ludwig Bechstein. Mahler's version is as follows:

Part I. A proud Queen declares that whosoever shall find a certain red flower growing in the forest shall win her hand. Two brothers go in search of the flower, the younger of a sweet disposition, the elder evil in character. The younger brother finds the flower, sticks it in his hat, and stretches out to rest. He is discovered asleep by his elder brother, who, jealous of his success, strikes him dead with a sword, steals the flower, and claims the Queen as his bride. The younger brother lies buried under leaves and blossoms beneath a willow tree.

Part II. . . . introduces the minstrel, who picks up a gleaming white bone, fashions it into a flute and plays upon it—when he is astonished to hear the flute pour forth its tale of murder, "sorrow and woe." The minstrel ventures forth to seek out the king and his bride.

Part III. . . . brings us to the castle. It is the Queen's wedding day and a feast is in progress. The minstrel enters the castle hall and plays his flute; it repeats once more the story of the murder. The guilty king leaps to his feet, seizes the flute and scornfully places it to his lips: the bone sings again its sorry tale of fratricide. The Queen collapses to the ground, the guests flee, and the castle walls begin to crumble [Mitchell, 1958, pp. 142–143].

In Ludwig Bechstein's fairy tale, the contenders for the flower are not brothers but brother and sister; and the prize is not marriage but succession to the Queen's throne. The Princess, the firstborn, finds the flower and lies down to sleep, whereupon she is murdered by her jealous brother. In later years a peasant boy picks up a bone and makes a flute from it; he is startled when a child's voice issues forth and tells the manner of the sister's death.

A knight takes possession of the flute and appears at the castle where the guilty brother is King and his mother still mourns her lost daughter. It is to the old Queen alone that the flute reveals the terrible truth. She then takes the instrument and herself plays it to her son before a festive assembly in the castle hall. The story ends on this note of chilling catastrophe, in which the mother is the final instrument of her son's doom [Mitchell, 1958, p. 143].

In the Grimm tale, "we find two brothers competing for a wife, a rivalry which ends in fratricide. The circumstances of the competition and the murder are quite different from those we find in the cantata, but the loquacious bone flute and details of the denouement are as we know them in Mahler's text" (Mitchell, 1958, p. 143).

Mahler combined these two tales. He eliminated the mother who destroys her guilty son, and substituted two brothers for Bechstein's brother–sister rivalry. Mitchell correctly but incompletely asserted that "it must be that the roots of Mahler's variations of Bechstein's story lay in his own psychological makeup, that the changed relationships were conditioned by emotional attitudes of Mahler towards members of his family" (1958, p. 144). I would ask if it was too close to Mahler's inner fears that a mother can destroy the surviving son after the first has died. Fratricide, evil as it is, is safer than filicide at the hands of the mother. And yet, it was the same cardiac illness that destroyed not only the mother but Ernst and eventually Gustav. Did Mahler suffer from survivor guilt regarding Ernst and Isadore? Did he fear that his music (the flute) might reveal this? Was there a fear of his own death? Mahler's music may reflect his pathological mourning and inevitable, tragic end. One can speculate about the meanings of the text Mahler chose for his cantata, though there is no definite proof. The evidence points toward unresolved problems and unfinished business connected with his childhood siblings' deaths.

While working on "Das klagende Lied," Mahler's concerns with death emerged in two letters, both written in 1879. In the first, dated June 18, 1879, he wrote:

Oh my beloved earth, where, oh when, wilt thou take the abandoned one unto thy breast? Behold! Mankind has banished him from itself, and he flees from its cold and heartless bosom to thee, to thee! Oh care for the lonely one, for the restless one, Universal Mother [Mitchell, 1958, p. 88].

In the second letter, also written in 1879, about the time of his brother Konrad's death and while working on "Das klagende Lied," Mahler stated: "The highest ecstasy of the most joyous strength of life and the most burning desire for death: these two reign alternately within my heart; yes, oftentimes they alternate within the hour" (Mitchell, 1958, p. 89).

Engel reported that while Mahler was working day and night to finish "Das klagende Lied," Mahler kept raising his tired eyes to watch a certain shadowy corner of the room. "All at once it seemed to him that the wall was coming to life. Someone was struggling furiously to come through it into the room. Now he could see the apparition's face contorted with the agony of hopeless struggle. Suddenly he knew it was his own face! Terror-stricken Mahler rushed from the room" (Engel, 1970, p. 32).

Ten years later, while working out the funeral march in his symphony, he had a similar experience.

> One night . . . he was very weary and lifted his eyes gradually from the intricate web of notes which he had just written. His tired gaze wandered about the room, finally coming to rest upon the wreaths of flowers, trophies of the "Three Pintos" [Mahler's successful completion of Weber's unfinished musical manuscript], heaped in profusion upon the table in the center. A moment later he attempted once more to concentrate upon the music, but an uncanny feeling had stolen upon him and again he looked up. Suddenly the appearance of the table had changed. It seemed to him as if it were now surrounded by weirdly flickering candles! And on the center, among the wreaths lay a shape,—a corpse! The features were his own! Horrified he rushed from the room [Engel, 1970, p. 63].

The similarity to Justine's early action with the candles is striking. One can surmise that the meaning of this hallucination dealt with Mahler's anxiety about his own survival—a manifestation of his early childhood concerns over his own death.

To jump ahead in time, in February 1889, Mahler's father died (at age sixty-two), to be followed by the death of his mother in October of that year (at age fifty-two). The household at Iglau was abandoned and the three eldest dependent children, Justine, Emma, and Otto, moved to Vienna where Mahler assumed the burden of providing a home for them. As indicated earlier, this was also the year that his oldest sister, Leopoldine, died. Mahler was beset by financial difficulties in meeting his new responsibilities. In the next few years, he began to work on his second symphony, entitled "Death and Resurrection," whose opening movement is entitled "Death-celebration," a funereal composition during which the dead hero is carried to his grave. The death music is "subjective and out of its sombre depths rise the ultimate human questions: Why have you lived? To what end have you suffered? Is it just a great, terrible jest? We must somehow answer this to prove life worth while, and death life's most magnificent step towards fulfillment" (Engel, 1970, p. 93).

Reik, for personal reasons, has extensively discussed Mahler's "Second Symphony." He quoted a letter from Mahler in which Mahler wrote:

I know that as far as I can shape an inner experience in words, I certainly would not write any music about it. My need to express myself musically and symphonically starts only where the dark emotions begin, at the door leading to the "other world," the world in which things are not any more separated by time and place [1953, p. 252].

Mahler described the last movement of the Second Symphony to another friend:

It starts with the cry of dying and now comes the solution of the terrible problems of life, at first as faith and church shaped it in the beyond. A trembling moves over the earth. Listen to the roll of the drums and your hair will stand on end! The Great Summons sounds. The graves open and all creatures emerge from the soil, shrieking and with chattering teeth. Now they all come a-marching: beggars and wealthy men, common people and kings, the ecclesia militans, the popes. With all of them the same anxiety, shouting and quivering with fear, because none is just before God. Between it again and again—as if from the other world—from beyond the Great Summons. Finally, after all had cried out in the worst turmoil, only the long-lasting voice of the death-bird from the last grave. It also becomes silent at last. And now nothing of all that which was dreaded comes; no last judgment, no blessed and no damned. None is good, none bad—no judge, low and simple the chorale sets in: Rise, yes, rise [Reik, 1953, pp. 253–254].

Mooney, who has also studied Mahler's life and works, commented that "Mahler's conscious preoccupation with problems of life and death is reflected in some way in almost every composition" (1968, p. 88). Mahler was frequently preoccupied, with understandable reason, with his own death and questions about the meaning of life, why there was so much suffering, if there was a reward or punishment in the "beyond," or even if there was a "beyond." Each of his symphonies was a new attempt at an answer. "And when he had arrived at an answer, the same question rose soon anew as an unquenchable cry of longing. He could not—such was his nature—hold positions conquered, because he was not constant" (Bruno Walter, cited in Reik, 1953, p. 257).

Mahler could not solve the problem of a finale to the Second Symphony. In a letter to Arthur Seidl (February 17, 1897) he related the experience which brought him his answer.

> Bülow died, and I attended the memorial service for him. . . . The mood in which I sat there and thought of the departed one was exactly that of the work which, at that time, occupied me constantly—at that moment, the chorus near the organ intoned the Klopstock chorale Aufersteh'n! It struck me like a bolt of lightning and everything stood clear and vivid before my soul. The creator waits for this bolt of lightning; this is his "Holy Annunciation." What I then experienced, I had now to shape into tones. And yet, if I had not carried that idea with me, how could I have experienced it? There were a thousand people with me in the church at that moment [cited by Reik, 1953, p. 264].

It is significant that the funeral celebration for a man who had helped Mahler and who suggested that he should become his successor stimulated and sparked the solution of the finale. The funeral, undoubtedly, reminded him of other very personal funerals he had attended from childhood onward. Resurrection was the answer he sought. "Rise, yes, rise wilt thou, my dust" were Mahler's words.

The last movement, the musical exposition of Resurrection, inspired by the choral setting of Klopstock's ode on Resurrection, which was given a choral setting at Bülow's funeral, was the answer to Mahler's questions. I believe, however, the three family deaths in 1889 served as the stimulus for this work and were in part Mahler's musical mourning for his parents and sister.

Gustav Mahler married Alma Marie Schindler on March 9, 1902, the day before his sister Justine was married. On November 3, 1902, the Mahlers had their first child, a daughter, named Marie after his mother. The name Marie was very important to Mahler; Mahler's "first impulse" was to convince Alma to change her own name to Marie after their marriage (Mahler, 1969, p. 175). This obviously did not occur, even though Alma's middle name was Marie. The second child, also a daughter, named Anna, was born on June 15, 1904.

Mahler was very attached to his daughter Marie. Alma Mahler wrote:

> Our elder child used to go to Mahler's studio every morning. They held long conversations there together. Nobody has ever known what about. I never disturbed them. We had a fussy English nurse who took her to his door, as clean and neat as a new pin. By the time Mahler brought her back she was usually smeared with jam from top to toe. It was my job to pacify the English nurse. But they were so happy together after their talk that I took a secret pleasure in these occasions.
>
> She was his child entirely. Her beauty and waywardness, and her unapproachability, her black curls and large blue eyes, foretold that she would be a danger later on. But if she was allowed only a short life, she was chosen to be his joy for a few years, and that in itself is worth an eternity. It was his wish to be buried in her grave. And his wish was fulfilled [1969, p. 105].

Marie died of complications resulting from scarlet fever and diphtheria, the disease that was so fatal for Mahler's siblings, on July 5, 1907. In addition to this blow, from which Mahler never recovered, the confirmed diagnosis of his own serious heart condition (from which he died on May 18, 1911), and his resignation of his Vienna post, all occurred in 1907. After Marie's death, Mahler then turned to the melancholy poems, "The Chinese Flute," which answered his own deep grief, and from these he wrote "Das Lied von der Erde" a year later. There is a clear connection between his mourning for Marie and this magnificent symphony. Alma Mahler noted that "he expressed all his sorrow and dread in this work—The Song of the Earth. Its first title was 'The Song of the Sorrow of the Earth'" (1969, p. 139).

Mahler's later Fifth, Sixth, and Seventh Symphonies form a trilogy dealing with death. The Fifth opens with a grim, long trumpet call in a minor key preceding a funeral march. The Sixth Symphony, called the "Tragic," is followed by the Seventh, conjuring up secrets and mysteries of goblins' spirits. As already indicated, the Ninth Symphony, "Das Lied von der Erde," was composed after the death of his beloved child Marie. "Mahler had always been superstitious about a ninth symphony" (Mooney, 1968, p. 91). And he did not wish to call his work the Ninth Symphony as he felt he might die after its completion since Beethoven, Schubert, and Bruckner had died after writing a ninth symphony. Although Mahler almost finished another symphony afterwards, the Farewell Song closing "Das Lied von der Erde" has been almost universally regarded as his own farewell to the world.

Mahler's heart condition, diagnosed by chance after Marie's death, marked the beginning of the end for Mahler. Initially he was very anxious about his health, feeling his pulse, ascertaining whether his heart beat was clear, rapid, or regular. The beginning of the end came in New York in 1911. He insisted on conducting what was his last concert on February 21, 1911. Among the works he conducted that night was the first public performance of Busoni's "Cradlesong at the Grave of My Mother." He went steadily downhill, and traveled from New York to Paris and finally to Vienna, where he died on May 18, 1911. The burial, close to that of his beloved child, Marie, may have had deeper significance. In some way he perhaps felt the reunion was not only with Marie, his dead daughter, but also with Marie, his dead mother.

Mitchell (1958) has said: "The state of mind in which the

Tenth Symphony was composed must have approximated very closely a private hell." Mahler has left evidence to indicate this in his exclamations on the manuscript, Third Movement (Purgatorio):

Compassion! O God! O God, why hast thou forsaken me? Death! Transfiguration!

Fourth Movement title page:

The devil leads me in a dance. Demolish me that I may forget my being! That I may cease to exist. . . . End of movement (muffled drum): None but you knows what it signifies! . . . Fare thee well, my lyre! Farewell, Farewell, Farewell.

Fifth Movement, Finale:

To live for thee! To die for thee! Almschi!

From Alma Mahler we learn what the muffled drum signifies. In 1907–1908:

[At the Hotel Majestic in New York] hearing a confused noise, we leaned out of the window and saw a long procession in the broad street along the side of Central Park. It was the funeral cortege of a fireman, of whose heroic death we had read in the newspaper. The chief mourners were almost immediately beneath us when the procession halted, and the master of ceremonies stepped forward and gave a short address. From our eleventh-floor window we could only guess what he said. There was a brief pause and then a stroke on the muffled drum, followed by a dead silence. The procession then moved forward and all was over.

The scene brought tears to our eyes and I looked anxiously at Mahler's window. But he too was leaning out and his face was streaming with tears. The brief drum-stroke impressed him so deeply that he used it in the Tenth Symphony [1969, p. 135].

Since this scene followed the relatively recent death of Mahler's daughter, one can assume the tears were for her death and for the part of him that died with her and for the remainder of himself that would soon join her. As Alma Mahler pointed out, Mahler wished to be buried in the same grave that held his little daughter, Marie. This was done. Mahler and his daughter are buried in the nonsectarian cemetery of Grinzing, a Viennese suburb. Mahler left specific instructions that not a word be said nor a note sung at the burial. In the teeming rain his coffin was lowered, but a rainbow appeared after the burial. Mahler did not live to hear either of his last two symphonies performed in concert.

Postscript

The Freud–Mahler Consultation, 1910

It has been well documented that Mahler saw Freud in 1910, not long before Mahler's untimely death in 1911. Mahler knew he was dying, but the ostensible reason for the consultation dealt with a marital problem.

Alma Mahler, brought to "a complete breakdown" in the summer of 1910, was in a sanatarium in Tobelbad. She was isolated and very melancholy and the head of the hospital introduced young people to her as company for her walks. One such individual was the architect, Walter Gropius, who fell in love with her.[4] He wrote a letter declaring his love for Alma and stating if she had any feeling for him she should leave all and go with him. Although the letter was meant for Alma, it was addressed and sent to Mahler. Mahler, opening the letter, was shocked and felt convinced that Gropius addressed the letter to him as a way of asking Mahler to release Alma so that she could marry him. An intense discussion with Alma ensued, during which she told Mahler of the great deprivation she felt. Even though she felt Mahler, being too self-absorbed, gave her little, she reassured Mahler that she could never leave him. Mahler became ecstatic but he became jealous of everything and everybody having contact with his Alma. Oftentimes Alma found Mahler lying on the floor, weeping in his dread that he

[4]Alma married Gropius after Mahler's death, but they were divorced under troubled circumstances. While Gropius was in the German Army in World War I, Alma had a passionate affair with the artist Oskar Kokoschka, who wanted her to divorce Gropius and marry him. Alma did not do this, but instead married the famous writer Franz Werfel.

might lose her or that he had already lost her (like he lost his mother and his daughter?). On the floor he said he was nearer to the earth. In Alma Mahler's account, she gives details of this entire episode and points out that it was at this time "he wrote those outcries and ejaculations addressed to me in the draft score of the Tenth Symphony" (Werfel, 1958, p. 175). Mahler realized he was very upset and decided to consult Freud who was then on holiday at Leyden in Holland. According to Alma Mahler Freud calmed Mahler and said:

> "I know your wife. She loved her father [who died when she was thirteen] and she can only choose and love a man of his sort. Your age, of which you are so much afraid, is precisely what attracts her. You need not be anxious. You loved your mother, and you look for her in every woman. She was careworn and ailing, and unconsciously you wish your wife to be the same" [Werfel, 1958, p. 176].

Alma Mahler stated that Freud was right in both of his statements, that she always looked for "a small, slight man, who had wisdom and spiritual superiority, since this was what I had known and loved in my father" (Werfel, 1958, p. 175). She also believed Freud's suggestion that Mahler had a fixation on his mother and transferred this to her, Alma.

Discussing only the Alma Mahler account at this point, I believe Mahler was more threatened at "losing" Alma, as a result of her hospitalization and her serious depression than by the rivalry with Gropius. The appearance of another male might have recapitulated the earlier situation when his brother Ernst was born and Mahler was one year old. The loss of the "mother" to the new rival and to her depression and absence from him, in addition to his own anxiety about his health, could have produced a panic state, out of which Freud helped him. After this psychoanalytic consultation, Mahler was very affectionate and self-confident with Alma.

On the train bringing him back from seeing Freud in Leyden, Mahler wrote a poem for Alma, the first lines of which Theodore Reik has translated:

They melt, the shadows of the night.
What always tortured me as fright,
Is blown away by power of one word.
My feeling, pressing to the height,
My thoughts, in danger of the glide,
They flow together into one accord:
I love you. . . [1953, p. 341].

In 1935, Reik wrote to Freud asking him about the meeting with Mahler in Leyden. Freud wrote back to Reik and in part of his letter, he stated:

> If I may believe reports, I achieved much with him at that time. This visit appeared necessary to him, because his wife at the time rebelled against the fact that he withdrew his libido from her. In highly interesting expeditions through his life history, we discovered his personal conditions for love, especially his Holy Mary complex (mother fixation). I had plenty of opportunity to admire the capability for psychological understanding of this man of genius [cited and translated by Reik, 1953, pp. 342–343].

Reik's researches allowed him to fix the date of the Freud consultation in Leyden as either August 26 or 27 of 1910. Mahler died on May 18, 1911. I would wonder if Mahler's libidinal withdrawal from Alma was an attempt to conserve his own biological and psychological integrity in the face of his oncoming death, which was not sudden when it occurred and in all probability was the result of streptoccal endocarditis secondary to rheumatic heart disease.

But before we leave the Mahler–Freud episode, let us have one last hearing—the report of Ernest Jones in his Freud biography. Jones (1955) wrote that Dr. Nepollek, a Viennese psychoanalyst, who was a relative of Alma Mahler, suggested that Mahler consult with Freud. Three times did Mahler make an appointment with Freud and three times did he cancel same. Finally he saw Freud in Leyden. Jones repeated what has been noted above; namely, that Mahler was closely attached to his mother. Jones wrote that the "analytic talk evidently produced an effect, since Mahler recovered his potency, and the marriage was a happy one until his death" (1955, p. 80). I would question that almost total recovery that Jones described. That Mahler was more involved, attentive, and loving is attested to by Alma Mahler, but Mahler knew he was steadily growing weaker and finally died in less than a year. Freud gave Mahler hope—hope to live and expend libido outwards toward his wife. But libido could not fight cardiac pathology, which unfortunately won out in a short time. And now in our age of mourning and nostalgia, we find Mahler resurrected through his music and perhaps a little more here, through a bit of his life.

References

de la Grange, H. L. (1973), *Mahler*, Vol. 1. Garden City, NY: Doubleday.

Engel, G. (1970), *Gustav Mahler*. New York: David Lewis.

Freud, S. (1900), The Interpretation of Dreams. *Standard Edition*, 4 & 5. London: Hogarth Press, 1953.

Gay, P. (1976), *Art and Act: On Causes in History—Manet, Gropius, Mondrian*. New York: Harper & Row.

Hägglund, T. B. (1976), *Dying: A Psychoanalytical Study with Special Reference to Individual Creativity and Defensive Organization*. Helsinki: Psychiatric Clinic, Helsinki University Central Hospital (Monograph 6).

Jones, E. (1953), *The Life and Work of Sigmund Freud*, Vol. 1. New York: Basic Books.

———(1955), *The Life and Work of Sigmund Freud*, Vol. 2. New York: Basic Books.

Klein, M. (1940), Mourning and its relation to manic-depressive states. *Internat. J. Psycho-Anal.*, 21:125–153.

———Riviere, J. (1953), *Love, Hate, and Reparation*. London: Hogarth Press.

Mahler, A. (1969), *Gustav Mahler: Memories and Letters*, rev. ed. New York: Viking Press.

Mitchell, D. (1955), Some notes on Mahler's Tenth Symphony. *The Musical Times*, December.

———(1958), *Gustav Mahler: The Early Years*. London: Rockliff Publishers.

Mooney, W. E. (1968), Gustav Mahler: A note on life and death in music. *Psychoanal. Quart.*, 30:80–102.

Pollock, G. H. (1961), Mourning and adaptation. *Internat. J. Psycho-Anal.*, 42:341–361.

———(1962), Childhood parent and sibling loss in adult patients: A comparative study. *Arch. Gen. Psychiat.*, 7:295–305.

———(1968), The possible significance of childhood object loss in the Josef Breuer–Bertha Pappenheim (Anna O.)–Sigmund Freud relationship. *J. Amer. Psychoanal. Assn.*, 16:711–739.

———(1970), Anniversary reactions, trauma and mourning. *Psychoanal. Quart.*, 39:347–371.

———(1971a), On time and anniversaries. In: *The Unconscious Today*, ed. M. Kanzer. New York: International Universities Press, pp. 233–257.

————(1971b), Temporal anniversary manifestations: Hour, day, holiday. *Psychoanal. Quart.*, 40:123–131.

————(1971c), On time, death and immortality. *Psychoanal. Quart.*, 40:435–446.

————(1971d), Some historical notes on Bertha Pappenheim's idealized ancestor: Glükel von Hameln. *Amer. Imago*, 23:216–227.

————(1972a), On mourning and anniversaries: The relationship of culturally constituted defensive systems to intrapsychic adaptive processes. *Israel Ann. Psychiat. & Rel. Discip.*, 10:9–40.

————(1972b), Bertha Pappenheim's pathological mourning: Possible effects of childhood sibling loss. *J. Amer. Psychoanal. Assn.*, 20:476–493.

————(1973), Bertha Pappenheim: Addenda to her case history. *J. Amer. Psychoanal. Assn.*, 21:328–332.

————(1975a), On mourning, immortality and utopia. *J. Amer. Psychoanal. Assn.*, 23:334–362.

————(1975b), On anniversary suicide and mourning. In: *Depression and the Human Existence*, ed. T. Benedek & E. J. Anthony. Boston: Little, Brown, pp. 369–393.

————(1975c), Mourning and memorialization through music. *The Annual of Psychoanalysis*, 3:423–435. New York: International Universities Press.

————(1976), Manifestations of abnormal mourning: Homicide and suicide following the death of another. *The Annual of Psychoanalysis*, 4:225–249. New York: International Universities Press.

————(1977), Mourning: Psychoanalytic theory. In: *International Encyclopedia of Psychiatry, Psychology, Psychoanalysis and Neurology*, Vol. 7, ed. B. B. Wolman. New York: Aesculapius Publishers, pp. 368–371.

————(1978), On siblings, childhood sibling loss, and creativity. *The Annual of Psychoanalysis*, 6:443–481. New York: International Universities Press.

————(1982), The mourning–liberation process and creativity: The case of Käthe Kollwitz. *The Annual of Psychoanalysis*, 10:333–354. New York: International Universities Press.

————(1985), Mourning mothers, depressed grandmothers, guilty siblings, and identifying survivors. In: *Parental Influences: In Health and Disease*, ed. E. J. Anthony & G. H. Pollock. Boston: Little, Brown, pp. 235–257.

————(1986a), Childhood sibling loss: A family tragedy. *The Annual of Psychoanalysis*, 14:5–34. Madison, CT: International Universities Press.

————(1986b), Simón Bolívar: Revolutionary, liberator, and idealist. *The Annual of Psychoanalysis*, 14:59–76. Madison, CT: International Universities Press.

————(in preparation), On Dahlberg.

Reik, T. (1953), *The Haunting Melody*. New York: Farrar, Straus & Cudahy.

Rentchnick, P. (1975), *The Orphans Lead the World*. Geneva: Ed. Med. Hyg.

Segal, H. (1952), A psychoanalytic approach to aesthetics. *Internat. J. Psycho-Anal.*, 33:196–207.

Werfel, A. M. (1958), *And the Bridge is Love*. New York: Harcourt, Brace.

2

Trauma, Loss, Restoration, and Creativity

WILLIAM G. NIEDERLAND, M.D.

> *Restoration hang thy medicine on my lips.*
> —Shakespeare, *King Lear*

> *The past is never dead; it is not even past.*
> —William Faulkner

Explanatory Notes on the Concept, Definition, and Range of Trauma

Trauma—according to Webster, "an injury or wound, or the resulting condition (in medicine); a mental shock, a disturbing experience to which a neurosis may be traced (in psychiatry)"—occupies a prominent position in psychiatric, psychoanalytic, and psychodynamically oriented thinking. From both a practical and theoretical viewpoint, a thoroughgoing investigation and clarification of the concept of trauma is central not only to psychoanalysis, but also to clinical and social psychiatry, psychology, the study of the creative process, as well as efforts in various mental health areas generally.

It may not be superfluous to mention that, historically

61

speaking, the somewhat loose terms *traumatic neurosis, war neurosis, accident neurosis,* and *postaccidental psychological illness* that have been part of our professional literature since the days long before World War I were originally and often erroneously used in medicine, finding entrance into early psychoanalysis primarily by dint of their employment in medico-legal issues, forensic psychiatry, disability problems in military medicine, and frequently vain or fruitless attempts at rehabilitation. Any study, even thought, of a possible relationship of trauma to creativity was totally omitted. A decidedly clinical approach to what were regarded as definitely clinical problems prevailed.

Of course, as early as 1895, Breuer and Freud began to investigate the nature and influence of trauma in the mental lives of patients, and discovered that these patients' symptoms "were founded upon highly significant, but forgotten scenes in their past lives (traumas)." Thus the pathway was opened for a more detailed examination of how traumatic events exert their influences on symptom formation, developmental and maturational processes, character structure, and psychic life in general. Originally, Breuer and Freud (1893–1895) had described trauma as an experience in which perceptual and affective stimuli overwhelm those psychic processes which bind them and which thereby ordinarily maintain a homeostatic equilibrium in the mental apparatus. In a number of follow-up studies, Freud (1916, 1920, 1926) elaborated on the initial definition and discussed the problem of trauma and the traumatic state more specifically. In 1920 he wrote: "We describe as traumatic any excitations from outside which are powerful enough to break through the protective shield . . . the concept of trauma necessarily implies a connection of this kind with a break in an otherwise efficacious barrier against stimuli." Breaking "the protective shield" or "barrier" refers, in Freud's formulation, to the inundation of the psychic apparatus with such large amounts of stimuli that they cannot be bound and/or mastered. In 1926 Freud spoke of "early . . . traumata which the immature ego was unable to master" and of "impressions of this [early] period [which] impinge upon an immature and feeble ego, and act upon it as trauma." To these characteristics he added, in 1933, the factor of helplessness as a further important criterion in defining psychic trauma: "The essence of a traumatic situation is an experience of helplessness on the part of the ego in the face of accumulation of excitation, whether of external or internal origin."

It is with more than theoretical interest that I cite these formulations in their original (if translated) wording. With the widening scope of analytic, psychodynamic, and psychothera-peutic approaches to mental illness, the current usage of the terms *trauma, traumatic state, traumatic experience,* and the like has undergone, perhaps inevitably, certain changes and modifica-tions. The frequent use of these terms, at times "overuse" (as Anna Freud has called it), tends to bring about, in addition to the familiar generalizations in today's parlance, a blurring of distinctions, and ultimately a decrease in conceptual meaning and clarity. It is equally important to add that in Freud's writings, from his earliest papers to his last contributions, the part played by experiences (including fantasies) involving trau-matic events is viewed as a major factor in pathogenesis. This has to be emphasized in view of occasional attempts to reduce Freud's concept of trauma to a sort of side issue by assigning it a transient or minor role. As an illustration, I mention Karl Jasper's (cited in Niederland, 1966) approach which restricts pathological reactions following a traumatic experience to a temporary condition, and postulates that there is a return to the *status quo ante* with regard to specific psychic mechanisms and functions. On the other side of the spectrum, Greenacre's (1952) view should be noted that no truly traumatic event is ever wholly overcome and that increased psychic vulnerability is the inevitable outcome of such experiences. Essentially, this coincides in a wide-ranging context with Freud's earliest em-phasis on the influence of overt sexual traumata in the causa-tion of neuroses.

More recently, attention has been focused on specifically defining the nature and effect of traumatic events. Kris (1952) has spoken of "chronic stress trauma" seen in persons subject to prolonged, day-to-day injurious conditions as opposed to "acute shock trauma" wherein a suddenly overwhelming stimulus (or series of stimuli) of a kind that cannot be mastered is operative. Not infrequently, closer study reveals a combination of both types, that is to say, a shock trauma superimposed on a vulnerable, previously and chronically traumatized ego acts in combination with protracted stress to produce certain effects or aftereffects. Some authors have used the terms *cumulative trauma* or *traumatic processes*. In many of these situations, clinical evaluation may present considerable difficulty. The nature and history of trauma, onset and progression of illness, presence or absence of disorders before trauma, developmental factors, pretraumatic condition, and other anamnestic data (including course and specific manifestations of posttraumatic illness) serve as important criteria in such evaluations. Though necessarily incomplete and schematic, a brief review of the principal traumatic influences, in a more or less chronological sequence, may be useful.

Prenatal, Natal, and Perinatal Trauma

During prenatal life there is a predisposition to anxiety and other reactions. On the basis of work done by neurologists, physiologists, pediatricians, and other researchers, there is reason to believe that intense fetal responses, especially during the latter months of pregnancy, can be elicited by certain stimuli, for example, of an acoustic or kinesthetic nature. These seem to provoke responses which are in the nature of reflex action and most probably devoid of psychic content.

Trauma in Infancy and Early Childhood

Painful and uncomfortable situations in the earliest postnatal weeks would have a traumatic effect on the developmental process and tend to increase the organic components of anxiety reaction. A marked elevation in early anxiety due to traumatic experiences results in an increase in narcissism, an inadequate sense of reality, and a predisposition to severe neuroses or borderline states. Examples of massive stimulation leading to overexcitement and disorganization are (1) repeated exposure to the primal scene, although whether such exposure is really traumatic is still an open question; (2) being tossed, played with, or tickled or teased violently; (3) frequent exposure to sudden loud voices and noises in early infancy; and (4) repeated anesthetic and/or operative procedures.

Physical restraint over periods of time is another form of trauma in infancy. Positive restraint consists in binding and holding in order to limit motion. Negative restraint results from the prolonged absence of activity-permitting situations. With intense and sudden restraint involving the entire body, including a variety of congenital deformities of the musculoskeletal system, the traumatic effect is quite marked.

The birth of a sibling is more traumatic in infancy than at a later age because speech and locomotion have not been established for the discharge of the infant's jealousy.

The traumatic experiences of separation and deprivation during the formative years are created by (1) the death or illness of one or both parents; (2) broken homes; (3) separation of parents; (4) psychotic parents, and (5) parents with antisocial character disorders, the first three obviously including object loss. Children who have suffered early separation deprivation and serious disturbances of the mother–child relationship manifest impairment of ego functions, disturbances of instinctual drives, and interference with superego development.

Frequent potentially traumatic experiences mentioned in the literature (Niederland, 1965, 1967) involve perceived body loss: (1) congenital or early acquired malformations; (2) childhood bodily illness; and (3) hospitalization and surgery.

Precocious experiences which have traumatic effects include (1) specific genital seduction in early infancy; (2) frequent forced feeding; (3) frequent and early enemas, administered forcefully; and (4) premature toilet training.

Trauma in Puberty and Adolescence

Little is known about prepuberty trauma except for one group of cases in which traumata are provoked by the victims and are compulsive repetitions of preoedipal conflicts influencing the intensity of the oedipal phase and subsequent severity and deformation of the superego. The occurrence of such traumata is favored by the combination of an increased thrust of activity during prepuberty years, with marked sadomasochism derived from pregenital phases, and a strong masculine identification during the latency period.

Trauma in Adulthood

Brutal and sadistic traumas inflicted on an individual or a group of individuals, such as inmates of Nazi concentration camps, are characterized by (1) constant pervasive threats and reality of torture and death, (2) extreme deprivation and suffering, and (3) the need for absolute control and suppression of any aggressive or altruistic reactions.

Personality changes in the survivors of such experiences are related to quantitative factors. Massive and repeated traumatic experiences of this type have devastating effects on ego organization. These sequelae, known as the "survivor syndrome," are:

1. Anxiety
2. Disturbances of cognition and memory.
3. Chronic depressive reactions.
4. Psychosomatic disorders.
5. Psychosislike picture manifestations.
6. Tendencies to isolation and brooding seclusion.
7. Disturbances of the sense of identity, and of body- and self-image.
8. Survivor guilt.

The above summary, though schematic and sketchy, may serve to facilitate the therapist's work in various ways. It focuses special attention on factors and manifestations not always designated as traumatogenic in the literature. It separates specific (traumatic) events from a variety of other pathogenic conditions. Finally, it is hoped that such a summary may reawaken interest in exploring further the injurious effects of trauma on psychic life. Traumatic events are part of mankind's universal experience and various aspects of trauma have become almost commonplace. Only well-defined inquiries into the nature and consequences of such experiences can throw light on the silent, persistent, at times compensatory and autoreconstructive features thereof, as I hope to demonstrate in the remainder of this chapter.

The Loss/Restoration Principle: A Dynamic Ingredient of the Creative Process

I should now like to explore some of the specific traumata to which, according to my research (1965, 1967, 1975, 1976, 1981), many poets, writers, artists, and scientists have been subjected in early life, mainly the traumata of object loss and what I have called body loss, the latter referring to physical handicaps, bodily malformations, protracted illness in childhood, long periods of frailty, and similar conditions. To a degree, the experience of object loss resembles that of body loss. Object loss relates to a love object in the external world; body loss relates to an object that once was part of the self. However, a sharp and fully determined distinction between the mental representations of the inner and outer world develops comparatively late in childhood. Even in adult life this lack of determinate distinction is not at all rare, especially under the impact of such serious bodily injuries as amputation and the like. The experience of "phantom limb" is too well known to require further elaboration. In these cases the human mind "creates" a limb that has ceased to exist. Artistic creativity, in particular, "intimately involves the body," as Fisher (1973) so aptly puts it.

With regard to bodily losses and their restorative–creative potential, a brief historical review may be useful. Hephaestus, the god of art and artisanship (there were no sharp differences between the two in those days), was lame. His masterwork, according to Homer, was the Shield of Achilles, replete with depictions of figures dancing, running, fighting—all of them in active and impressive motion. Among all the gods on Mount Olympus the "renowned lame god," as Homer calls him, was the one who understood, promoted, and created art. Homer himself, according to tradition, was blind. Socrates, the great philosopher of antiquity, was physically misshapen, had a bulbous nose, and was otherwise unattractive in physical appearance. To go still further back, Moses, the most prominent figure of the Old Testament and founder of the Hebrew religion, was *aral sefoyajim*, as the scriptural text has it; that is, he suffered from a speech defect of such intensity that his brother Aaron had to serve as his mouthpiece for his talks with Pharaoh, to "let my people go." We all know, of course, the story of Demosthenes, the greatest orator of the classical Greek world, who, impelled by a most serious speech defect, forced himself to practice speaking through a mouthful of pebbles in order to overcome that deficiency. In early Persian literature a poet was viewed in two ways: in one, he was likened to a butterfly flying about a burning candle and being seriously injured by its flame; in the other, he was identified with a lovesick nightingale which bleeds on the thorns of bushes, yet creates its beautiful songs.

Turning to less ancient sources, I should mention Cervantes, whose left arm was wounded by a bullet during the battle of Lepanto. It remained paralyzed "ad majorem gloriam dextrae," as he later wrote—for the "greater glory of my right arm and hand," with which he created his immortal *Don Quixote*. Cervantes thus expressed, almost in analytic terms, the shift of body cathexis from the deficient body part to the healthy and active one which he used in creating his celebrated work.

Christy Brown, the crippled Irish author of, among other novels, the best-selling *Down All the Days* (1970), died in 1981 at the age of forty-nine. Brown was a victim of congenital cerebral palsy. In his early years he could neither stand, walk, nor feed himself, and his speech consisted largely of grunts understood only by family members and close friends. He could not control any part of his body except his left foot. With this foot he learned to write by holding a paint brush with his toes. In analytic terms, his one intact body part became compensatorily hypercathected. Robert Collis, a physician who specialized in cerebral palsy, encouraged him to write and use his foot in this way. Therapeutically speaking, such medicopsychological support is of extreme importance—helpful guidance and prudent encouragement reinforce the patient's own restorative efforts. To quote Brown:

From very early on I had the urge to write. As far back as I can remember I was always writing bits and pieces—poems, short stories, essays. That was my release. My brothers got it kicking footballs or loving women, but I had to compensate for being handicapped, and the only way I could do it, was to put my thoughts down on paper [Brown, 1982, p. 90].

Two other Irish authors, O'Casey and Joyce, less handicapped and much more prominent in literature than Christy Brown, may also be considered in this connection. Both had serious visual deficiencies from childhood on. O'Casey, who lost his father at an early age, suffered from greatly impaired vision. Joyce probably offers the supreme example as far as the relationship between creative achievement and visual defectiveness is concerned. In *Ulysses* he virtually makes us see Dublin, the Liffy River, Leopold Bloom and his wife, the city by night and day, local places and all the rest, as though we were with him in person sharing all those sights and experiences. Let us note, therefore, that in 1920, still working on *Ulysses* and approaching middle age, Joyce was in a state of near-blindness. Before that time he had undergone at least ten eye operations and could often barely see. Entire chapters or subchapters of *Portrait of an Artist as a Young Man* deal with his eye troubles and the incapacity of schoolteachers and other adults to understand them. This same man, so close to blindness, *sees* the world as it really and symbolically is, and makes us see it too, in his creative work.

The French painters Degas and Monet were likewise afflicted by poor vision, the former from childhood on, the latter during the final period of his life—one of the most creative and exciting in his artistic career. It was during that period that Monet worked on the completion of his famous Water Lily series with its numerous revisions and variations, while repeatedly undergoing eye operations for a "degenerative cataract" condition which, according to his Paris eye doctor's diagnosis, had reduced the painter's vision to one-tenth in the left eye and to only perception of light with good projection in the right. Degas, on the other hand, with his difficulty in seeing landscapes and countryside, concentrated on painting ballet dancers and racehorses throughout most of his life. As his eyesight continued to fail, he undertook to work with new media and techniques, especially sculpture, engraving, and experimentation with lithography, wax, and so on. At the age of seventy or so, when he was almost totally blind, he persisted in working with these new techniques. Both artists overcame the "degenerative" processes in their visual systems by what I am inclined to call "generative-creative-restorative repair" in the very areas threatened or reduced through loss.

Allen (1974, p.111) has focused our attention on "the ability to be inwardly curious, to employ self-directed scoptophilia without hampering anxiety," a capacity which he describes as "a fundamental first step in the creative process." Indeed, this "wish to look," often sexually and erotically tinged (i.e., scopophilia), and the permission to do so, may play a great role in the exploration of new fields and the attraction of the unknown, or in the search for the "hidden deep" which I have described in my papers on river and water symbolism (1956, 1957). According to Allen, the exploratory endeavors of Freud, Darwin, Pasteur, Einstein, and others are notable examples of this capacity, which, in accordance with my findings, may be intensely stimulated by preceding losses and, if dormant, set into motion by such losses.

An impressive example of the loss/restoration principle in poetry and fiction is offered by Kipling, who in his early life suffered both object and body loss later followed by such generative–creative activity. Object loss is not always caused by death. Early separation and abandonment, in symbolic meaning and psychological reverberations, can approximate it. At the age of six, Kipling—born in Bombay, India, in 1865—was taken by his British parents to England for schooling and "deposited" by them in a foster home at Southsea. He later named this home in which he remained for five years "the house of desolation." His parents left him in the care of the owners of that "house of desolation," "Uncle Harry" and "Aunty Rosa," and returned to India without telling the young boy of their imminent departure. Throughout his life, he suffered from impaired vision, a case of extreme congenital myopia which was neither recognized nor treated by his real or surrogate parents during those early years. After the much belated recognition of his impairment, two types of spectacles were required in order to correct it. Subsequently, as a writer, he composed a collection of reminiscences, impressions, and fantasies (in my experience as a psychoanalyst, I have often found fantasies to be distorted, at times not so distorted, memories) which appeared in the literature as a novel under the ominous title *The Light That Failed*. Much later, in our time, the novel was produced as a film with the same title.

Of further interest in the present context is this fact: Kipling, who in childhood had lost his parental home in distant India and along with it his parents, with whom he was reunited only after a number of years, was able to express the loss/restoration principle or process poetically by giving lyrical expression to its roots and meaning. In his poem "The Explorer" it appears characteristically as an imperative, which, indeed, it often is:

> Something *hidden*. Go and find it. Go and *look*
> Behind the Ranges—
> Something *lost* behind the Ranges. *Lost* and
> *Waiting for you*. Go! [Italics added.]

Precisely so did Kipling's career evolve—ceaseless traveling, writing, exploring, and moving from place to place, across the seas, mountains, and valleys. His literary achievement has sometimes been attacked by the imputation that he made of himself the poet of the British Empire, glorifying its existence and extolling its might. This may be so. But even a brief glance behind the poet's "inner" ranges sheds light on this attitude and much of his literary work. How intensely a gifted little boy, abandoned in the "house of desolation" of Southsea, trapped in its narrow streets and in the dimness and constriction of his myopia, must have longed for the spaciousness of the Empire, which in his day was worldwide and virtually without limits. The striving for expansion and mobility is one of the elements of the creative experience, certainly understandable in the case of Kipling.

Another example of early corporeal traumatization is that of

Sir Walter Scott, who was stricken by polio at the age of two and walked with a permanent limp. As a writer, he created the figure in *Ivanhoe* of the invincible knight in shining armor who helps the downtrodden and infirm, turning his enemies into limp and stricken figures while he himself is never defeated.

Byron likewise was lame. His lameness, not the result of polio but caused by a birth defect, was incurable at the time and his need to wear an "iron on his leg" up to his college days is described by friends and biographers. As an author of poetry and drama, Byron matured with amazing speed and created an enduring literary universe of rhyme, lyrics, narratives, impassioned confessions, and brilliant letters. Without going into the detail of this superbly creative output, suffice it for us to witness *Childe Harold's Pilgrimage* from country to country, sea to sea, across rivers, lakes, and mountains—not unlike Kipling's at a later date. Quite clearly, the hero of the pilgrimage is Byron himself, or more precisely, he represents the poetically and wishfully projected image of the physically unimpaired, bodily perfect, and magically restored Byron. In fact, just before his death in Greece in 1824, while fighting on a desolate battlefield for Greek freedom, his last words reportedly were : "AVANTI, AVANTI" ("Forward, Forward")—the lame poet transmuting and denying his lameness until the very last moments of his turbulent life.

What about the lives of highly creative individuals in other fields? Mention of polio brings quickly to mind Franklin Delano Roosevelt's life and achievement. Stricken by the disease before reaching middle age, he lost the use of both his legs. Five years later, he became President of the United States and subsequently, with Churchill, the leader in the war against Hitler. Equally important and lasting were his creative efforts in the field of social security, which, against weighty opposition, he introduced as an innovative institution on a nationwide basis while simultaneously fighting for the acceptance of many related social services never before considered either necessary or important for the well-being of the government of the United States and its people.

His wife, Eleanor, was plagued by the triple handicap of early object loss—her mother and father died when she was eight and ten years of age, respectively—physically unattractive appearance, and marked resultant shyness and isolation. Later, the plain, shy, and awkward girl turned into an eloquent, active, and almost ubiquitous figure. During the last fifteen years of her life she became the American voice of humanity, a woman of unbroken inner strength (in spite of a virtually broken marriage with Roosevelt before his death), and sovereign in her own right.

This leads us to a consideration of physical ugliness as a leitmotif in the careers of certain creative personalities. Michelangelo, whose glaring facial disfigurement due to a distorted and misshapen nose, fractured in a preadolescent fistfight which made him the ugliest among hundreds of his fellow Renaissance artists, walked alone through the streets of Rome "*Solo come un boia,*" "lonely as a hangman," according to his contemporary Raphael. This unusually ugly man created, among his many outstanding artistic works, two of perhaps the most impressive examples we know of masculine beauty—the statues of David and Moses.

With regard to physical ugliness as a potential *stimulus creandi,* I have referred above to Socrates and his misshapen figure. The list includes at least four other great philosophers: Hans Christopher Lichtenberg, Emanuel Kant, Moses Mendelsohn, and Søren Kierkegaard, all crippled at an early age, hunchbacks in fact. Moreover, Kant was known as the shortest man in Koenigsberg where he taught philosophy, and Arthur Schopenhauer was so characterized in Danzig, Goettingen, and Frankfurt. Physical "short" comings of this type, later converted into spiritual greatness, are not limited, of course, to one or two nationalities. The Americans Ralph Waldo Emerson and Theodore Dreiser were known as "ugly ducklings" among their contemporaries. So was the Russian Nicolai Gogol, with his enormous nose and conspicuously short stature. His schoolmates called him the "mysterious dwarf." John Keats was small, stocky, and never grew beyond five feet, four inches in height. Gustave Eiffel, the builder of the tall, erect Tower, was short and stooped. So was Alexander Pope who suffered from a marked curvature of the spine. An even more surprising addition to this list of creative "shorties" is the best known artist of our century—Pablo Picasso, whose height was five foot, two inches. Unconsciously, like children, we are prone to think of great men and women as being great—tall and big—in bodily terms as well. Often, the reverse holds true and promotes restorative action. The crippled Toulouse-Lautrec said it directly: "If my legs had been a little longer, I would never have become a painter."

William Faulkner, Sir Arthur Evans, discoverer of the Palace of Knossos on the island of Crete, and the original Dr. Faustus whom Goethe celebrated in his greatest work, belong to the same category of defective body growth. They were all abnormally short and of poor physique. The lifelong emotional reverberations reemerge, at least in part, in their very accomplishments. Evans excavated the giant palace and Dr. Faust, the legendary alchemist, tried forever to find the gold of physical beauty, eternal renewal (rebirth), and the fountain of youth. Victor Hugo, whom his biographers describe as looking like "a deformed dwarf," created the grossly misshapen yet immortal figures in literature Quasimodo and Rigoletto.

Though being short in a taller world does not exactly belong to the category of "body loss" in the sense described above, the subjective experience of such an individual may approximate that of defective body growth, of having been wronged or literally kept "down" by Mother Nature. It is known that Picasso frequently expressed concern about his small physical stature, brooding and talking about it in worried terms. Gogol's work, too, offers an almost classical example. In one of his wondrous tales the pimpled nose of a conceited bureaucrat, Kovalev, disappears mysteriously. During the night it has stealthily detached itself from the face of its bearer and, in broad daylight, parades gloriously attired down the street. In another satirical story, the inhabitants of the moon are nothing but grotesque and mobile noses. One of Gogol's poems depicts his whole body transformed into a stately and upright nose, a fantasy which suggests to the analytically trained reader the familiar "body–phallus" equation.

All this is not to say that bodily imperfections or deficiencies produce creative work. Such a simplistic view would be absurd and must be rebuked. Physical defectiveness, rather, tends to stimulate the imagination, to activate a rich and florid fantasy life, compensatory mechanisms, reaction formations, symbolic processes, restorative ego functions, and, in gifted individuals, to promote creativity. The influence of narcissistic injury to the body image and self-representation certainly is marked. Moreover, the *doors of perception* (to use Aldous Huxley's term) are more widely opened while the superego's control over thoughts and feelings are reduced. The same holds true for object loss, if and when the intense reactions of grief, sorrow, anger, rancor, and embitterment are gone or alleviated.

Huxley, whose defective eyesight interrupted his education at Eton and who wrote not only the lucid "Doors of Perception" but also "Eyeless in Gaza" and "Brief Candles," was able to enlighten us more with his half-blind eye than most people can with perfect vision. In his many brilliant writings he offered luminous glimpses of his world and personal tragedy, especially his lifelong fight against blindness. So did James Thurber, whose left eye, at the age of six, was destroyed by an arrow accidentally shot by his brother William. Before long his good right eye began to go bad so that late in midlife he became totally blind. Though he never got over the shock which he sustained as a young boy, he continued working creatively as an artist and writer until the end of his life.

Under certain circumstances the creative process may be set in motion with a sort of blitzkrieg intensity and speed. Petrarch, who is generally thought to be the spiritual father of the Renaissance, was fourteen years old when his beloved young mother died. On his return from her funeral, he wrote his first poem, which begins with the words: "of thy glory my tongue will sing forever." Peter Weiss, author of *Marat/Sade*, and a painter as well as producer and director of famous Swedish films, was a refugee from Nazi Germany whence he fled with his Jewish family as a young adolescent. In his autobiographical novel *Exile* he describes his incestuous love for his sister, who died in his presence a short time after their escape from Germany. On the day following his sister's death, he created his first piece of art—a painting. Auden's comment on art as "our chief means of breaking bread with the dead" relates to these occurrences almost point blank.

A touching episode from the life of W. Somerset Maugham highlights the enduring impact of early object loss. Maugham's mother died when he was a young child. His nephew Robin (cited in Niederland, 1976) reports the following event which took place during the writer's last period of life:

> A few years ago I was alone with him . . . and his mind sometimes wandered. Suddenly he muttered: *"I shall never get over her death. I shall never get over it."* For an instant I supposed he was referring to my much beloved sister Kate who had died recently, but as he went on talking, I realized that he was thinking of his *mother who had been dead for over eighty years* [italics added] [p. 204].

The creative work of Edgar Allan Poe cannot be understood, in my opinion, without specific reference to the nature and influence of object loss in his early childhood. His father deserted the family when Poe was two, and his beautiful young mother was dying of pulmonary tuberculosis before he had reached the age of three. The little family, consisting of the tubercular mother, the future poet, and his one-year-old sister, lived in one small dingy room in a boarding house in Rich-mond, Virginia, during the final months of her illness. Almost daily her condition grew worse. The young Edgar (the middle name Allan was added much later, after the mother's demise) not only observed for days and weeks the mother's hopeless struggle with her illness, but also witnessed her death in that dingy room on a cold night in December. Indeed, there is reason to believe that he stayed close to the mother's lifeless body throughout that entire night until neighbors entered the next morning and separated the child from the mother's corpse.

The influences of these highly traumatic experiences are strikingly concatenated in much of Poe's creative output—from the earliest poems about the sorrow that comes to a lover on the death of a beautiful woman through the ever-recurrent theme of "the lost one" to the macabre croak of "The Raven"; from the deadly mystery hidden in "The Fall of the House of Usher" to the sinister content of "The Oblong Box"; the writhing corpses in "The Premature Burial" and the terrifying "Facts in the Case of M. Valdemar." They all reflect the "terrifying facts" in the poet's own early life, particularly those of that dark night in December when the young child was in close contact with his mother's body, as the closing stanza of "Annabel Lee" describes it:

> and so all the night-tide, I lie down by the side of my darling, my darling, my life and my bride in the sepulchre there by the sea, in her tomb by the sounding sea [1962, p. 135].

I am inclined to assume that both the noise of the "sounding sea" and the raven's endless croaking have something in common with the young boy's traumatic experience—the sound of the death rattle in the lungs of the dying mother during that very night.

> Ah, distinctly I remember, it was in the bleak December . . . [1962, p. 109].

It is easy to dismiss these lines as an obvious rhyme, and leave it at that. Searching a little more deeply, however, I discovered that the date of the mother's death was indeed the night of December 9. It is of course unlikely that the future poet, then only close to three, would have known that the traumatic loss was suffered precisely in December. To the analyst, however, the date serves to reaffirm the way in which later knowledge and early trauma tends to coalesce in the mind, especially in the creative mind.

In the end, the poem is the essential thing. By rigorously analyzing Edgar Allan Poe's poetry or Somerset Maugham's novels, with a clear view of their personal lives and avoiding all peripheral detail, one arrives at the true significance of their, in a sense, profoundly autobiographical literary works. Analysis demonstrates, futhermore, that these works were, in effect, the expression of intense strivings for restoration in which memory and images, experience and perception, facts and fantasies coalesced in a consuming search for survival and truth. Besides Somerset Maugham's early object loss, we know that he hated his short physical stature so much that he was always pulling himself up and bracing his shoulders in order to appear taller. He was also a chronic stammerer. Thus, the fact that the hero of his greatest novel, *Of Human Bondage*, has a clubfoot is not incidental to his story but all important. To the nonanalytic reader this may appear farfetched. To the analyst, the indication of a marked shift of body experience and body cathexis, creatively elaborated, is evident. It requires a Cervantes to express it in the much more convincing terms already cited.

Theoretical Considerations

In studying the roots and vicissitudes of the creative process, it is difficult to avoid the recognition that hardships, handicaps, early losses, physical infirmity, or related traumata play a significant, often decisive, role in promoting artistic productivity. Certain illnesses—bodily, mental, or both—have long been recognized as unconsciously motivating and propelling forces in the formation, maintenance, and direction of the creative process. In the prolific work of Thomas Mann, it is mainly the routes of physical illness (*The Magic Mountain, Dr. Faustus*) or weakness and frailty (*Tonio Kroeger*) which lead to creative strivings. In an earlier novel, *Royal Highness*, Mann has one of the protagonists, a poet, say outright: "My health is delicate. I dare not say unfortunately, for I am convinced that my talent is inseparably connected with bodily infirmity."

Freud, to be sure, is more circumspect. In his paper on Dostoevsky (1928) he refers to the great Russian novelist as "the creative artist, the neurotic, the moralist, the sinner" and then poses the question: "How is one to find one's way in this bewildering complexity?" In the same essay, Freud speaks of "the unanalyzable artistic endowment," and reiterates this position with equal restraint a few years later (1933).

Edmund Wilson's *The Wound and the Bow* (1941) emphasized the "literary value" of trauma and the conception of "superior strength as inseparable from disability." In this sense, Wilson can be viewed as the originator of the "wounded man" theory of creativity, though his approach—so popular in America—lacks the specifics of Freud's findings and the analytic data provided independently by Greenacre (1957, 1963), Rochlin (1953), Stamm (1971), and myself.

My theory of the loss/restoration principle is based essentially on Freud's 1908 statement that everything we lose must be *replaced,* and is supported by my psychobiographical studies and clinical observations (1965, 1967, 1975). This principle reflects the view that a human being cannot be without an object, and when loss does occur—be it body or object loss—the object or body part must be replaced, because the individual can achieve only partial compensation or substitution within him- or herself. Narcissism represents but a partial substitution and certainly not a solution; it is, obviously, a pathological formation. Object loss is also a critical factor in the psychogenesis of certain emotional disorders such as grief, depression, anxiety, survivor guilt, and psychosomatic pathology. The object cannot be lost altogether, however; via the creative process it is restored through externalization on canvas, stone, paper, marble, or even the little black dots which, in musical composition, can turn into rousing, "living" symphonies or operas. Pollock's (1971) "mourning–liberation" process pertains here.

In body loss, the body image and self-representation are intensely affected. Under normal conditions, the body image is felt as a coherent and complete unit. When physical defectiveness occurs, in fact or fantasy, strivings to restore the lost sense of coherence or completeness set in and take the pathway, in talented individuals, of creative action or reaction.

With respect to this last point—talent, gift, innate endowment—it should be said that the sources of such apparently genetic factors are most difficult to determine and, up to the present, uncertain. As a pertinent example, let us consider the famous Bach family. Johann Sebastian Bach was just one of a series of great musicians in a line that included his grandfather, uncle, father, sons, and various other family members. Johann Sebastian himself became an orphan at nine years old. When both his father and mother died in rapid succession, he was "farmed out" to an older married brother in whose house he spent several miserable years. Thus, it is quite difficult to decide how much of Johann Sebastian's creative capacity was due to innate endowment, early object loss, identification, or traumatization. As far as our present-day knowledge goes, we are not able to arrive at a satisfactory answer with regard to these questions. Further research, including thoroughgoing psychobiographical, psychosocial, and clinical studies, will be needed to draw meaningful conclusions and arrive at fully convincing validation. In this sense, the present chapter is intended to promote further study in a field for which additional scientific data on the correlations between the lifework of an author or artist, his or her creative career, actual life events, traumatic experiences, fantasies, and inborn capacities are indispensable.

The aftereffects of trauma are multifarious and complex. Most studies of these effects have focused, understandably, on psychopathology following the traumatic event or events. My approach indicates that, although many traumatized individuals continue to suffer from major emotional problems, a number of such persons can overcome the trauma, at least to an extent, via creativity, which, in this aspect, represents a self-healing, autoreconstructive, and adaptive process. This process, in the concreteness of the creative experience (in writing, painting, sculpting, composing, as well as in scientific creativity), works *from the inside out* and thus turns, in essence, into a *procreative* act. Thomas Mann, in *Death in Venice*, speaks of the artist's "secretive procreative delights," which, in my opinion, are present in every creative person's unconscious mind and may make him or her feel godlike, or close to it. Eissler (1971a) postulates the presence of what he calls the *doxatheleic** function of the ego, which protects the artist, in phases of high creativity, against the onslaught of overwhelming inner stimuli, omnipotent or magical thinking, and archaic and hallucinatory experiences, a function which does not always operate adequately, however, as the tragic cases of Van Gogh, Sylvia Plath, and others indicate.

Still, in the great majority of cases, the ego functions of creative people, in particular those afflicted by body loss, object

*From the Greek *doxa*, meaning illusory, delusional-minded, and *aletheia*, referring to the cognitive and confirmable realm of knowledge.

loss, or both, are such that they help them see things in a novel or different way and to produce on this changed "background within" something which did not before exist—that is, something new, original, and, if successful, of lasting value. In closing I wish to mention that in the present chapter I have focused my research on the loss/restoration principle and its significance for the creativity of famous figures in literature and art, without presenting affirmative findings from clinical studies and observations already presented in my previous publications on the subject. Ameliorating the emotional impact of grievous loss, amputation, and disfigurement was the primary aim of those earlier studies.

References

Allen, D. W. (1974), *The Fear of Looking.* Charlottesville, VA: University Press of Virginia.

Breuer, J., & Freud, S. (1893–1895), Studies on hysteria. *Standard Edition,* 2. London: Hogarth Press, 1955.

Brown, C. (1970), *Down All the Days.* New York: Stein & Day.

———(1982), *Contemporary Authors,*Vol. 105. Detroit: Gaale Research Co.

Eissler, K. R. (1971a), *Talent and Genius.* Chicago: Quadrangle.

———(1971b), *Discourse on Hamlet and Hamlet.* New York: International Universities Press.

Fisher, S. (1973), *Body Consciousness.* Englewood Cliffs, NJ: Prentice-Hall.

Freud, S. (1895), Studies on hysteria. *Standard Edition,* 2. London: Hogarth Press, 1955.

———(1908), Creative writers and daydreaming. *Standard Edition,* 9:143–153. London: Hogarth Press, 1959.

———(1910), Leonardo da Vinci and a memory of his childhood. *Standard Edition,* 11:63–137. London:Hogarth Press, 1957.

———(1914), On the history of the psychoanalytic movement. *Standard Edition,* 14:7–66. London: Hogarth Press, 1957.

———(1916), Introductory lectures on psychoanalysis. *Standard Edition,* 15. London: Hogarth Press, 1963.

———(1920), Beyond the pleasure principle. *Standard Edition,* 18:7–64. London: Hogarth Press, 1955.

———(1923), The ego and the id. *Standard Edition,* 19:12–59. London: Hogarth Press, 1961.

———(1926), Inhibitions, symptoms and anxiety. *Standard Edition,* 20:87–172. London: Hogarth Press, 1959.

———(1928), Dostoievsky and parricide. *Standard Edition,* 21:177–196. London: Hogarth Press, 1961.

———(1933), Preface to Marie Bonaparte's *The Life and Works of Edgar Allan Poe, A Psychoanalytic Interpretation.* London: Imago, 1949.

————(1936), A disturbance of memory on the Acropolis. *Standard Edition*, 22:239–248. London: Hogarth Press, 1964.

————(1939), Moses and monotheism: Three essays. *Standard Edition*, 23:7–137. London: Hogarth Press, 1964.

Greenacre, P. (1952), *Trauma, Growth and Personality*. New York: W. W. Norton.

————(1957), The childhood of the artist. *The Psychoanalytic Study of the Child*, 12:47–72. New York: International Universities Press.

————(1963), *The Quest for the Father*. New York: International Universities Press.

Kris, E. (1952), *Psychoanalytic Explorations in Art*. New York: International Universities Press.

Niederland, W. G. (1956), River symbolism: Part I. *Psychoanal. Quart.*, 25:469–504.

————(1957), River symbolism: Part II. *Psychoanal. Quart.*, 26:50–75.

————(1965), Nacissistic ego impairment in patients with early physical malformations. *The Psychoanalytic Study of the Child*, 20:518–533. New York: International Universities Press.

————(1966), Review of K. Jaspers, *General Psychopathology*. *Psychoanal. Quart.*, 35:130–135.

————(1967), Clinical aspects of creativity. *Amer. Imago*, 24:6–33.

————(1975), Scarred: A contribution of the study of facial disfigurement. *Psychoanal. Quart.*, 44:450–459.

————(1976), Psychoanalytic approaches to artistic creativity. *Psychoanal. Quart.*, 45:185–212.

————(1981), The survivor syndrome: Further observations and dimensions. *J. Amer. Psychoanal. Assn.*, 29:413–425.

Poe, E. A.(1962), *The Poems of Edgar Allan Poe*, ed. K. Campbell. New York: Russell and Russell.

Pollock, G. H. (1971), On time, death, and immortality. *Psychoanal. Quart.*, 40(3):435–446.

————(1975), On mourning, immortality and utopia. *J. Amer. Psychoanal. Assn.*, 23:334–362.

Rochlin, G. (1953), Loss and restitution. *The Psychoanalytic Study of the Child*, 8:288–309. New York: International Universities Press.

Stamm, J. (1971), Vincent Van Gogh: Identity crisis and creativity. *Amer. Imago*, 28:363–372.

Wilson, E. (1941), *The Wound and the Bow*. New York: Oxford University Press.

3

Mourning a Lost Childhood: The Problem of Peter Pan

Nancy Mann Kulish, Ph.D.

Introduction

Never-Never Land, the island home of Peter Pan, exerts a powerful lure for all children and adults who have heard the story. With its beautiful blue lagoons, mermaids basking on the rocks, thrilling adventures with pirates and Indians, and sparkling fairies, it promises an endless, happy childhood. It is this promise that makes Peter Pan, "the boy who would not grow up," such an alluring figure. Many people look back nostalgically to childhood as a happy time of family picnics in the park and endless summer days filled with exciting adventures. It is my contention that very often this notion of a happy childhood like the story of Peter Pan, is a myth. It is a myth or fantasy constructed to hide and to defend against pain and loss incurred in the process of development.

The arrival of adolescence signals the inevitable ending of childhood and its pleasures. Normally, adolescence sets in motion processes of mourning, partially for our lost childhood. Clinically, many adolescents hold back these progressive pro-

83

cesses and hold onto the hope of childlike pleasures, often in the form of a fantasy of remaining a child forever. A crucial task in the psychoanalysis or psychoanalytic psychotherapy for such individuals, then, is giving up this fantasy and mourning for a lost childhood.

The Myth of Peter Pan

Before discussing the role of mourning in adolescence, I will briefly examine the myth of an endless happy childhood as depicted in the story of Peter Pan. The story, *Peter Pan, The Story of Peter and Wendy* (1911), was written by James M. Barrie after almost seven years of successful productions of his play *Peter Pan* (1904). The opening words of *Peter Pan and Wendy* point to the theme of growing up:

> All children, except one, grow up. They soon know that they will grow up, and the way Wendy knew was this. One day when she was two years old she was playing in a garden, and she plucked another flower and ran with it to her mother. I suppose she must have looked rather delightful, for Mrs. Darling put her hand to her heart, and cried, "Oh, why can't you remain like this forever!" This was all that passed between them on the subject, but henceforth, Wendy knew that she must grow up. You always know after you are two. Two is the beginning of the end [p. 1].

Clearly, growing up is coupled with separation and death, the plucked flower, "the end." The book and the original play both restate the theme in a last chapter or scene called "When Wendy Grew Up."

Thus, Barrie sets forth for us the dazzling prospect of a Never Land where we can escape that inevitable "end." Barrie's Never Land is a topographical representation of the unconscious and its timelessness. The agent of repression is the mother, Mrs. Darling, who tidies up the children's minds at night by folding up "the naughtiness and evil passions" (pp. 6–7) and placing them at the bottom of the mind. As he so beautifully puts it, the island can be found on the map of a child's mind. When the Darling children first land on Never

Land, it is familiar to them, full of their own forgotten possessions.

Within the context of the story itself, however, we can discern the brittleness of the myth of an endless childhood and what it seeks to cover. Peter Pan is a brash and cocky fellow, the epitome of the macho phallic little boy. But Peter, without admitting it, desperately needs and wants a mother because he has been deserted by his own. He had flown away as a baby, we are told. (All children were once little birds.) Once when Peter flew home to his mother, he found that the window was barred and another baby boy had taken his place. Barrie first tells this sad little episode and introduces Peter Pan in "Peter Pan in Kensington Gardens," which is actually a child's story within an adult novel, *The Little White Bird* (1902). Themes of separation and reunion, desertion, and revenge recur throughout the story as Peter leaves, returns, and finally leaves the mother; as Wendy and her brothers follow Peter to fly away from their parents, who are left to suffer; as the dog–nurse Nana is dispatched unfairly to the doghouse by Mr. Darling.

Thus, the story of Peter Pan clearly covers over, compensates for, and masters loss and separation. At the same time, the flight to Never Land provides for fantasied temporary solutions to many central conflicts of childhood. Meisel (1977), providing a psychoanalytic perspective, sees the myth of Peter Pan as a repair of childish narcissistic injuries. For example, disillusionment with the father, Mr. Darling, who is depicted as a somewhat childish, pompous figure, sets the story in motion; the four-year-old girl Maimie in "Peter Pan in Kensington Gardens" (Barrie, 1930) runs away from disappointment with an admired older brother. Meisel describes Peter Pan as a "bisexual narcissistic fantasy" (p. 546) with Peter, who in the stage version is depicted by a female actress as an alter ego of the heroine Wendy.

I find the oedipal motif in the story even more compelling. Shifting triangular relationships abound: Tinker Bell jealously competes with Wendy; the Indian Princess Tiger Lily is another admirer of Peter. While Wendy is mother to Peter, he is too dense to see that she is, or would like to be, his wife. The sinister Captain Hook, played by the same actor who plays father

Darling, is vanquished by young Peter. Literary biographers such as Harry Geduld (1971) have taken up the frank oedipal themes running throughout the Peter Pan stories and the whole of Barrie's works.

James Barrie and the Boy Who Would Not Grow Up

The clear key to understanding the meaning underlying the myth of Peter Pan, however, comes from an examination of the background of the author, J. M. Barrie (Mackail, 1941; Dunbar, 1970; Geduld, 1971; Birkin, 1979). James was one of many children of David and Margaret Ogilvy Barrie. James, even as a child, was exceptionally short and not good looking. His mother's favorite was an older brother, named David after the father. David was described as tall and handsome, self-confident, a tree-climber. All her hopes were pinned on his becoming a minister. When James was almost seven, David, then thirteen, was killed accidentally as he was ice skating. His mother, who never fully recovered from this tragedy, took to her bed. James himself poignantly describes what happened when as a little boy he took courage to go to her. He entered the darkened room and was scared and quiet:

> . . . after a time I heard a listless voice that had never been listless before say, 'Is that you?' I thought it was the dead boy she was speaking to, and I said in a little lonely voice, 'No it's not him, it's just me.' Then I heard a cry and my mother turned in bed, and though it was dark I knew that she was holding out her arms [Barrie, 1913, p.165].

Later Barrie writes that she repeated this scene by calling eagerly from her deathbed, "Is that you, David?" (Barrie, 1913, p. 264).

Thenceforth, Barrie devoted his whole existence to trying to comfort his mother, and consciously to take this brother's place, first in literally charading in his brother's clothes, and later in his literary efforts in which his mother took special interest. "At first, they say, I was often jealous, stopping her fond memories with the cry, 'Do you mind nothing about me?' but that did not last; its place was taken by an intense desire . . . to become so like him that even my mother should not see the difference" (Barrie, 1913, p. 166). He continues, "She lived twenty-nine years after his death. . . . But I had not made her forget the bit of her that was dead. . . . When I became a man . . . he was still a boy of thirteen" (Barrie, 1913, pp. 167–168). Thus, the mother's need to hold on to the memory of the son as forever a boy became inspiration for Barrie's creation of the figure of Peter Pan years later.

Barrie, like his literary creation, Peter Pan, did not want to grow up. He wrote of himself, "The horror of my boyhood was that I knew a time would come when I also must give up the games, and how it was to be done I saw not . . ." (Barrie, 1913, p. 173). In the autobiographical novel *Tommy and Grizel* (Barrie, 1900), *The Little White Bird* (Barrie, 1902), and in numerous other works, Barrie's central figures express sentiments of not wanting to grow up, and instead extol the glories of childhood.

James paid idealized homage to his mother in his book about her, *Margaret Ogilvy* (1913), and in his literary figures such as Mrs. Darling:

> She was a lovely lady, with a romantic mind and such a sweet mocking mouth. Her romantic mind was like the tiny boxes, one within the other, that come from the puzzling East, however many you discover there is always one more; and her sweet mocking mouth had one kiss on it that Wendy would never get, though there it was, perfectly conspicuous in the right-hand corner [Barrie, 1911, p. 1].

Later, Peter Pan is also described as "very like Mrs. Darling's kiss" (Barrie, 1911, p. 13). This is a beautiful description of the little boy's tie to the mysterious, illusive oedipal mother. That Barrie had not resolved his oedipal conflicts with his mother is abundantly clear in his lifelong devotion to her, his adoration of women who belonged to other men, notably Sylvia Davies, his conflicted relationship to his wife, and the figures of the Madonna versus the whore (e.g., Wendy vs. Tiger Lily) that run throughout his literary works (Geduld, 1971). The vanquished, disdained oedipal father is combined in the figures of the bumbling Mr. Darling and the castrated, one-armed Captain Hook, usually played by the same actor in the play *Peter Pan*.

It was the death of his rival that doomed Barrie to a hopeless oedipal and sibling struggle. Themes of death mark the story of *Peter Pan*. The Never Land in the earlier "Peter Pan in Kensington Gardens" and in *Peter Pan* is populated by lost boys who have slipped out of their perambulators and flown away. The lost boys are dead boys and the island, an island of the dead. The boys sleep in the womb or coffinlike underground beds, to rise to the surface at daybreak. In the original story of Peter Pan in *The Little White Bird*, as a ruse to give baby clothes and become close to a young married woman and her infant, the narrator, a lonely man, invents a fantasied baby who has died. He then tells the story of Peter Pan to her child named David. Lest there will be no doubt that Peter Pan is tied to the dead brother, Barrie (1911) first introduces the personage of Peter in a link with the dead: Wendy casually lets drop to her mother she saw Peter Pan in the manner in which children "may remember to mention, that when they were in the wood they met their dead father . . ." (p. 10)

Anna Freud's (1967) essay on being lost and losing further illuminates the theme of being lost which runs throughout *Peter Pan*. Individuals who frequently lose objects or find themselves lost, she said, are identified with lost objects and themselves feel deserted, rejected, or alone. The idea of "lost souls" in literature symbolizes the emotional impoverishment felt by a survivor of a loss. Barrie's preoccupation with lost boys is a good example of such a literary image.

In a fascinating short piece on the origins of Peter Pan, Karpel (1956) suggests that Peter Pan combines the figures of David and the mother who died before the writing of Peter Pan. She points out how the initials D. B. (for David Barrie) recur throughout J. M. Barrie's works in *Better Dead* and *Boy David*, for example. Further, in Barrie's works mother and children are always coming back from the grave, often through a window as in *Peter Pan*.

Thus, Barrie reveals his guilt-ridden conflicts regarding his dead brother in the recurring theme of death and rebirth. He would kill him off and at the same time bring him to life again for his mother. And bring him to life again he did, forever, encapsulated in the literary creation of the Peter Pan who never grew up. The brother who was killed on the ice becomes frozen in time. Thus, Peter Pan is the dead, cocky, tree-climbing brother David, and the wished-for image of Barrie himself.

Never-Never Land is a land in which one never grows up, but also one never dies. It is reminiscent of Edna St. Vincent Millay's (1934) poem "Childhood Is the Kingdom where Nobody Dies." As Stern (1968) has pointed out, the fear of death has been largely ignored in psychoanalytic thinking as a crucial determinant in neurosis and mental life. Certainly in its denial of the inevitability of death, the myth of Peter Pan gains in its allure.

Barrie himself asserted that the origins of Peter Pan lay outside these internal realms and in his experiences with the five sons of Sylvia and Arthur Davies. Barrie's peculiar relationship with the Davies family began in Kensington Gardens where he and his wife and dog took walks. He became attracted to two small boys and struck up a friendship with them. Later he met the mother, a beauty with a crooked smile, whom he consciously used as a model for Mrs. Darling. He worshipped Sylvia, pushed himself into the family's lives, became a constant playmate to the boys, and was tolerated by the father. With the boys one summer, he vacationed on a beautiful lake, played pirates, and acted out boyish adventures and fantasies which he soon incorporated into the play *Peter Pan*. Later, after their parents' tragic deaths, he adopted the boys, and the oldest became known worldwide as the original Peter.

Yet, we can recognize that Barrie's relationship with Sylvia Davies and her sons was, to begin with, an overdetermined acting out of his deep, central conflicts involving his brother and mother. Barrie's seeking out friendships with little boys was a search for the lost boys of his childhood—David, himself, and the son he could not have.

Moreover, Barrie's relationship with his wife, Mary, was unhappy, strained, and ended in divorce when he discovered she was having an affair. Biographies and contemporaries suggested that the childless marriage was never consummated and that he was impotent (Dunbar, 1970; Birkin, 1979). In any event, Barrie's own words indicate sexual fears and inhibitions. In his notebook, he described a recurrent nightmare:

> One of the horrors of my dream was that I knew how it would come each time, and from where. . . . I do not recall it in my childhood, but they tell me that, asleep in my cot, I would fling my arms about wildly as if fighting a ghost. It would thus seem that my nightmare was with me even then, though perhaps only as a shapeless mass that a too lively imagination was soon to resolve into a woman. My weird dream never varies now. Always I see myself being married, and then I wake up with the scream of a lost soul clammy and shivering [Birkin, 1979, pp. 26–27].

Clearly, Barrie connected marriage, perhaps equated with sexual union, with death.

In his revealing novel, *Tommy and Grizel* (Barrie, 1900), Barrie echoes this conflict: "'Grizel, I seem to be different from all other men; there seems to be some curse upon me. I want to love you . . . but apparently I can't.' . . . They had a honeymoon by the sea. . . . Tommy trying to become a lover by taking thought, and Grizel not letting on that it could not be done in that way. . . . He was a boy only" (pp. 465–466). It would appear that the seven-year-old Barrie, in resolving to take the place of his dead brother and rival for his mother's love, came to an unconscious conclusion that gratifying his oedipal wishes meant he would have to be dead. His mother had embraced a dead boy.

This equation of death, punishment, and oedipal strivings is reiterated in the ending of his novel *Tommy and Grizel*. Tommy has fallen victim to the seductress Lady Pippinworth, who has stolen his manuscript which he calls his "baby." When he leaves Grizel to claim the missing book, he is wearing a dead rival's overcoat which he obtained by pretending an affection for him. On leaving the seductress, Tommy finds himself trapped inside her locked garden. He endeavors to escape by climbing over the garden gate, but his overcoat catches the iron spikes and he is suffocated inside of it. As Geduld (1971), a literary biographer, concludes, "Thus Barrie—as Tommy—destroys himself inside his brother's clothes, and the manner of his hero's death recalls the child . . . dressing up as his dead brother in order to assume David's identity. The iron spike and the over-coat . . . anticipate . . . the iron hook and the crocodile that destroys the villainous captain in Peter Pan" (p. 51).

Barrie's inability to have his own children, whatever its cause, deeply pained him. He wrote of this disappointment in his journals, acted it out in adopting other people's children, and put it into the hearts of many of his literary characters, including Peter Pan.

Barrie held on to his dream of childhood not only to dispel loss, but to avoid adult sexuality. As Peter Pan said, "I don't want to go to school and learn solemn things. . . . I don't want to be a man. O Wendy's mother, if I was to wake up and feel there was a beard!" (Barrie, 1911, p. 205). When Barrie himself reached his adolescence, he also entered Deemfries Academy. There, with a companion, he threw himself into acting out adventures such as playing pirates in the trees of the garden. Very short and shy, he did not have success with girls.

Thus in summary, Barrie's nostalgic clinging to the fantasy of a carefree childhood and fear of growing up had sources in his own past. It was a denial of his brother's death, and the associated losses and disappointments with his mother. It represented a defensive regression from adult sexuality and a competition tied to oedipal fears and guilt. His genius allowed him both to immortalize and transcend his problems in his work. In his own words again: "the next best thing to being boys is to write about them. What is genius? It is the power to be a boy again at will" (Barrie, 1900, p. 249).

Adolescence as a Process of Mourning

As the child enters adolescence, crucial and difficult psycholog-ical tasks lay ahead. The adolescent must come to grips with heightened sexual feelings and a developing adult body, sepa-rate from infantile parental objects to achieve independence, and solidify a separate adult identity.

Freud (1905) described the adolescent's necessary detach-ment from parental authority as one of the most significant albeit painful psychic achievements. The adolescent process is one of giving up ties of old objects and replacing them with new objects, similar to mourning. Mourning, as Freud (1917) cogently described it, is a painful and protracted process in which the grieving individual struggles to acknowledge the reality of a loss of an object to which he or she was strongly cathected. Memories of the loved object are, bit by bit, compared with the reality of the present loss.

Wolfenstein (1966) likened adolescence itself to mourning. She believed that adolescence marks the development of the capacity to mourn. It is not only characterized by mourning for infantile objects, but by a new feeling for the past: "There is a nostalgia for the lost past, a combined yearning and sense of irrevocability" (p. 114). Wolfenstein (1969) presented a case of an adolescent in which a death of the father, coupled with earlier disappointment in mother, brought nostalgic evocation of the lost home and vivid memories of a happy childhood. Root (1957) described a case of an adolescent girl whose symptoms reflected her failure to mourn her mother's death in prepuberty. According to Root, this trauma complicated the psychological task of mourning during adolescence: "every adolescent must make a real psychical renunciation and suffer the 'loss' of childhood and its aims and objects" (p. 332). Krystal (1975) emphasized that for adolescence to proceed successfully, the individual must be able to bear mourning and to tolerate the affect of depression.

According to Kaplan (1984), the sense of nostalgia appears for the first time during adolescence and arises from the struggle between the desire to relinquish the past and to never let it go. Most adults have repressed the painful emotions associated with becoming an adult and imagine adolescence as those "happy days." The idea of infancy as the golden age of humankind—such as Never-Never Land—has its origin in adolescent nostalgia.

Levin (1966) suggested that the wish to return to childhood may have a meaning other than grief over infantile losses. Rather, it may represent a regressive pull to escape adult sexual experience. Obsessive–compulsive personalities may be especially prone to such regressions. Lorand (1947) observed that obsessive–compulsive individuals constantly vascillate between the wish to remain a child and the wish to grow up. Their ambivalent wavering between the anal and the phallic/oedipal stages and their regressive backing away from oedipal conflicts would incline them to such fantasied solutions.

Case Illustrations

For many individuals commonly seen in clinical practice, the necessary processes of mourning during adolescence have been incomplete, arrested, or have never taken place. The following are brief illustrations taken from cases in which the wish not to grow up was a prominent feature of the symptomatology. Thus, the giving up of and mourning for the fantasy of a happy childhood became an important part of the psychoanalytic therapeutic process. The cases illustrate, in various degrees, the prominent features of the case of James Barrie—denial of death and early losses, defenses against infantile disappointments, and regression from adult sexuality.

Case 1

Although Miss B. was twenty-four years old, she appeared much younger, more like a scruffy young teen-ager. Her hair hung unevenly around a face devoid of makeup. She always wore jeans. She complained that she was discontented with her job as a school aide. Also, she was tied up in a love relationship with her supervisor, a "nice man" older than herself. She voiced these complaints about her life not going anywhere in a mild and vague fashion. She felt her childhood had been happy. Only when questioned did she reveal that her mother had died when she was thirteen, after a protracted illness. During the mother's increasingly frequent stays in the hospital, the patient and her siblings were told that her mother was "visiting." When the mother died, the father informed them she was on a trip and they did not attend the funeral. The patient had all along known but denied the truth. Childhood, before this, she insisted, was happy, her mother a good and loving woman. The denial of the mother's death in this familiar clinical picture was obvious. For example, the family kept the mother's clothes and makeup untouched. For the patient, time had stopped since the mother's death and she remained suspended, unable to complete the tasks of adolescence.

In the brief once-a-week therapy, the patient worked very hard. I felt that the immediate task for the therapy was to help the young woman accept the loss of her mother, complete the mourning, and get on with her life. In the subsequent months, the patient suffered intensively through a period of mourning for her mother, but her courage, intelligence, and will to get better kept her going. The fantasy of a happy childhood broke down as well, although memories of the mother remained positive. She remembered much friction between the parents and saw that she had to assume a motherly role toward her father and siblings. Within a year, the patient's whole demeanor, looks, and life had changed. She almost aged before my eyes from a scrawny adolescent to a poised young woman. When I heard from her several years later, she seemed deliriously in love with a new young man to whom she was engaged; later I heard she graduated from professional school. Thus, in this case, the fantasy of a happy childhood was, as in Peter Pan, woven within the problem of severe and unresolved loss in early adolescence.

Case 2

Mrs. T., a thirty-three-year-old, had begun treatment after watching a recent series on television about child abuse. As she watched, she found herself with tears running down her cheeks. The tears puzzled her as her personality was unusually cheery. Other than this occurrence, all she could articulate were ill-defined desires to find a career for herself.

Mrs. T.'s appearance was striking. Her blonde curly hair was tied with a bow. She dressed herself in ruffles, puffed sleeves, and pastel colored dresses. She was perky and bubbly and outgoing. For her the word *cute* was, indeed, appropriate. With her manner of dress, her coyness, and her big blue eyes, she was like a three-year-old little girl. She, too, proclaimed a happy childhood for which she should be grateful, and compared it to the horrible histories she had seen on television and read about in the newspapers.

Shortly after she began treatment, she developed an intense eroticized narcissistic transference. I was an idealized mother, from whom she wanted care, adoration, and physical contact and toward whom she had frank oral fantasies of burrowing at my breast, crawling into my lap, even into my womb. A problem of object constancy took the following form: I would not remember her between sessions, or be transformed into a totally different Dr. Kulish from one session to the next. She, in turn, at times needed concrete transitional objects to tide her over—my voice on the telephone, my appointment card tucked into her bra, or my name whispered over and over.

While she still clung to the notion of her happy childhood, the following picture of her history emerged very slowly. Her mother, both from the patient's concurrent interactions and her memories, appeared to be an extremely beautiful but narcissistic woman for whom no one existed but herself. All conversations were turned back to her accomplishments. Her husband and, at his orders, the children, waited on her hand and foot, while she did no household chores or cooking. Three memories will suffice as examples. She served the patient, aged six, soup during her lunch hour in the first grade. Her face was cold, turned away, and not a word was said. This memory is undoubtedly a screen memory for the earlier infantile feeding experiences. Again, the patient, somewhat older, hit by a car, was carried by a policeman to the porch where her mother sat gossiping with a group of ladies. The mother, annoyed at being disturbed, did not touch or say anything to the girl. In fact, the patient remembered that the only time she touched her was when she gave her, while face down, enemas on the cold bathroom floor. Another memory concerned being taken to sit on the sidelines to watch her mother perform in amateur stage productions.

The father apparently was warmer; with his joking, he was outgoing and well liked. He found the patient "cute" and played with her in a rather frenetic manner by tickling or twirling her by the arms. She seemed to have identified with his outgoing traits. He, however, was scornful of any display of emotion whatsoever. Moreover, the only person for him seemed to be his wife whom he idealized. He spent any spare time with his hobbies. The household was silent, dark, ill-cared for, and with almost no conversation, and certainly no support between parents and children, or among the children themselves. There was almost never any company or special family festivities, except activities at the fundamentalist church to which they belonged. The patient did poorly at school.

In contrast to this bleak picture, the patient consciously tried to make her adult life over in the image of a happy, warm home with happy children. She wanted starched, ruffled curtains at the windows; she literally contrived to have the smell of cookies envelop the house; she made elaborate fusses and meals at holidays about which she was very sentimental; that is, she was creating all the trappings of a happy childhood. In fact, in her interests, tastes, and sentimentality, she seemed childlike. It is a tribute to this woman's denial and creativity that she was able to put on a cheery demeanor, pour energy into keeping up the image of a home, and still maintain her fantasy of a happy childhood.

Finally, in the final phase of treatment, the idealization of the therapist crumbled. She had tried endlessly with many maneuvers to get the therapist to gratify her infantile needs and to act out, but the therapist was able, by and large, to maintain neutrality. Predictably, the realization, which came after years of work, that she would not be able to "get me," that is, have her infantile needs met by me or by her mother, ushered in a prolonged depression and a period of mourning. In a session during this period, after she had decided to go back to school to become a teacher, she put these feelings clearly into words:

"I am so depressed. Now that I see you are a real person, there is no chance of finding the secret of being happy. I see there are no secrets. My mother was unhappy herself. I realize I *am* going to die. Now that you are real, it means there is no utopia and *there never was*. There is no chance. But, funny, now I feel more like an adult." At this point the patient was not sure these new feelings spelled improvement; we would be convinced otherwise.

In this case, similar to that of Barrie, the fantasy of a happy childhood and the wish to remain a child covered intense narcissistic rage and disappointments. The bubbly, cute little girl was a persona, a "false self" she constructed for herself, which in many ways served these needs well.

Case 3

Mr. M. sought treatment for classic obsessive–compulsive symptoms. He, too, appeared younger than his thirty-three years. He dressed very casually and boyishly in jeans, T-shirt, and sneakers. He was undecided about a career. His love life was unsatisfactory as he could not seem to "get it all together" to find the right woman, settle down, marry, and have children. He felt he had no right to have any problems as his childhood was ideal in all respects. His parents were loving and kind. There were never any problems or friction of any kind.

As treatment progressed, it became obvious that the ambivalence characteristic of obsessive–compulsive neuroses pervaded his life and prevented him from achieving any stated goals for himself. His ambivalence between growing up or remaining a child is revealed in the following dream which he associated with Peter Pan:

"He is in his parent's bedroom, flying about. His father is lying on the bed as if dead while he flies and darts in and out at him. Then the scene switches—he and a brother are sneaking homemade chocolate chip cookies, and replacing them as they eat them with store bought cookies. He hates to leave this scene and, in fact, to wake up."

In his associations, the patient immediately thinks of the story of Peter Pan, a favorite. The darting in and out reminds him of the fairy Tinker Bell and all the flying children. The homemade chocolate chip cookies symbolize mother's old-fashioned nurturing. He speculates that he does not want to leave the scene because he does not want to grow up, like Peter Pan.

Other less immediate associations are to sexual issues and conflicts: allusions to the primal scene and the wish to observe the mother (as a tiny almost invisible fairy), and phallic concerns and rivalries. With this patient, as with Barrie, the wish to remain a child reflects a regressive flight from higher-level sexual conflicts and guilt. His sweeping generalizations about an ideal home cover typical memories, disappointments, and anxieties of childhood he has repressed. In his regression from the phallic/oedipal conflicts to solutions and style of the anal period which are revealed in his obsessive symptoms, he gets secret infantile satisfactions, as in the chocolate chip cookies he steals.

Discussion

In these cases in which the fantasy of remaining a child was central, the patients shared some common characteristics. They were indeed childlike in outward appearance, interests, and interpersonal relationships. Below the surface, they were markedly unhappy. Their fantasies of a happy childhood were constructed both to hide deep disappointments or losses in childhood and to gratify unconscious infantile aims. The fantasies in these cases, and most especially the second, were more than simple verbal denials; rather, they represented unconsciously organized and embedded constructions which seemed to dictate and shape the individuals' lives.

Margaret Mahler (Mahler, Pine, and Bergman, 1975) observed that a backward longing for closeness with mother was most pronounced in children whose earliest symbiotic relationships with her had been unsatisfactory. Analogously, as a lost object which has been ambivalently loved is idealized, so is a childhood which was far from perfect idealized in such nostalgic fantasies. Clinging to the past, we are afraid to let it go and lose the chance to find happiness. We can bid a happy childhood good-bye without a backward glance; we cling to our dashed hopes and cover them over with nostalgia. Nostalgia is an incomplete form of mourning.

In these cases, the mourning for a lost object or for an important, related fantasy became important tasks in the treatment. Several writers have stressed the importance of mourning in general in the psychoanalytic process. Karush (1968) links mourning with the concept of "working through," which he describes in terms of overcoming resistances and structural reorganization. He wrote that "In many ways successful working through repeats a universal developmental process by which energy is provided both for the renunciation of infantile aims and for their replacement by new and more socially acceptable ones" (p. 501). Karush's description of this process of working through as a slow and reluctant one echoes Freud's (1917) description of mourning as a slow and reluctant submission to the reality principle. Karush emphasized two ideas in the relationship between mourning and working through: first, working through as mourning for renounced gratification, and second, working through as mourning for a lost object.

Wetmore (1963), in a too often overlooked paper, pointed to the important role of grief in psychoanalysis. His hypothesis was that little permanent change can occur without a long period of grief for that which has been discontinued. He felt that because children cannot grieve effectively, they hold on to infantile objects, aims, and defenses, and are destined to repeat old patterns via the repetition compulsion. The neurotic patient's wish for recovery, then, contains unconscious hopes for infantile gratification from the analyst. Fantasies which protect against the experience of painful affects of neglect, rejection, and disappointment are also tightly held. The giving up of such fantasies during the course of psychoanalysis is accompanied by mourning and grief. We are reminded of how painful an experience effective psychoanalysis can be because of the grief it entails—grief, often, for the loss of the most cherished fantasies we hold for and about ourselves. One such fantasy is that of an endless, happy childhood as depicted in *Peter Pan*. Our nostalgia for the past betrays our sense of loss and softens our grief.

References

Barrie, J. M. (1900), *Tommy and Grizel*. New York: Charles Scribner's Sons.
———(1902), The little white bird. In: *Collected Works of J. M. Barrie*. New York: Charles Scribner's Sons.
———(1911), *Peter Pan, The Story of Peter and Wendy*. New York: Grosset & Dunlap.
———(1913), *Margaret Ogilvy*. London: Hodder & Stoughton.
———(1904), Peter Pan or the boy who would not grow up. In: *The Plays of J. M. Barrie*. New York: Charles Scribner's Sons, 1928.

————(1930), *Peter Pan in Kensington Gardens*. New York: Charles Scribner's.

Birkin, A. (1979), *J. M. Barrie and the Lost Boys*. New York: Clarkson N. Potter.

Dunbar, J. (1970), *J. M. Barrie; The Man Behind the Image*. Boston: Houghton Mifflin.

Freud, A. (1967), About losing and being lost. *The Psychoanalytic Study of the Child*, 22:9–19. New York: International Universities Press.

Freud, S. (1905), Three essays on sexuality. *Standard Edition*, 7:125–145. London: Hogarth Press, 1946.

————(1917), Mourning and melancholia. *Standard Edition*, 14:237–258.

Geduld, H. M. (1971), *James Barrie*. New York: T. Wayne.

Kaplan, L. (1984), *Adolescence: The Farewell to Childhood*. New York: Simon & Schuster.

Karpel, M. (1956), The origins of Peter Pan. *Psychoanal. Rev.*, 43:104–110.

Karush, A. (1968), Working through. *Psychoanal. Quart.*, 36(4):497–531.

Krystal, H. (1975), Affect tolerance. *The Annual of Psychoanalysis*, 3:179–220. New York: International Universities Press.

Levin, S. (1966), Depression and object loss. *J. Amer. Psychoanal. Assn.*, 14:142–153.

Lorand, S. (1947), Compulsion neurosis. *The Yearbook of Psychoanalysis*, 3:129–140. New York: International Universities Press.

Mackail, D. (1941), *The Story of J. M. B.* London: P. Davies.

Mahler, M., Pine, F., & Bergman, A. (1975), *The Psychological Birth of the Human Infant*. New York: Basic Books.

Meisel, F. T. (1977), The myth of Peter Pan. *The Psychoanalytic Study of the child*, 32:545–563. New Haven, CT: Yale University Press.

Millay, E., St. Vincent (1934), Childhood is the kingdom where nobody dies. In: *Collected Lyrics*. New York: Washington Square Press, 1963, pp. 203–205.

Root, N. N. (1957), A neurosis in adolescence. *The Psychoanalytic Study of the Child*, 12:320–334. New York: International Universities Press.

Stern, M. (1968), Fear of death and neurosis. *J. Amer. Psychoanal. Assn.*, 16:3–31.

Wetmore, R. (1963), The role of grief in psychoanalysis. *Internat. J. Psycho-Anal.*, 44:97–103.

Wolfenstein, M. (1966), How is mourning possible? *The Psychoanalytic Study of the Child*, 21:92–126. New York: International Universities Press.

————(1969), Loss, rage, and repetition. *The Psychoanalytic Study of the Child*, 24:432–460. New York: International Universities Press.

4

Vicissitudes of Psychic Loss of a Physically Present Parent

Peter C. Shabad, Ph.D.

In the course of making the normal developmental journey toward adulthood, we all experience, to a greater or lesser degree, the intangible loss of childhood and all that goes with it: a playful spontaneity, a subjective, idiosyncratic view of the world, and a bygone innocence. With the mediating assistance of a relatively successful resolution to the oedipus complex, the child learns to compromise, to subordinate individual needs and wishes to the realistic requirements of his given culture. Because our particular cultural norm of maturity incorporates a great deal of what we refer to as secondary process thinking—often to the great detriment and exclusion of the passion and vigor that primary process thinking infuses into our lives—we can see how the socialization process inevitably entails a gradual "loss."

As we increasingly discover the imperfections of our parents, our childlike spontaneity and innocence are no longer safe-

Thanks go to Drs. E. J. Anthony, George Feden, Steven Gryll, Irwin Hoffman, and Paul Holinger for their careful reading and helpful editorial comments for this chapter.

guarded from the pitfalls and unpleasant realities of the adult world. Without this protective umbrella of idealized parents, we are exposed to what seems to be an ever-widening life-space. And what was our grandiose importance in the small, familiar context of the family becomes diminished in the face of a far larger, more alien life-space of strangers.

Growing up thus necessitates some degree of mourning the discrepancy between the ideal and real, of accepting imperfections in our parents and in our own developmental histories. This process of "letting go" requires a working through of the repeated indignities and small narcissistic insults experienced at the hands of our parents. When these little traumata do not overwhelm a person's sense of goodness and completeness, it is more or less possible to accept oneself and proceed onwards with life.

However, sometimes very real narcissistic injuries disrupt the gradual shedding of a childhood skin, and make it very difficult to relinquish salvation fantasies of ideal parents. Here, the self-protective need to retain such fantasies hinders the necessary work of growing up. While remaining unconsciously fixated upon particular themes of trauma with their accompanying repetitious fantasies of restitution and mastery, such individuals may drift into adulthood with only a phantom existence.

While perhaps unconsciously sensing this powerful regressive pull to undo previous psychic harm with idealized reparative fantasies, the child also consciously recognizes the need to move forward in life. Thus, such individuals may renounce their wishful fantasies with excessive rigor. In so doing, many such persons may eventually become alienated from that which is at all true or meaningful in themselves.

For these adults the bygone memories of a childhood innocence may seem an inaccessibly remote island on the far side of adolescence. Indeed, it is precisely because of this self-imposed sense of distance that such alienated individuals, when in treatment, convey nostalgic longings for an inadequately mourned childhood. And yet there is often no evidence of overt physical loss in the histories of these patients; typically, they grew up within two-parent households. Instead, we might say that the accumulated weight of repeated little deprivations, narcissistic injuries, and "petites" traumata—experienced as loss, but unmourned—weave their way into the fabric of character and its defensive armor. I have chosen to refer to this intangible, subtle sort of loss experience as *psychic loss*, following Anthony's (1973) use of the term to describe the loss of a parent via psychosis.

This chapter will attempt to reconstruct a pathway by which the experience of psychic loss leads to the development of a specific kind of characterology. First, I will describe more precisely what I mean by psychic loss. I will then examine how the inherent aspects of this type of loss prolong and severely interfere with the mourning process, thus leading to the establishment of a particular array of characterological defenses. Finally, I will briefly discuss some of the implications and challenges involved in the diagnosis and treatment of such individuals.

Physical Loss versus Psychic Loss

Historically, loss has typically been conceptualized as an overt, physical separation of one person from another person. The vicissitudes of loss, such as grief and mourning, are usually viewed as reactions that correspond directly to a demonstrable physical abandonment. Although mourning is not an absolute process (i.e., we can probably never completely overcome the loss of a loved one), I would like to briefly outline how a child may work through the death of a parent in a relatively healthy manner. I have assumed that the child of whom I am speaking has the requisite object constancy, ego strength, and support of the surviving parent to successfully engage in the mourning process.

Mahler, Pine, and Bergman (1975) have described how a child's ego may split upon being physically separated from his mother. The absent, imagined mother is idealized, while other physically present figures are viewed as all bad. In the initial grieving phase following a loss, this idealization of the lost object is often coupled with a devaluation of the self. Indeed, Freud (1917) suggested that the mourner's self-reproaches cleanse the lost object of any wrongdoing; such self-derogation may protect the image of the abandoning parent from the disappointed yearnings, reproaches, and rage that Wolfenstein (1969) and Bowlby (1979), among others, see as common reactions of a child to the physical loss of a parent.

Anthony (1973) has pointed out that when a child loses a parent, an essential core of good feeling is magnified, with the consequence that an idealized picture emerges of the parent. Although the child who mourns the physical loss of a parent is vulnerable to becoming fixated upon this idealization phase of the mourning process, it is my view that idealization, if worked through, is a temporary but important prelude to the introjection and identification necessary for productive mourning. By encapsulating the child's rage, idealization permits the representation of the physically lost parent to remain "good enough" and palatable enough for introjection. The child can then fashion this relatively benign image to his own needs and assimilate the lost parent into lasting memory.

Pollock (1961) has pointed out that productive mourning can only occur when the introject is assimilated into the ego. Fenichel (1945) noted that the establishment of the introject helps facilitate the loosening of the binds to the lost object. Freud (1923) has said: "It may be that this identification is the sole condition under which the id can give up its objects" (p. 29). Assimilating the lost object into the ego, establishing an introject, and identification are all ways of describing a process by which the mourner gradually internalizes the image of the lost person, thus enabling a final parting with that person.

The adaptive sequence in this mourning process, of idealization, introjection, and the relinquishment of objects, is based upon a lasting physical loss. Yet, when we define loss solely in terms of physical loss occurring at a certain time and place, we are not doing justice to the phenomenology of the loss experience. A truly psychoanalytic theory of mourning would not be based only upon the objective reality of loss, but would also encompass the subjective perception and personal experience of loss. Because a sense of loss can be experienced even while another person is physically present, it is useful to distinguish loss as a physically evident fact from loss as a subjectively felt state.

In his classic work "Mourning and Melancholia," Freud (1917) captures well the subtle, often unconscious aspect of what could be viewed as psychic loss:

> The object has not perhaps actually died, but has become lost as an object of love. In yet other cases one feels justified in concluding that a loss of the kind has been experienced, but one cannot see clearly what it is that has been lost, and it is all the more reasonable to suppose that the patient cannot consciously perceive what he has lost either [p. 245].

In the same paper, Freud also states that "the occasions giving rise to melancholia for the most part extend beyond the clear case of a loss by death, and include all those situations of being wounded, hurt, neglected, out of favor or disappointed" (p. 251). Rochlin (1965) has taken notice of an important aspect of psychic loss—the tearing down of a child's self-image. He states: "The self, when demeaned, produces conflicts and responses similar to those that may be observed in object loss . . . loss and hence damage to self-esteem remain bound" (pp. 2–3).

Elsewhere, Rochlin and other psychoanalytic observers have commented that the loss experience need not be conceived only as physical absence, but may also refer to an emotionally neglected empty relationship (Rochlin, 1953), a lack of responsiveness and accessibility (Bowlby, 1979), and the psychotic transformation of a parent (Anthony, 1973). In this chapter, I will address myself to this internal experience of loss, or psychic loss, when it occurs in the continued physical presence of the parent.

The Traumatic Theme and Psychic Loss

It is often not possible to point to an objectively verifiable determinant that corresponds to a sense of loss. In contrast to the acute and overt trauma of physical loss, psychic loss may derive from relatively chronic and intangible traumata. Greenacre (1952) has noted that "prolonged traumata may suffuse the organism with stimulation" (p. 295). Kris (1956) describes "strain trauma" as "the effect of long-lasting situations, which may cause traumatic effects by accumulation of frustrating tensions" (p. 73). Kohut and Wolf (1978) also note the narcissistic injury resulting from a "chronic ambience created by the deep-rooted attitudes of the selfobjects" (p. 417). Khan (1974) uses the term *cumulative trauma* to describe "the significant points of stress and strain in the evolving mother–infant relationship" (p. 55).

Although Khan emphasizes early mother–infant interaction (specifically, the breach in the mother's role as a protective shield for the infant) as the major determinant of cumulative trauma, it seems that the concept of cumulative trauma could be extended to refer to traumata that accumulate throughout childhood, and in relation to any significant familial figure. The traumatizing aspects of such prolonged, relatively intangible trauma for a child often seem to derive from the constancy of a parent's unconscious characterological *faults* (to use Balint's term [1979]) that the parent has not assimilated into his or her ego. Because these split-off aspects of the parent's ego are governed by the repetition compulsion, they are acted out repeatedly upon the child. Gradually, a specific thematic chronicity may begin to emerge in the interplay between parent and child that corresponds closely to the most problematic aspects of the parent's character. I will use the term *traumatic theme* to describe this chronic pattern of frustrating experiences that are passively suffered in childhood.

In using the term *traumatic theme*, I would like to especially emphasize the patterned imprint that the ongoing experience of accumulating trauma stamps upon the child's developing personality. The traumatic theme thus forms a chain of repetitive, concrete experiences from which the psychic loss of a physically present parent gradually emerges. What then are some of these traumatic themes?

If one night, for example, a father sits quietly in his living room without speaking to his child, the child will most likely not be traumatized. However, if night after night, year after year, the child is ignored by that same father, a traumatic pattern may establish itself that then constitutes the basis of the psychic loss experience. The traumatic themes of a parent's exploitation of a child for narcissistic purposes, the withholding of love, harsh criticisms, moody silences, and excessive intrusiveness all may induce feelings of psychic loss to a greater or lesser degree. The omission and commission of little acts such as never being kissed good night, having small promises consistently broken, or being called a stupid child, when repeated over a number of years, may each develop into a traumatic theme. A mother's excessive martyrdom or a father's explosively drunken rages may each leave a cumulative traumatic imprint upon the developing child. For some individuals many such traumatic themes of varying severity may accumulate throughout childhood.

It may seem like this list of traumatic themes is too varied to be encompassed by a single term such as *psychic loss*. However, it must be remembered that the developmental requirements of the child are also quite numerous, and often seem to contradict each other.

At first glance, the regressive tendency toward object relatedness may seem incompatible with the progressive drive toward increasing individuation and autonomy. We are aware from Kris's (1956) work, however, that the process of regression does not only serve the pleasure-seeking id, but also is essential to the ego's drive toward mastery. Regression and progression may therefore be viewed as complementary, mutually reinforcing aspects of a single developmental process leading to psychological growth. Thus, either the extreme intrusiveness of a mother or the empty silence of a father may inhibit and alter the course of development from different end points; blocking the fulfillment of either regressive or progressive tendencies may be experienced as psychologically depriving.

Usually, it is only in later years, when as clinicians we observe the repetitive urges to undo the experience of the psychological deprivation and master the traumatic theme, that a specific psychic loss can be reconstructed. The term *psychic loss* is thus used mainly for heuristic purposes: to complete the picture of regressive longings, repetitive acting out, and sense of incomplete mourning that is often conveyed in clinical practice.

The Problem of Mourning Psychic Loss

The inherent qualities of psychic loss do not lend themselves easily to a healthy mourning process. Unlike a tangible, physical loss which must necessarily occur suddenly, overtly, and often conclusively, psychic loss will develop slowly, covertly, and often indefinitely. Because we are speaking of a sense of loss, there is no objective reference point by which to validate the child's feelings. On the contrary, the continued physical presence of the parent would seem to contradict and thus invalidate the child's private experience. It is this pernicious, hidden quality of psychic loss that makes it difficult to grasp, and which delays its eventual conscious realization. Unlike the sometimes too painful objective reality of physical loss, psychic loss is a far subtler deprivation; to a great extent, psychic loss is likely to be experienced unconsciously. Consequently, the child's reactions to psychic loss are likely to be muted as well.

Without a conscious recognition that something has been lost, the child will be unable to express "the overt yearning for the lost object" that Bowlby (1979) sees as necessary to healthy mourning. Instead, because this type of loss is so difficult to objectify, the child often bears the burden of his feelings alone, without the adequate reality testing or outside support crucial to adaptive mourning. Within the private recesses of his imagination, the child is thus more prone to hidden, magical fantasies of restitution, more sensitive to those fantasies never coming to fruition, and finally, more susceptible to the formation of defenses that would shield him from his helplessness. All of these vulnerabilities of the child make it more likely that a particular psychic loss will have a pathogenic effect upon an individual's development rather than be adequately mourned.

The incompleteness of psychic loss hinders the adaptive aspects of a mourning process that are typically based upon the finality of physical loss. The idealized image of the psychically lost parent, formed during the parent's periodic physical absences, becomes increasingly difficult to maintain in the face of the very real reappearances of that same frustrating parental figure.

Mahler (1971) has observed that "the mother after separation," or what Bowlby (1958) has called the "mother in the flesh," is always disappointing. Mahler, Pine, and Bergman (1975) have noted that this returning mother is seen as unreliable and intrusive, and remains an "unassimilated foreign body." Each time the parent reappears, then, the idealization and consequent internalization of that parent's image are thwarted, and the mourning process is brought to a halt. Instead, as long as the parent physically returns from an absence, the child's hope is forever renewed that the parent will be somehow magically transformed into a needed restitutive figure—only to have that hope dashed anew by that parent's same depriving actions. Because mourning is so difficult to bring to some closure, psychic loss is continually reexperienced, like salt rubbed into an open wound.

I would like to illustrate this cycle of hope and disappointment with a brief example. A small boy has seldom received love or attention from his father. But because on this particular day he has received a B in math (unusually high for him), he believes that his father will finally have some warm, kind words to say to him. He eagerly awaits his father's return from work. When the father does finally come home, however, he nods indifferently to news of his son's grade. He then becomes engrossed in his newspaper, and later in the TV. He breaks the monotony of television watching only to remind his son to take the garbage out before going to bed.

After years of such indifferent or critical treatment from his father, this boy may begin to experience the effects of this particular traumatic theme as a psychic loss. Each day as his father goes to work, the boy's unconscious hope begins to grow in his father's absence: maybe today things will be different. Indeed, perhaps if the father's absence were to become permanent at this point, his son would be able to "freeze" the sequence of frames at this optimistic moment and internalize the benevolent, idealized image of a rarely seen, caring father. He could then retain the comforting illusion that had his father lived, he finally would have received his father's love. Instead, with the return of his still uncaring father at the end of the day, the experience of psychic loss is reconfirmed once again.

With each parental reappearance, then, the child is caught in a vicious cycle. The failure to fully mourn the psychic loss of the parent leaves the child exposed not only to the painful reexperiencing of that loss, but with it, the rekindling of never-to-be fulfilled yearnings. The renewal of hope, in turn, interferes with the acknowledgment of the relative finality of psychic loss. It is this treadmill-like quality of wish and disillusionment that torturously protracts the child's frustration and helplessness.

A number of psychoanalytic observers (Deutsch, 1937; Lindemann, 1944; Bowlby, 1979) have noted that ego strength is a key factor in successful mourning. It enables the child to tolerate the helplessness that accompanies loss, or as Bowlby has pointed out, to bear with the "pining for the lost object." Zetzel (1965) has also made the observation that the ego's capacity to tolerate depression is essential to the acknowledging of separation and loss. Ego strength thus enables the mourner to "stay with" the acute pain of grieving, to retain an identification with the grieving self victimized by psychic loss rather than to resort to psychic escape in the form of defensive detachment. Unfortunately, the often demoralizing experience of psychic loss usually serves to deplete the child of the very ego strength that is necessary to mourn this sort of loss.

Significantly, Bowlby (1979) suggests that because of the relatively weak egos of young children, the "despair" stage of grieving over a physical loss of the mother may prematurely give way to a "detachment" stage. In other writings, Bowlby (1973) has described detachment behaviorally as a defensive nonrecognition of the mother after her return from a prolonged separation. Because in the situation of psychic loss, the capacity for hopefulness and sense of psychological potency is continually undermined, we would expect the child to proceed relatively quickly from grief to detachment.

However, the mother is not the primary source of emotional torment. It is the child's own desperation to overcome the void left by psychic loss that perpetuates the child's sense of anguish. As Joffe and Sandler (1965) have pointed out, the loss of an object also signifies the loss of an aspect of the self that reflects the relation to the object. Thus, not only does the child overtly detach from the mother, but also, because the child's misbegotten wish for the ideal restitutive parent leaves him vulnerable to seemingly interminable narcissistic deflation, the child detaches from the major internal source of disappointment—his own tendency toward idealization. Joffe and Sandler (1965) thus argue that detachment occurs when the child settles for "its actual state of the self. It is a type of resignation which can be seen as an attempt to do away with the discrepancy between actual self and ideal self, and in this sense it is a form of adaptation which stands in contrast to processes of mourning" (p. 409). As a consequence of this detachment, the fragile longing for the ideal restitution of psychic loss proceeds underground into the protected confines of the unconscious. Concurrently with this defensive detachment, such a child may gradually develop, at least consciously, a fatalistic outlook toward his life and future. After all, fate, as personalized by the child, seems to have powerfully thwarted his wish for a parental metamorphosis at every turn.

The contrast between bearing with the pain of grieving and its accompanying idealization, or detaching from that grief can sometimes be observed in two distinctive character styles of leavetaking. When taking leave of a loved one, some individuals will cling and seek to prolong the departure; they bear with the pain of anticipating the impending loss. Such persons seem to be well able to tolerate, if not actually to immerse themselves in their grief. Because they are prone to idealization, such individuals are also often likely to stay in contact with others over distant spaces and times. These may also be the people whose "hearts grow fonder" in the absence of the loved one.

Other individuals, manifesting the defensive detachment described above, do not seem to be able to tolerate a protracted anticipation of loss. Although such persons may be depriving themselves of precious time with a person whom they dearly love, they cut the leavetaking short. In quickly disengaging themselves from the loved one, these persons attempt to deny the wish to hold on to the other, a wish that will be inevitably frustrated when the loved one departs. Their actions seem to well fit the saying "out of sight, out of mind." Thus, such individuals do not easily write letters or make telephone calls over long distances, for that would arouse the pain of yearning in the face of loss. Instead, such practical, perhaps opportunistic persons have learned to "love the ones they are with" rather than long for the ones they are without.

The experience of severe psychic loss may also influence an individual's capacity to mourn the subsequent physical loss of that person. The rage and frustration that results from psychic loss may sometimes overwhelm what little "core of positive transactions" that had existed with the departed one. Because these individuals have defensively detached from their idealizing tendency in reaction to the protracted despair of psychic loss, they may exhibit a similar defense in response to a subsequent physical separation from that person as well. Their reaction to physical loss may then resemble the schizoidlike state that H. Deutsch (1937) described as "absence of grief."

In contrast, it seems that individuals who have not experienced severe psychic loss are able to retain the capacity for overt wishing and idealizing. By using idealization, they may be better able to establish the introject necessary for mourning a physical loss such as death. It is my impression that if such persons do develop psychopathology in response to physical loss, they are likely, because of their idealization of the lost person, to convey a sense of incompleteness and inadequacy typically indicative of depressive symptomatology.

The difficulty inherent in mourning psychic loss may have problematic repercussions for personality development. The traumatic theme forms the developmental blueprint of the psychic loss experience that we could least tolerate, and yet could do nothing to overcome. As such, the traumatic theme and its accompanying feeling of psychic loss come to form a personally defined construct of helplessness. Instead of assimilating the loss experience within the ego, the child's personality gradually coalesces around the specific traumatic theme(s) in characterological defense of its own fragile helplessness. Without adequate mourning, the psychic loss experience may then become fixed as an imprint upon the developing character of the child.

Because of the drive toward ego integration, the urge to

overcome psychic loss may increasingly preoccupy the individual's life. Given the ego's need to undo the passively undergone experience of psychic loss and change it into an active one, the individual will seek to reenact a scenario of the traumatic theme with a far different outcome than had occurred in the past.

Characterological Defenses Against Psychic Loss

With increasing age, the defensive detachment from an overtly idealizing aspect of the ego becomes more pronounced in the face of the ongoing frustrations of psychic loss. However, beneath such determined defense there burns a cauldron of unconscious fantasy and hope. The more strongly the child consciously renounces his wishes for the restitutive parent, the more tenaciously he holds on to those unconscious fantasies. In this sense, such detachment may begin to manifestly resemble the ego splitting described by Freud (1938) and Wolfenstein (1969). Wolfenstein has observed that a child will react to the death of a parent by consciously acknowledging the loss, while unconsciously denying it. In the situation of psychic loss, a child may thus come to consciously recognize that his parent will never meet his needs, while still unconsciously yearning for ultimate fulfillment with that psychically lost parent.

In clinical work we often see adolescent and adult patients who, voicing the conviction that a parent will never meet their needs, either swear off that parent or take an apparently indifferent stance toward him or her. Although such patients may live in the same town as their parents, they make a conscious effort to see them only rarely, if at all. These patients seem to need and make use of the external structure of physical distance to ensure that they do not yield to an unconscious wish for reconciling with the psychically lost parent—only to have that wish disappointed again.

Given the adolescent task of mourning childhood and fashioning an identity fitted to the harsh rigors of adult life, we should not be surprised at this conscious attempt to renounce the childlike and vulnerable wish for the ideal parent. Furthermore, in adolescence we also see an urge to render previous passively undergone experiences into active ones, an urge toward reintegrating earlier identifications. Yet psychic loss, with its vicissitudes of a failure to mourn and consequent splitting of the ego, has created an emotional chasm between the adolescent and the lost parent, making such reintegration problematic. Instead, an either/or choice of identifications is set up between the split off, despairing self, victimized by psychic abandonment, and the powerful parent who psychically abandoned the child. By attempting to identify with the parent as psychic abandoner, the child's ego splitting becomes a prelude to a self-perpetrated psychic loss that duplicates the parent's psychic abandonment.

To the extent that this abandoner is also perceived as a type of aggressor, the attempt to identify with the psychically abandoning parent strongly resembles the dynamic of the identification with the aggressor described by Anna Freud (1936). She noted, however, that identification with the aggressor is not really an identification with the person of the aggressor, but with the aggressive behavior itself. In this sense, identification with the aggressor or the psychic abandoner may best be thought of as a form of imitation, an imitation of the abandoning behavior of the psychically lost parent.

In an interesting article, Gaddini (1969) has compared the concepts of identification and imitation. He describes the process of identification as referring to the verb *to have*; it is a process by which reality (or the other person) becomes introjected, possessed, and assimilated. Identification enables the developing child to re-create, or, according to Loewald (1962), "reconstitute the object" within himself. This identification process eventually leads to deep structural change and development.

In contrast, Gaddini says that imitation refers to the verb *to be*; it is an attempt to adapt to the other's reality. Imitation installs itself in the absence of an object, and increases as oral frustrations increase. As such, the imitative process, by reestablishing an omnipotent fusion of the self with the object, becomes a means of attempting to overcome a sense of separateness.

Anthony (1973) also has noted that a child will seek to overcome the loss of a parent via psychosis by an "identification with the crazy one." He points out that this folie à deux bridges the psychic gap between parent and child.

Imitation may thus be viewed as an attempt to compensate for the failure to identify with and internalize the person of the psychically lost parent; it is instead an identification with the psychically abandoning behavior of that parent. Schecter (1968) has compared such pseudoidentifications to superficial imitations, which he suggests are repetitive attempts to introject the parent.

In clinical practice, we typically see patients who are their own worst enemies. Paradoxical as it may seem, many of these persons are perpetuating the psychic loss from which they previously suffered, by duplicating the very behavior which had victimized them as children.

One patient of mine recounted how distressed she would become whenever her mother blamed herself for the ills of the world, which she did repeatedly. In spite of all the daughter's reassurances and attempts to cheer up her mother, it was to no avail; her mother would continue to flagellate herself. As a child, this patient's traumatic theme had arisen from the continuous experience of helplessness in not having an impact upon her mother's mood. Her psychic loss derived from the loss of mutuality, of the give and take with her mother essential to the development of healthy narcissism. This patient's mother could not accept the symbolic gift of love or reassurance offered by her daughter. Instead of mourning this psychic loss, the daughter reenacted the pain and helplessness of her narcissistic wounds by subsequently taking on her mother's stance and behavior of moral masochism in her own adult life, which eventually led her to seek help.

Other familiar examples of this imitative process can be observed when women verbally abuse their children with the same words that their own mothers had used against them, or when men ignore their children in the identical fashion that their fathers had ignored them.

Sometimes such imitation seems so uncannily accurate that we know that the imago of the parent has not been adequately "chewed up" and internalized. Rather, a fixed imprint of the psychically lost parent has remained at the more superficial, behavioral level. Pollock (1961) has noted that when the death of a loved one is denied, an "encapsulated image" retaining the characteristics of the external object sometimes exists separately as a result of a lack of assimilation. When a failure in assimilating the representation of a parent has occurred, we often see the adult blatantly manifesting that parent's behavior, unaltered and frozen in the transmission from one generation to the next. This immutability of behavior suggests an arrest in development, and more specifically, a fixation upon a specific aspect of the parent's character.

Instead of a deeper, more personal, internally restructuring identification with the parent that would have permitted the child to gradually mourn and let go of that parent, imitation belies a short-circuiting of the mourning process. The split-off aspect of the ego that sought to undo psychic loss, now governed by the repetition compulsion, is given expression through an imitative fusion with the lost parent. Such persistent imitation, reflecting as it does a failure to fully mourn, can become characterologically entrenched.

The denied wish for a relationship with the psychically lost parent may thus become reenacted as a type of characterological imitation of that parent's psychically abandoning behavior. Pollock (1961) uses the concept of a primitive introjection without identification to describe the continuing existence of a separate parental imago in the child. The question arises, then, of whether characterological imitation is not really a form of primitive introjection. And if so, to what extent does such introjection occur? Because Loewald's (1962) concept of degrees of internalization highlights the dimension of intrapsychic depth, it is useful in addressing these questions.

According to Loewald, parental introjects may shift in degrees of internalization, of greater or lesser distance, from the superego on the periphery of the ego system to a central ego core. Loewald further notes that when a loved object dies, ties with the external object become gradually loosened. At the same time, what was originally an ego ideal or superego element while the parent is living, then becomes internalized into progressively deeper aspects of the ego system upon the parent's death.

In case of psychic loss, however, the parent continues to be physically present. Because of this continued physical presence, we would expect that the parental image would not receive the necessary impetus for further internalization. Instead, it would remain fixed on the periphery of the ego system, as if "stuck in the craw." Identifying with precisely those parental behaviors that produced psychic loss is a makeshift attempt at healing both the rift between child and parent, and at the same time, the intrapsychic split within the ego system.

Unfortunately, this imitative identification with the parental imago on the periphery of the ego system is also a defensive desertion from the person's own ego core, and thus it is duplicative of the parent's psychic abandonment of the child. It is through this compulsive attempt to repetitively and defensively render passive aspects of the psychic loss experience into active ones, that imitation gradually entrenches itself into the constancy of character. Characterological imitation can then be viewed as a counterphobic reaction to the soft underbelly of childhood helplessness as concretized by the psychic loss experience. From this view, it can be considered an essential aspect of the defensive armor that gives form to adult character.

The defensive evolution of this experience of distance from a central ego core can be illustrated by tracing the child's need to shield himself from the emotional impact of the present moment. Because the child, in the midst of experiencing psychic loss, has been hindered too often in pursuit of his most treasured ideals, he begins to lose his healthy narcissism, his sense of illusion concerning his impact upon the world around him. From this child's point of view, it is external reality, in the guise of the idealized, all-powerful adult world, that seems to hold ultimate sway over the giving and withholding of the necessary life-giving "manna from heaven." For the child experiencing the emptiness of the psychic loss of the present, the hope for restitution in the future may be the only source of solace. Eventually, this hope may become psychically activated through a defensive shift of identifications from the passive helplessness of childhood to the active potency of adulthood.

As a means of warding off a gnawing sense of loneliness,

then, a child may attempt to seek salvation by prematurely joining the entitled "promised land" of the adult world. For this child, "growing up" quickly may mean a caricaturing mimicry of what it means to be adult. Such a child, for example, may perceive that identifying with his powerful antagonist of external reality, or the "fate" represented by a frustrating parent— and thereby becoming "realistic"—is a necessary rite of passage into the adult community. As these children progressively renounce their childlike propensities of imagining, hoping, and wishing for what is possible, all of which have only brought unbearable vulnerability and tremendous frustration, they may instead develop a character structure suited to the necessary: serious, pseudomature, conventional, and at all times, practical.

Kierkegaard (1849) has well described this superficial veneer of conventionality:

> By seeing the multitude of men about it, by getting engaged in all sorts of worldly affairs, by becoming wise about how things go in this world, such a man forgets himself. . . . [D]oes not dare to believe in himself, finds it too venturesome a thing to be himself, far easier and safer to be like the others, to become an imitation, a number, a cipher in the crowd [pp. 166–167].

The clinical observations of later psychoanalytic theorists nicely extend Kierkegaard's basic insight. Helene Deutsch (1942) describes the "as if" personality as one whose "apparently normal relationship to the world corresponds to a child's imitativeness and is the expression of an identification with the environment" (p. 304). Winnicott (1965) similarly sees the "false self" as an impersonation, a defense against the exploitation of the "true self." In a formulation similar to one of the theses of this chapter, Khan (1974) has theorized that the false self emerges from a premature defensive organization resulting from cumulative trauma.

Detached from themselves and encapsulated within this world of the "other," these individuals continually miss the emotional richness of the current moment. Such a person's life may, upon reflection, take on an illusory, dreamlike quality—as if time had passed without having been genuinely lived. Because such individuals are not truly inhabiting their own egos, they often exhibit the obsessional quality of second-guessing themselves. It seems such persons need to verify externally through their own self-consciousness, that what had not been experienced from within, had nevertheless actually occurred. From this point of view, obsessional thinking is a fruitless, and, therefore, endless quest to capture one's own experience. Elsewhere, I have examined how this feeling of unlived life may eventually culminate in a sense of regret, becoming then a source of resistance in the treatment of such patients (Shabad, 1987).

This type of obsessionality may also manifest itself in an emphasis upon the objective and rational at the expense of the subjective and irrational. After all, the child's subjective experiences and yearnings were repeatedly rebuffed by the objective realities of psychic loss. Initially, the private experience of psychic loss itself seems irrational in the face of the parent's continued physical presence. In time, however, after the psychic loss is consciously recognized, the irrational unconscious wishes to undo that loss are felt as a great source of frustration and are forsaken. A life of the mind may consequently become a refuge from emotional pain, and self-denial may masquerade in the guise of objectivity and rationality.

In sum, the imitative identification with the psychically abandoning behavior of the parent, the future, the conventionally "adult," and the cerebral, all encapsulated at a psychic distance from a central ego core, leave such a person with the alienating sense of being "on the outside looking in." Indeed, feeling as if one were on the outside looking inwards may be the narcissistic experience, par excellence. The prototypical narcissistic characteristic of self-preoccupation can be viewed as a means of compensating for the psychic absence of the other, of relating to oneself as if from without. In the final analysis, the imitative fusing with the hallucinatory image of one's psychically lost parent—putting oneself in the place of a parent who was not really there—may well be a way of keeping oneself company in the face of devastating loneliness.

Diagnostic and Treatment Implications of Psychic Loss

Before examining specific treatment issues, there are certain diagnostic implications of the psychic loss of a physically present parent that are worth considering. As the defensive reenacting of characterological imitation proceeds, the outside observer may be clued in to the specific traumatic theme that forms the basis of the patient's psychic loss experience. Without having been worked through, the hated aspects of the parent's abandoning image have remained fixed or "encapsulated" in the individual's character. Now, however, in a desperate attempt to escape the helplessness that was previously experienced passively, the patient reenacts the drama of the traumatic theme in imitation of the parent's actively traumatizing behavior.

In this defensive transition from passive to active, the traumatic theme, still governed by the repetition compulsion, remains unaltered by the vagaries of development. The patient's active role thus becomes a reflective mirror of those traumatized aspects of personality that have not been adequately mourned or assimilated.

A characterological envy, for example, is often visible in persons who have experienced rather severe psychic loss. Such envy allows us a reflective view into the emotional deprivation such patients had suffered earlier in life. Patients who envy the success of a spouse or a friend have frequently been deprived of their own pleasures. Such patients have often been victimized by the conscious or unconscious sadistic maneuverings of narcissistic parents, who begrudged their child any enjoyment that may have been derived from an object or person other than themselves. In such a way, a narcissistic parent might cast an envious "evil eye" on a toy, a favorite food, or a good friend, and thus spoil that pleasure for the child. Unfortunately, this child, in imitative fusion with the depriving actions of the envious parent, often becomes the self-denying adult who envies others.

The continued usage of characterological imitation as a counterphobic defense provides a mirror of the patient's profound fear that the helplessness of his specific psychic loss will be perpetuated, unless a more active stance is taken. Elsewhere, I have made the point that types of fears of death (burning, stabbing, drowning, etc.) can be viewed as metaphors for the private, idiosyncratic meanings of helplessness symbolizing a person's traumatic theme (Shabad, 1983). The notion of characterological imitation thus enables us as clinicians to diagnose the patient's specific psychic loss in a clear dynamic fashion without reference to general categorical labels.

In the case of the woman who as a child was repeatedly exposed to her mother's martyrdom, we see that in adulthood she resolutely clings to that very same moral masochism and suffering in her marriage and in her treatment. Indeed, the specific scenario of her traumatic theme was repeatedly acted out in the transference. Week after week, this woman came to her sessions with self-derogatory remarks about her intelligence, her sexual inadequacy, her weight, and her overall appearance.

At one level of diagnostic interpretation, we can see evidence here of obsessional and depressive symptomatology. At another level of interpretation, however, we can see how this patient has reversed the roles of her traumatic theme. In repeatedly reenacting the part of her self-abusive mother, this woman was also attempting to engender a helplessness in the therapist to facilitate change and influence her—the very helplessness that she had experienced as a child.

It may be added, in general, that when treatment begins to drift and we sense an immutability to change, we may be seeing a repetition of the patient's psychic loss experience. As the patient had once waited without success for the psychically lost parent to change, so the patient may now challenge us to wait for him or her to be "cured." Following from this line of reasoning, psychoanalysis and psychoanalytic psychotherapy can be potentially mutative for the patient. As the traumatic theme becomes reconstructed within the transference and interpreted and as the therapist is internalized, the original experience of psychic loss can begin to be properly mourned. The relinquishment of the unconscious wish for a parental turnabout in the future occurs concurrently with the patient's internalization of a nonparent, the therapist, in the present.

The internalization of the therapist and the mourning of psychic loss can only occur, however, when the patient fully acknowledges his wish to receive from the therapeutic relationship, and subsequently allows himself to do so. Yet, because such patients identify with the self-prohibiting and self-denying image of the psychically lost parent, the consciousness that one is receiving from the therapist can paralyze the therapeutic process; for the original purpose of the splitting of the ego was to detach from the wish to receive from a parent who did not give what was needed.

By initially coming for help, the patient may feel that he is already putting himself in the vulnerable position of receiving from the therapist; to do further would challenge long-entrenched defenses designed to fend off the passivity of receiving. From the beginning of treatment, we may thus encounter strong resistance to the wish to receive and to the crucial therapeutic process of internalization.

As a patient gradually reconciles himself to the therapeutic process of receiving help and begins to internalize the therapist, a new subtle problem may begin to emerge in treatment—the problem of regret over lost time. Elsewhere, I have written in greater detail about this problem (Shabad, 1987). Here I will touch upon it briefly.

When a child fails to identify with and internalize the psychically lost parent, ego development becomes fixated, to a greater or lesser degree, upon the parent's abandoning behavior. By having split off from the wish to undo the psychic loss, the patient has also detached himself from living, from fully experiencing himself and others. Years of psychic drifting may pass by between childhood and adulthood; years that were based upon an unconscious hope that the ideal parental figure will appear someday to fill the void left by psychic loss. Life had usually been comprised of a series of active attempts to ferret out such an idealized figure: frenetic activity which masked an underlying passive demand that such a figure should be made readily available.

By coming for treatment then, the patient is also implicitly requesting a return to the mainstream of his life again. The establishment of the transference and its subsequent analysis enables the patient to distinguish between the psychic loss of the past with the accompanying wish to undo that loss in the future, and the genuine emotional experience of the present.

Although the major task in the treatment of such individuals is to facilitate the mourning of psychic loss and the working through of the fixation, the intervening years since childhood have subtly and characterologically strengthened the patient's resistance to insight and change. For working through the irretrievable psychic loss of the parent at this late date puts the patient face-to-face with an unpleasant personal reality; many years were devoted to the pursuit of an unrealizable ideal. Being able to acknowledge and accept the inevitable limitations of life and time now leads to a new regret: the relationship with the therapist and the attainment of personal responsibility could have taken place years earlier.

One patient, after a particularly unsettling memory of his mother's neglect, asked the therapist reproachfully: "Where were you when I needed you?" This significant question clues us in to the tortured despair of regret, and is a warning to the danger of resistance. For now the patient is tempted to justify the wasted years by retaining his symptoms, by proceeding as if he continues to be helpless to alter his destiny.

As clinicians, we must beware of being seduced by patients who immerse themselves repeatedly in memories of past traumata, and of thus collaborating with the perpetuation of symptoms that justify and maintain their neurosis. Indeed, a preoccupation with the psychic loss of a parent may be a means of escaping a more immediate self-hatred for having wasted precious life.

Because of the rage that may well have been consequent upon the psychic loss of the physically present parent, the patient's self-disgust may now be comfortably projected upon the parent. This rage, in turn, perpetuates the unconscious demanding, clinging, and yearning that the parent finally change. To mourn that parent at this late date would also mean "letting him or her off the hook," to implicitly admit that long years of waiting had gone for naught. Such mourning would also require that the patient completely restructure new purpose and meaning in his life, because previously that meaning had been derived from the preoccupation with the psychically lost parent.

Ironically enough, sometimes even when parents do occasionally mellow and become more or less emotionally available, the adult patient is not always able to recognize that altered reality. Still operating by the fixed imprint of the psychically lost parent experienced as a child, the adult has detached himself from his wish to receive. The ideal of undoing psychic loss, borne out of deprivation and nurtured in fantasy, has no basis in reality. Therefore, the patient may not believe that a parental change has occurred, even after it has become apparent. Furthermore, if the parent does indeed change, it may be disappointing for the adult patient; to his disillusionment, the patient may learn that the psychic loss of another time cannot be made good at a later date. From a developmental point of view, each phase has its own critical requirements, and is lived but once.

I saw one patient in treatment who, as a child, had felt especially neglected by a father who rarely showed him affection. When his father recently visited him from out of town, he hugged his adult son. While recounting this episode in treatment, this patient began doubting his own perceptions and experience to the point that he could no longer accurately remember whether or not his father had actually hugged him.

At this point in treatment, resistance is no longer exclusively concerned with the original psychic loss, but with the regret-laden implications of belatedly accepting that loss. The therapeutic task becomes one of mourning the undeveloped, "lost" intervening time. This treatment challenge often preceding termination parallels Erikson's (1950) eighth stage of ego integrity versus despair. Like the resolution to that stage, the goal of treatment necessitates the compassionate acceptance of one's personal past as one that had to be; the path taken was the only one that was apparent at the time, and, therefore, the only one upon which the patient could have embarked. Ironically, this final acceptance of one's life, as one that was individually fated, paradoxically enhances the patient's willingness and capability of more realistically exercising a genuine freedom of will in the present.

References

Anthony, E. J. (1973), Mourning and psychic loss of the parent. In: *The Child in His Family*, ed. E. J. Anthony. New York: John Wiley & Sons.
Balint, M. (1979), *The Basic Fault*. New York: Brunner/Mazel.
Bowlby, J. (1958), The nature of the child's tie to the mother. *Internat. J. Psycho-Anal.*, 39:350–373.
———(1973), *Separation*. New York: Basic Books.
———(1979), *The Making and Breaking of Affectional Bonds*. London: Tavistock Publications.
Deutsch, H. (1937), Absence of grief. *Psychoanal. Quart.*, 6:12–22.
———(1942), Some forms of emotional disturbance and their relationship to schizophrenia. *Psychoanal. Quart.*, 11:301–321.
Erikson, E. (1950), *Childhood and Society*. New York: W. W. Norton.
Fenichel, O. (1945), *The Psycho-Analytic Theory of Neurosis*. New York: W. W. Norton.
Freud, A. (1936), *The Ego and the Mechanism of the Defense*. New York: International Universities Press, 1946.
Freud, S. (1917), Mourning and melancholia. *Standard Edition*, 14:237–258. London: Hogarth Press, 1961.
———(1923), The ego and the id. *Standard Edition*, 19:13–66. London: Hogarth Press, 1961.
———(1938), Splitting of the ego in the defensive process. In: *Collected Papers*, Vol. 5. New York: Basic Books, 1964.
Gaddini, E. (1969), On imitation. *Internat. J. Psycho-Anal.*, 50(4):475–484.
Greenacre, P. (1952), *Trauma, Growth and Personality*. New York: International Universities Press.
Joffe, W., & Sandler, J. (1965), Notes on pain, depression and individuation. *The Psychoanalytic Study of the Child*, 20:394–424. New York: International Universities Press.
Khan, M. (1974), *The Privacy of the Self*. New York: International Universities Press.
Kohut, H., & Wolf, E. (1978), The disorders of the self and their treatment: An outline. *Internat. J. Psycho-Anal.*, 59:413–424.
Kierkegaard, S. (1849), *The Sickness unto Death*. New York: Anchor, 1954.
Kris, E. (1956), The recovery of childhood memories in psychoanalysis. *The Psychoanalytic Study of the Child*, 11:54–88. New York: International Universities Press.
Lindemann, E. (1944), Symptomatology and management of acute grief. *Amer. J. Psychiat.*, 101:141–148.
Loewald, M. (1962), Internalization, separation, mourning and the superego. *Psychoanal. Quart.*, 31:483–504.
Mahler, M. (1971), A study of the separation–individuation process and its possible application to borderline phenomena in the psychoanalytic situation. *The Psychoanalytic Study of the Child*, 26:403–424. New York: Quadrangle.
———Pine, F., & Bergman, A. (1975), *The Psychological Birth of the Human Infant*. New York: Basic Books.

Pollock, G. (1961), Mourning and adaptation. *Internat. J. Psycho-Anal.*, 42:341–361.

Rochlin, G. (1953), Loss and restitution. *The Psychoanalytic Study of the Child*, 8:288–309. New York: International Universities Press.

———(1965), *Griefs and Discontents*. Boston: Little, Brown.

Schecter, D. (1968), Identification and individuation. *J. Amer. Psychoanal. Assn.*, 16:48–80.

Shabad, P. (1983), Orientation to death as a mirror of personality. Paper presented at the American Psychological Association 91st Annual Convention.

———(1987), Fixation and the road not taken. *Psychoanal. Psychol.*, 4(3):187–205.

Winnicott, D. W. (1965), *The Maturational Process and the Facilitating Environment*. New York: International Universities Press.

Wolfenstein, M. (1969), Loss, rage and repetition. *The Psychoanalytic Study of the Child*, 24:432–460. New York: International Universities Press.

Zetzel, E. (1965), Depression and the incapacity to bear it. In: *Drives, Affects and Behavior*, Vol. 2, ed. M. Schur. New York: International Universities Press.

Part II

Developmental Perspectives

5

Some Effects of the One-Parent Family on Personality Development

Erna Furman
Robert A. Furman, M.D.

During the last twenty years our Cleveland group of child analysts has worked on understanding some of the vicissitudes of the child's development in the one-parent family. Initially our interest was focused on the study of parentally bereaved children and twenty-three such cases were reported in *A Child's Parent Dies* (E. Furman, 1974). Since that time we have treated another thirty children who have lost a parent by death, bringing the total of such cases we have studied now to fifty-three. In addition, we have extended our research to cases in which one parent was absent for other reasons, such as parental separation or divorce, or where children were raised out of wedlock. Forty-nine children comprise this latter group.

As with the previous study of mourning, our data derive

We are greatly indebted to our Cleveland colleagues for sharing their material and allowing us to learn from and with them. We do, however, bear sole responsibility for the contents of this chapter.

from five times weekly analyses of children of all ages (a few seen privately, the majority at the Child Analytic Clinic of the Cleveland Center for Research in Child Development) and from two to three years of observation and treatment via the parent at the Hanna Perkins Nursery School and Kindergarten (R. Furman and Katan, 1969). Of the fifty-three bereaved children, twenty were in analysis and thirty-three in treatment via the parent. Of the forty-nine cases from one-parent families without bereavement, twenty-three were in analysis and twenty-six were treated via the parent at Hanna Perkins. In most of the analytic cases in both groups analysis followed prior treatment via the parents.

As with the previous study also, none of these patients came to us because we sought them out or publicized our interest and no family indicated their concern about the effects of the bereavement or absence of one parent as the main reason for referral. They wanted help for their children with a wide variety of symptoms, most of which seemed manifestly unrelated to the one-parent family constellation. In some cases the parents could more readily recognize the connection. This was especially true with those instances where the parental death or divorce happened during the child's treatment and in those where current experiences served to revive the past and occasioned upset or exacerbation of difficulties in the child. However, even in these situations the child's response could be fully understood only through the slow and painstaking therapeutic work which enabled patients, parents, and therapists gradually to unravel the individual underlying causes and shed light on their connections with the manifest pathology.

We have compared the material gained from the therapies of children with similar losses; we have compared cases of bereavement with those whose parents were absent for other reasons; we have compared those who did and did not have access to parent-substitutes; and we have compared these individuals and groups of patients with the analytic data of children who grew up with both parents. Throughout we have tried, as best possible, to separate out the specific effects of growing up in a one-parent home and to distinguish these from difficulties in coping with the events and circumstances which caused the other parent's absence, be it a death to be mourned, a divorce to be mastered, or other cause to be understood and accepted. The great amount of available information has not made our task easier. The more cases we see and the more closely we study them, the more do we appreciate the myriad of diverse factors at work and the complexity of their interaction. It is very difficult to pinpoint a few single determinants even in individual instances. General conclusions inevitably risk over-simplification and distortion. With this caution in mind, we shall nevertheless attempt to describe some areas of personality development which seem particularly difficult for the child in a one-parent family and to delineate some of the factors which appear to contribute to putting him or her at risk. Not all such children are burdened enough to run into problems, and indeed some children who have both parents in the home encounter similar difficulties. The total or partial unavailability of one parent has, however, proven itself to carry a potential danger for every child thus affected and therefore has to be viewed as a significant developmental interference.

Gathering of observations and material has proceeded grad-ually, and understanding has come piecemeal as one or another clinical aspect forced itself to the fore, sometimes in its striking manifestations in one case, but more often through its subtler but repeated occurrence in many. It is noteworthy, however, that with this, as opposed to other developmental interferences, the behavioral manifestations of difficulties have been such that their profound effect on the total personality functioning is easily overlooked, underestimated, or attributed to other fac-tors. In many instances only the exploration of later pathology shed light on earlier factors and manifestations whose signifi-cance we had not appreciated, and prompted us to study them more closely and in greater detail in statu nascendi with younger children. For example, when enormous problems in superego integration surprised us in youngsters who had functioned well within the normal range until then, the analytic understanding of their pathology helped to pinpoint early forerunners in the nature and regulation of self-esteem. At the same time, our understanding was sometimes halted by the fact that the patients' pathology alerted us to general developmen-

131

hich in themselves required further elucidation. ofar as we have formulated our findings in of the papers addressed one or another of these example, the transition into latency from the issistic phase (R. Furman, 1980); the role of the fa.... e during the child's phallic–oedipal phase (R. Furman, 1986; E. Furman, 1987); normal and pathological aspects of superego integration in early latency (E. Furman, 1980a,b); the role of drive fusion in the oedipal phase (E. Furman, 1983), the relationship between drive fusion, integration, and neutralization in normal and pathological development (E. Furman, 1985); aggressive and homosexual aspects of object removal in adolescence (R. Furman, 1988).

At this time it seems appropriate to bring together the various strands of this research in progress, to begin to see how they interweave to make up the fabric of the growing personality of the child in the one-parent family and to use the emerging developmental patterns as a base which may facilitate further investigation.

Briefly stated, we find that many youngsters in one-parent families start to show manifestations of difficulty in the very earliest stages of phallic–narcissistic development, that their conflicts in this phase are exaggerated, and that its attendant drive, ego, and relationship characteristics tend to persist. These boys and girls have great difficulty in progressing to the oedipal phase proper and/or in achieving oedipal phase dominance. This affects the nature of their superego formation and its integration, as well as their ego identifications during latency, and later presents them with special difficulties in resolving the developmental tasks of adolescence.

In discussing some aspects of each of these maturational phases in greater detail, the clinical manifestations will be described, causative factors highlighted, and chances of helpful intervention indicated.

The Phallic–Narcissistic Phase

This phase, described by Edgcumbe and Burgner (1975), spans the developmental period between the earlier toddlerhood and the later oedipal phase proper and shows some overlap with both. The phallic–narcissistic phase, with its instinctual focus on bodily comparisons and adequacy and with its still primarily dyadic relationships, is the earliest phase during which difficulties related to the one-parent family constellation manifest themselves. It is also the phase during which these early troubles are most easily overlooked, in part because they appear phase-appropriate. Most prominent is a lowered self-esteem which affects many areas of functioning. It may show in exaggerated concern about bodily intactness and adequacy as well as about mental competence, especially in comparison with peers. At entry to nursery school and sometimes already in the toddler group, many of these children are so convinced that everyone else is bigger and better that they either shrink in fear from interaction, imitate the activities of others, or defensively boast and belittle their fellows. They are reluctant, however, to compete for real, do not offer their own ideas or do not follow through on them, expend little effort on tasks or easily abandon started projects, and when they do accomplish something, it gives them little pleasure. Indeed, they rarely feel good in themselves. They tend to keep busy with a restricted range of familiar materials and activities, to persist with what they feel they are already acceptably good at, and to avoid new challenges. Often they refuse suggestions with an "Oh, I want to do something else," or "I just want to play now," but their play also lacks zest and creativity. Role play, especially in the housekeeping corner, is limited, and, even when they do participate, they do not seem to know how to interact, conveying the feeling that they do what they have seen or been told but not what they have experienced and felt. For example, one three-year-old boy, fatherless since birth, liked to be the daddy, put on a big hat, carried a briefcase with lots of papers to his "office"—as indeed his grandfather did—but going to the office and then returning was the only thing he could do. Neither his grandparents' home life nor his mother's boyfriend's visits in his home had enlarged his concept of a man's role and function in the family. He did not know how to spend the early morning with his pretend family or have dinner with them, how to go on an outing—all the things his playmates took for granted as part of their game.

What was striking, however, with him as with many others, was not just that he did not know but that in this as in all other situations he was extremely touchy about not knowing.

Indeed, the tendency to have one's feelings hurt too easily is another very marked characteristic. Not only is the least criticism, admonition, or reprimand felt as major injuries, but slight or rejection is readily misperceived even in unrelated and unintentional behavior. For example, a remark directed to someone else is taken personally, an accidental brush by a passing child is mistaken for an attack, not being noticed right away on entering the room is viewed as a deliberate snub. Some children deal with their extreme vulnerability by avoiding situations in which they might expose themselves. Some turn the tables defensively and become standoffish to the point of rudeness, or become brusque and insensitive to the feelings of others. Steven, who had lost his father through suicide when he was barely three and whose treatment was detailed earlier (E. Furman, 1981), actually did not greet people because he thought they did not want to have anything to do with him.

A number of youngsters respond to real or imagined hurts to their feelings with quick flares of exaggerated anger, anger untempered and untamed by caring consideration, anger which does not allow them to feel regret or to forgive easily. These angry upsets, though not necessarily part of an overall excessive manifest aggression, highlight the major third area of observable difficulty, namely an inability to cope with ambivalence and a reluctance to invest in loving relationships with peers and adults outside the family. Of course, not all children show all these behaviors or to the same extent. Nevertheless, close observation usually reveals direct or defensive signs of them in most areas and it is their very concomitance, rather than single occurrence, which seems significant.

It is also striking that, with most of these children, these difficulties do not show themselves in the home, especially not with the parent, or at least much less so. One reason for this is that the child uses the loved adults in the family for narcissistic supplies, even to the extent of overestimation, and adapts his or her behavior so as to elicit the most positive response from them. Whatever especially appeals to the parent is what the child says, wears, and does. With some this may be an emphasis on their good looks or athletic prowess, with others it is an excited sensual interaction, or a special form of aggression, and others yet work, play, and pursue neutral activities with the parent with a concentration, perseverance, and even enjoyment which altogether fails them when they are on their own. The parent's appreciation (and the teacher's, if they can engage her to fill the same role) is used to an excessive extent to compensate for the hidden lack of self-worth. Often it is only with entry to nursery school that the difficulties surface. This is a surprise and hurt to the parents as they observe their child's response to the separation, difficulty in functioning on his own, distress as others fail to admire what the parent admired, and frequent complaints about not liking or being liked at school. To some extent all children experience a diminishment in self-esteem and an increase in phallic anxieties on entry to nursery school because all of them age-appropriately rely on parental narcissistic supplies (E. Furman, 1969). It is an important part of their adjustment process to transfer that parental love into self-love or, as one little girl put it to her mother, "When I am at school I love myself a little more because then you are not there to love me." For the one-parent child, however, this process is especially difficult. Also, all children act in such a way as to elicit parental appreciation, especially during the phallic phase when they wish to impress the parent and when being admired constitutes such an important gratification in their relationships. The one-parent child's wish to please the parent is thus easily seen as a part of his or her phallic dyadic relationship. What differentiates it, however, in these youngsters is the pressing need to maintain this relationship, sometimes to the point of surrendering their own aspirations, the inability to draw on their own resources, and the difficulty in extending the relationship to others. They either do not trust that anybody other than the parent could admire them or they do not trust themselves to be able to meet other people's different expectations.

What these nursery school observations in fact reveal is that the child's functioning is not merely affected by phase-appropriate phallic concerns, but rather that the conflicts of this phase are so hard to cope with because they touch on and exacerbate a diminished libidinal investment of self and others. This libidinal investment proves inadequate to regulate self-esteem, to invest in new objects for their own sake and without threat to the existing relationships, to bind and attenuate the excessive aggression, and to thus free energy for integration and neutralization (E. Furman, 1985). Although we see all this in children who live with both parents and suffered different interferences, and although even the children from one-parent families have had other experiences which contributed to their troubles, their therapeutic material shows time and again how diminished and wounded they feel by not having a complete family and by missing out, partly or wholly, on the opportunity to love and be loved by both parents. This finding emerged earlier and was reported in connection with bereaved children (E. Furman, 1974). It applies just as much, if not more, to children of divorced or separated parents for, although their parent may remain partly available, his or her absence from the home was consciously willed and hence is more readily felt as a rejection. Moreover, the break in the parents' relationship with each other is a formidable reminder that love really can disappear and mutual anger or dislike can really overtake it, something young children struggle so to master in their own personalities and usually rely on the parents' help and example to accomplish in time.

The parent's absence causes not only libidinal depletion and hurt but anger: at the remaining parent and anger at the absent parent, anger that is very difficult to express and to master because it threatens to overwhelm the inner loving ties and to bring about disastrous consequences in the external world. It is hard indeed to recognize and voice the full extent of one's destructive wishes to the sole available parent one needs so much or to the wholly or partly unavailable one who cannot be reached and whose return may be jeopardized. This is especially so when lasting separation and loss of object have really happened and therefore constitute a real threat. When both parents are in the home, the child has more opportunity for love and loving, less arousal of aggression, and can more readily distinguish imaginary from real consequences of aggression. Thus, especially prone to an unfavorable imbalance of the drives and especially handicapped in tolerating and verbalizing anger, many of these youngsters face serious problems with ambivalence. Their primitive unattenuated aggression tends to invade their self-investment as well as their relationships, surfacing in projections with fears of retaliation, in displacements from the parents to peers and adults outside the family, and later, as we shall see, in primitive instinctual identifications. Since the difficulty with drive fusion also affects integration and the capacity for neutralization, these children's ego energy becomes only partly deinstinctualized and their functions tend to lag in achieving secondary autonomy. As reported earlier (E. Furman, 1974), sometimes the loss of the parent during the first two years even results in inadequate initial investment of developing functions which creates a lasting weakness and susceptibility to later interference.

As soon as we learned that these difficulties did not subside with maturation but actually interfered with it, we began to study what helped some children to experience a lesser measure of trouble and how we could intervene to ameliorate the more serious conditions. Obviously, access to skilled observations in a sound preschool setting is most helpful to evaluation (E. Furman, 1978), especially when the nursery, like our Hanna Perkins School, includes opportunities for analysts to observe and to work with the parents as part of the program. Even if the child is taken into analysis, it is, at this stage, mainly the parents who need to be helped to be in tune with the child so that they can fulfill their important role of what A. Freud, as quoted by Rosenfeld and Sprince (1965), called the mediator between their child's id and ego. The parent's task here consists of assisting the child's ego in containing and integrating feelings and in mastering the stress of the external reality. Children were greatly helped when they could understand and cope with the cause and circumstances of one parent's absence, however painful or problematic, and when they could be assured that the fate of the parent or of the parental relationship was not caused by them and would not be repeated with them. One boy announced with relief, "My Mommy is divorced from my Daddy but I will never be divorced from my Daddy."

It also helped when the child could be supported in forming a realistic and detailed inner representation of the absent parent, in contrast to having to rely on a fantasied and therefore mainly instinctual image. In the case of death this included memories, photos, material possessions, and above all the surviving loved ones' descriptions of the personality and activities of the deceased. In the case of divorce, it implied regular contact with and parental functioning by the absent parent, in keeping with the child's needs rather than the parents' convenience. Of course, each parent's attitude to the partner as well as the nature of the relationship with the child are most important, a point discussed also by Neubauer (1960). Just as important is the parent's help with feelings. The partial or total absence of a parent creates an inevitable void which the child recognizes and feels, usually from toddlerhood on, even if he or she has never lived with both parents. It is a void that cannot be filled by the remaining parent trying to be both mother and father, nor can it be sufficiently filled by substitutes. It helps most when this void and the many feelings about it are acknowledged with the child, when sympathy is extended and discussion and expression of feelings are encouraged and accepted. Then, at least, the parent's unavailability does not become an insurmountable wall in the existing relationship and the child can put to better use what the parent has to offer.

The Oedipal Phase

In "Some Vicissitudes of the Transition into Latency" (R. Furman, 1980) some of the clinical findings were described which led to the conclusion that children may "move into latency from many points along a continuum from the phallic–narcissistic phase through the oedipal phase" or, put differently, that "an almost infinite variety of combinations of various aspects of the phallic–narcissistic and oedipal phases . . . can be operative at the time of transition into latency" (p. 38). Children who maintain a predominantly phallic–narcissistic position may show some true oedipal feelings and conflict but of very limited duration and intensity. In contrast to true oedipal phase dominance, their relationships are dyadic rather than triadic, lacking in thoughtfulness and consideration for the loved one, and focused on the aggressive envy and resentment of the other parent as an intruder whose primitive retaliation is feared. The emphasis is on acquiring bodily attributes rather than on engaging in mutually giving love and the primitive aggression toward the intruder, projected and feared, differs from the painful inner conflict the truly oedipal child experiences in being angry with a loved rival. In these instances the oedipal disappointment is experienced as an unforgivable narcissistic blow and the attendant ego and superego identifications bear the marks of inadequate drive fusion and insufficiently neutral ego participation. Whereas during the phallic–oedipal period these differences may be overlooked, the later consequences in early latency are often so striking that we soon learned to pay closer attention to the developments which immediately preceded them.

Phallic–narcissistic predominance may be related to several factors, among them identification with phallic–narcissistic parents, prephallic and phallic stresses, as well as innate disposition. However, we found it to be such a frequent occurrence among boys and girls in one-parent families, regardless of the parent's sex, that we could only conclude that the total or intermittent absence of the other parent played a significant part. Particularly important is the absence of an ongoing marital relationship between mother and father in the child's home life. In this connection it was of interest that, in discussing this issue with unselected classes of high school students, who, after giving it careful thought, arrived at this conclusion: For the healthiest and happiest resolution of early childhood there should be a family unit that consists of mother, father, and child. Uncles and aunts, grandparents, boy- and girlfriends of the parents, all can help, and something is better than nothing, but it is just different from the child's mother and father being married and all living together (Maynard, 1985; R. Furman, 1986).

There are, nevertheless, children who achieve sufficient oedipal dominance to assure healthy phase resolution, even though they live with but one parent. This happened with some of our bereaved children who delayed decathexis in mourning and could fully utilize their rich memories of the deceased parent, or who, after the completion of mourning, could build new relationships with stepparents. In some instances belated but intense unfolding of oedipal relationships took place when an absent parent was restored. Some children could also make sufficient use of very intermittent contacts or of parent substitutes. Many youngsters, however, failed to progress toward oedipal development although parents or substitutes were partially available, and could not even catch up when, for example, through remarriage, they lived with a couple. Such was the case with the girl of divorced parents, reported by Neubauer (1960). The difficulty, in these cases, lies in the child's personality, especially in the primitive unattenuated ambivalence embedded in the prephallic and phallic object relationships and self-investment, and intensified by the libidinal deprivation of missing out on the relationship with the unavailable parent during the phallic phase.

We consider these children to be at risk as their conflicts, fixations, and pathological formations endanger the resolution of the oedipal complex and we class them in a diagnostic category specifically so designated (E. Daunton, 1969). Our experience suggests that analysis and sometimes even treatment via the parent can help such children resolve their difficulties. With improved drive fusion, their object relationships become less ambivalent and conflict-laden, and their self-investment more positive and harmonious. They also take concomitant progressive steps in other ego manifestations, in the areas of integration and frustration tolerance, in the functions of reality testing, secondary process thinking and verbal mastery, in their ability to pursue and enjoy neutral, non-instinctual activities and to develop sublimations. They are able to experience a wider range of affects which are more subtle and modulated and can feel good (E. Furman, 1985). These youngsters can then achieve oedipal personality development and utilize their memories of the absent parent, or even very limited contacts with a parent or parent substitute, to form meaningful oedipal relationships. A case vignette, some aspects of which were also described earlier (E. Furman, 1983), may help to clarify and illustrate these points.

Case Example 1

Evelyn entered Hanna Perkins school in her fifth year and began her analysis a few months later, following preparatory work via her mother. She was physically well developed and of superior intelligence, gifted and precocious in some of her ego functions and activities. Her large, expressive brown eyes and animated features mirrored an everchanging inner turmoil of moods. The driven quality of her insistent talking and restless, rather jerky, motility impressed and dominated her surroundings. Despite her good capabilities, she could not concentrate and learn, in part because she could not tolerate the slightest imperfection in herself or the greater knowledge of adults or peers. Her self-initiated projects, imaginative and of grand verbal design, were invariably abandoned as soon as her actual skills and perseverance proved inadequate to accomplish the fantasied task. Although Evelyn crumpled up her drawings, demolished her block buildings, mistreated and lost her possessions, and dishevelled her hair and clothes, she was unaware of her deep self-hatred and never acknowledged that anything was wrong. Instead, she was quick to pick out others' weaknesses or shortcomings and criticized them mercilessly. When the teachers offered a suggestion or tried to reassure her about a little mistake, she turned on them viciously and blamed them for interfering and spoiling her efforts.

Evelyn's relationships were stormy but invested with depth and zest which endeared her to most adults. She could be genuinely loving and affectionately demonstrative with her mother and other women, as well as helpful and protective with younger children, including her little brother. The next moment, however, she would become angry, mean, and spiteful, burst into temper tantrums, and, especially with other children, was not only verbally but also physically abusive. Sometimes these changes followed a minor frustration, or when the other person's refusal to comply with Evelyn's wishes interfered with her need to be fully in control of them; at other times her switch of mood seemed prompted only from within. Evelyn's love and hate were not always genuine. Excessive shows of devotion could thinly disguise mounting inner aggression, and provocative meanness could serve to solicit anger and punishment from others for sins they, and even she, often did not know about. Her extreme, unmitigated ambivalence also played a part in her severe separation fear (she was frantic for mother's safety and felt deeply rejected by her absences), and in her constant complaints of not being liked. She would go out of her way to be nasty to newcomers, expecting them to find her unacceptable.

Her relationships with men and boys were quite inappropriate. She sought out men, even when she hardly knew them, absorbed their attention with brash excited talk and bodily seductiveness and, given the least encouragement, she hung and climbed on them, kissed them, provoked them to tussle with her or swing her around, and begged them to live in her home and be her daddy. With boys, her mixed feelings, her fear of not being liked, and her sadomasochistic sexual fantasies were evident as she complained of their meanness, provoked their attack, and masochistically exaggerated her suffering.

In contrast to her bright precocious demeanor, Evelyn's self-care was infantile and symptom-ridden. She had a severe eating disturbance, sleep difficulties, occasionally soiled and wet herself, dawdled over dressing, did not bathe independently, cared poorly for her toys and possessions, and could not tolerate being on her own. Her analysis revealed quickly that this often highly competent little girl's personality structure was very vulnerable and subject to disintegration. When I would speak to her in but a couple of sentences, she would cry out "Stop, stop" and cover her bowed head with her arms. We came to understand that, if she could not control my words, they represented an intolerable intrusion, overwhelmed her ego functions, and split up her body image. She called these episodes her "muddled thinking" and described how, at these times, her hands, feet, and other body parts did things she didn't even want them to do.

Evelyn came by her strengths and weaknesses honestly. She was the wanted child of an intelligent middle-class couple who loved her, not wisely but too well. From the start, the parents' handling alternated between intrusive sensuous overstimulation and emotional withdrawal or absences. Well intentioned, they made her a part of their own primitive, fiercely loving relationship and overwhelmed her as a witness and as a partner. During Evelyn's toddlerhood, they welcomed and extolled her precocious intellectual and verbal development, but abused her with harsh physical punishment and exposed her to repeated sexual perversions with an adolescent boy. The mother's difficult pregnancy and birth of the younger brother contributed to the deterioration of the marriage. Physical violence between the parents intensified, leading to a partial separation when Evelyn was two and one half. The father was murdered at his place of work when Evelyn was about three and one half. During the hectic chaos of the next year, the idealized image of the father became a near-concrete presence for her distraught mother, and Evelyn received little help in understanding and containing the confusing circumstances surrounding the father's death itself. Evelyn often introduced herself to people by shocking them with: "My daddy is dead. He was shot and killed."

Like her mother, Evelyn was eager for help and hoped to gain mastery of her inner distress through treatment. The first months of analysis were largely devoted to a repetitive shared game in which an intact puppet family of four got up, had breakfast, and drove off to school and work. We also played card games in which it was very important for Evelyn to win and not to possess black cards, spades and clubs. In time we understood that the family's contented mornings masked the agony of her own mornings, spent in compulsive phallic and anal masturbation. Unable to get ready, she usually provoked an altercation with her mother who retaliated with frustrated yelling and hitting. The black cards, we learned, signaled the danger of the black queen who stood for the "witchy" mutual "killing feelings" between mother and child and were encapsulated in her guilt and shame ridden sadistic masturbation fantasies. The analytic work focused on the question to which Evelyn devoted most of her unconscious, and later conscious, mental efforts: "How can one love a person?" How could she make sure that her intense but fragile love would not be swept away by her boundless hatred, and kill her mother? And how could she be sure that this would not also happen to her mother's love for her, the mother who was her only remaining parent but whose aggression was so dangerous?

We worked on Evelyn's past and current developmental conflicts and real experiences which had so greatly exacerbated her anger and convinced her of its danger. At times she was helped by gaining insight, by linking her anger to its true content and mastering it verbally. Many times, however, her angry thoughts and wishes threatened to engulf her and she could not draw on her positive feelings to fuse and attenuate them. It then helped to remind her that she also loved mommy, or the therapist, wanted to keep her, appreciated her care, and enjoyed their good times. As Evelyn's personality achieved better integration of her aggressive impulses, she developed acute anxieties and phobias in lieu of the earlier sadistic outbursts. Evelyn was delighted when she managed to complete a nice Mother's Day present, but she decided to give it several days early lest "my meanness ruins it by Sunday."

Evelyn's love for herself was similarly precarious. With analytic work, her investment of herself, as of her loved ones, became more stable and effective and she began to view herself more kindly. Prior to her birthday party she told me: "I know what you'll wish me most: that I'll be able to like myself because then I'll be nice to my guests." She could now enjoy learning and working as she could forgive herself for her mistakes and forgive others for their superiority. She was calmer, warmer, and functioned in a more integrated manner.

Her relationship with men and boys took a new turn. The oedipal theme of "Can one love two people?" became the focus of the analysis. Evelyn's excited provocative approach to males and her desperate demand for a father contained primarily her need of their penis. She even tried to produce one for herself with her masturbation. It would not only satisfy her phallic wishes but protect her from her aggression toward her mother and change her into an acceptable love object, like her brother, father, and mother's boyfriends. Now these same males became people she loved and longed for. She became friendly with mother's boyfriend, gave presents to her teenage half-brother, and was especially warmly enamored of a classmate. For the first time she brought her real unhappy memories of her father. He had hit her, exposed himself, fought with mother, and disregarded her pleas to stop. Perhaps he had not loved her. Then one day she brought to her session a toy she had found in a forgotten basement corner, a toy her father had expertly crafted for her. We talked about how much love and care must have gone into making it and she recalled good times of playing and learning her ABCs with him. The toy became newly precious. This helped her to integrate her image of her father and to fuse her feelings for him. She asked for his picture to keep in her room. He would not have been an ideal daddy but nice enough. She also thought she had wanted to live with him, had wanted mother to die instead of him, and had suspected her of killing him.

The therapist's husband became an important love object. Evelyn had known him even before her analysis from his weekly observation visits in her classroom. She had always tried to seduce and control him as she did with all males, and, at the start of treatment, had tended to follow up these encounters by provoking me to punish her for wanting to take him away from me. In time she adapted to the routine of his visits, her attitude softened, and she was often warm and charming with him. She was also less concerned with my response until we learned that the beloved classmate was a displacement for my husband whom she longed for as the most desirable daddy. To her happy surprise, one day she met Dr. Furman in my home as she was leaving her session. That night she had a nightmare which we understood in terms of her oedipal aggression to me. She was deeply chagrined and said, "But I like you too and I don't really want you to die." The following week she baked cookies, brought two for Dr. Furman, but, after some conflict, decided that I should keep one and give him the other.

Although her earlier defenses and conflicts were often still in evidence, Evelyn's personality strides included a marked affective change. She could sustain rich loving warmth as well as true sadness, could feel scared and helpless but also kind and concerned. Soon we began to see the beginnings of oedipal resignation. Evelyn was now about six and one half. On one of his visiting days, Dr. Furman briefly returned to her classroom later in the day, and Evelyn, like many of her peers, begged him to admire yet another something she had accomplished. He told her he really did not have time but reminded her that he had looked at some of her other work earlier. Much to his surprise she replied nicely, "I know you did. Thank you." When we discussed this event in her analysis and I wondered what had made it possible for her to accept the disappointment so well, Evelyn said: "I have come to feel that something is better than nothing." Another day she commented that the flowers in my office were wilting. What would I do with them? I told her I would dig them into a flower bed so that, as they turn into earth, they would enrich the soil and help new flowers to grow better. This led to renewed discussions of death, and, for the first time ever, Evelyn could integrate the concrete aspects of her father's death without terror or excitement. A week later, she talked about her father with sadness. She then said quietly, "But he also lives on with the things I do, that he did with me, and liked, and did for me." After a pause she added, "And my children will do the things I like when they grow up and after I am dead, and so it will go on always."

This condensed and selective account may raise more questions than it answers and may not adequately illustrate the point that oedipal development depends on a necessary degree of drive fusion and its concomitant ego manifestations. We do not know to what extent the therapist's husband represented a real or transferred love object for Evelyn, how much the analytic work or the therapist's real relationship with her helped her toward better integration, or how much difficulty she would have encountered in establishing oedipal ties if both parents had continued to be available to her. However, the same theme has emerged prominently in several other cases. Some of these were treatments via the parent where the transference played no part but where the children could utilize minimally available parent-figures after they had been helped. In other cases, children could not progress to a viable oedipal phase, even though they lived with both parents, until they achieved drive fusion, integration, and resolution of earlier conflicts.

The oedipal experience in these cases does not insure untroubled further development but it mitigates later difficulties and makes them more accessible to therapy. We therefore conclude, with Evelyn, that something is better than nothing.

Superego Formation and the Latency Period

In contrast to some of the subtler manifestations of difficulty during the phallic–narcissistic and oedipal phases, early latency pathology is often ushered in with a bang. The case of Steven (E. Furman, 1981) described how this seemingly well-progressing boy with appropriate preoedipal reaction formations and impulse control suddenly turned into a most provocative, unmanageable behavior problem on entering our Hanna Perkins Kindergarten after the summer vacation. As he put it, "There are no rules for me!" Prompted by the understanding of his symptom as well as by the observations and material gained from therapeutic work with our many other patients in this developmental phase, we learned that all youngsters experience difficulty in integrating their newly harsh superego; that all use the defense of externalization of superego to some extent to ward off the intense anxiety generated by the unfamiliar structural conflict; and that all experience a regressive exacerbation of phallic–narcissistic concerns (E. Furman, 1980 a,b). However, the most marked pathological exaggeration of difficulties in the new phase was experienced by children from one-parent families, like Steven, and others who for various reasons formed their superego when phallic–narcissistic personality characteristics predominated and when progressive drive fusion was impeded by an excess of aggression over libido. Also, their symptoms did not subside with maturation and required therapeutic help, whereas the children within the normal range could, merely with sound educational support, achieve superego integration and use their conscience to consolidate a latency adjustment.

With some of the youngsters, as with Steven, the new symptom showed mainly in unruly behavior, giving the impression that they not only had not developed a conscience but had lost all previously acquired inner controls. With others it manifested itself in severe temper outbursts, which often started out with teasing provocative interplays but ultimately crested in frenzied screaming and attacking of others and self as well as destruction of materials. Some even ran into the street traffic or dashed onto precipitous ledges threatening to kill themselves before they finally crumpled into a fetal position, overwhelmed, helpless, whimpering, and in need of comfort. We learned that the initial stage of provocative misbehavior served to externalize the unbearable threat of the punishing superego introject, entrusting the much kinder caring adults with the role of controlling and punishing their transgressions. The later stage of feeling that they had to hurt, even kill themselves, and collapsing overwhelmed, represented the failure of the earlier defense and the ensuing anxiety attack, experienced when the internal superego retribution seemed imminent. Neither permissiveness nor punitiveness helps. The attending parents or teachers are left in no doubt as to the child's harrowing anxiety because he or she does, to an extent, spread and/or externalize it to them, and, although tempted to act on this anxiety, they assist the stricken child best by protecting him from harm, by pointing out that the turmoil stems from within, and soothing sympathetically when it subsides.

Some children with similar inner conflicts do not succumb to such anxiety attacks and even their misbehavior is less clearly geared to eliciting external punishment. They appear as though they had not formed a superego at all and are easily misdiagnosed as arrested at the phallic or prephallic levels. However, observations and treatment data gained from work with them during the preceding period clearly shows that superego formation was beginning, and, although their defenses are so strong and effective, it often surfaces in isolated anxieties, especially in night fears and bad dreams.

It is striking with these children, whose superego gives them so much trouble, that its threatening manifestations and the transition into latency come much more quickly and suddenly, even at a relatively earlier age than the more normal onset, which tends to take place later, gradually, and in a "two steps forward, one step backward" progression. In the pathological instances, it is not uncommon to see a child transformed during a summer vacation or even within a week or two. This suddenness, along with the extreme harshness and unintegratability of the superego provide clues to the nature and causes of the difficulty. Instead of piecemeal accepting an oedipal resignation and preserving the aim-inhibited aspects of the positive relationships with both parents, the more primitive personality of the phallic–narcissistic position with its unfused instinctual impulses, narcissistic vulnerability, and insufficient capacity for integration and neutralization, responds to the obstacles to oedipal fulfillment with hurt, fury, and fear.

The parental images, distorted by projected aggression and unmitigated by loving consideration, are primitively introjected and cannot be assimilated by the personality. At best, such introjects burden children with greatly troubled consciences, causing them chronic discontent with themselves and tending to make them appear rather nasty and selfish in relation to others. Children of one-parent families are, of course, not helped by their diminished opportunities for loving interactions and for comparing their distorted image of the parent with his or her real behavior. However, the forces which shape the inner image, especially the imbalance of the drives, predominate even over the actual experiences with the available parent. The tendency to set up harshly instinctual introjects has been noted by several authors who studied children of one-parent families, among them M. Meiss (1952), A. Reich (1954), P. Neubauer (1960), and was also described in *A Child's Parent Dies* (E. Furman, 1974).

As mentioned earlier, therapeutic intervention at an earlier time does not prevent this difficulty with superego formation, even when the child could be helped to achieve a good measure of oedipal dominance, but it does appear to make it less severe and more amenable to treatment. With children who are not yet in therapy, the mere dramatic nature of their symptomatology serves as an impetus for analysis, but even the more muted manifestations of superego pathology are valid indications for treatment, especially as they usually coexist with difficulties in ego identifications and availability of neutral energy for latency pursuits.

Latency is the time of consolidation and modification of ego identifications with the parents, a process not unlike that which progresses in the integration and maturation of the conscience. By ego identifications we refer to various character traits that a child will acquire to assist him in mastery of his latency developmental tasks. These tasks are primarily concerned with learning how to get along and function with his peer group, both at school and at play, and with the learning or educational tasks set before him at school. In these areas we hope to see children able to control their instinctual side, assisted by their conscience, so that they can be firmly protective of their bodies, their rights, and their needs. We hope they will be able to be kind and considerate of others, abide frustration, and accept delays in gratification; able to persevere with tasks; be inquisitive, alert, and discriminatory; to have fun and enjoy themselves as they learn about the world outside of home and family.

The more children enter latency from the phallic–narcissistic position and the less favorable their drive balance, the more their motivation is derived from instinctual fears, the more primitive and hard to modify will be the identifications they make in this process. By contrast, the more the move into latency results from phallic–oedipal conflicts of resolving the aggression to beloved parents, the more neutral and modifiable will be the emerging identifications (R. Furman, 1980). An example of the more primitive type of ego identification in action may be helpful here.

Case Example 2

Not too long ago, in working with a midlatency boy, the analyst became concerned with the boy's constant neglect and dismissal of his homework, his inability each night to apply himself to some relatively simple tasks. Unfortunately, in one sense, this boy was bright enough to get good grades with even the most perfunctory approach to his assignments. If the analyst was after him enough, to please him or to silence the complaints, the boy would have periods of application to the tasks at hand. But there was no gratification for him at these times, nothing that rewarded him so that he wanted to persist in these efforts.

Pointing out the reality of the need to learn to enjoy studying while it was still easy, as a preparation for the increasingly difficult academic tasks that awaited him down the road, was of no use. The boy felt he would come to these in time; right now he wanted nothing to interfere with his just having fun, such as in watching television. When the boy was approached about how he felt about himself, whether he was aware of his lack of persistence and task application, his lack of standards for himself, his faulty reality perception, there was no distress whatsoever.

When the analyst asked how the boy's father dealt with his work, his father being a most successful and enterprising businessman, the boy replied, "I do just like him!" It turned out that all the boy saw of his father at home, and that had never been very often as the father traditionally worked long hours, was his father at play, partying, drinking, taking it easy. The boy had long since made this early ego identification with his father, an immature and unmodifiable one. The boy was now old enough to know, and it had been discussed often enough at home, how hard and successfully the father worked at his job. There was much that was admirable in the father that the boy could inquire after, seek out, learn about, and emulate, but he did not.

Unfortunately this was a distant father, one actually little involved with his son and unable to demonstrate in activities with him the attributes that made the father so financially successful. Instead, what he demonstrated in his interaction with his son was either his temper, when it seemed the boy misbehaved, or else his rather excited ways of relaxing.

One can describe the mechanism of acquisition of this boy's identification with his father in a number of ways. Annie Reich (1954) described early narcissistic identification with early glorified pictures of the parents, identifications put in place to overcome the hurts or narcissistic wounds endured, such as feeling ignored or uncared for by a parent. These very early, distorted identifications are difficult to integrate, to assimilate, to use to enhance one's own character because they are so unrealistic. Even when partly recognized as unrealistic, they are clung to. Another way of looking at this problem is to focus on the primitive, unfused, unneutralized energy that fuels the identificatory process and makes it so hard for the ego to modify and integrate the identifications which, through the instinctual energy involved, are much more under the control of the id. One could also focus on the fact that some children often have stayed much too long involved, fixated at the phallic–narcissistic phase for any of a number of possible reasons, simply leaving too little time for involvement with phallic–oedipal conflicts before the curtain of repression descends and latency arrives (R. Furman, 1980). Edith Jacobson (1954) pointed to yet another factor of unresolved ambivalence when she described two variants of mourning and its accompanying identifications. In the melancholic type of resolution there is an ego identification with the lost loved one, an introject upon which the superego vents its aggression, as Freud described so long ago (1915). In health, we are familiar with the identification with the lost loved one that leads to modification of the ego, taking on ego-syntonic constructive aspects of the deceased. Identification is operative in each instance, but in healthy mourning, ambivalence is mastered leading to an adaptive resolution. This is lacking in the melancholic.

All children make the early, more primitive identifications. One factor that can lead to their modification over time is the presence of the reality of the parent, available with his or her more neutral ways of relating that offer the child the constant opportunity to correct and modify his earlier impressions and identifications. These are difficult to modify later in analysis and take a great deal of work, work that is successful in part as the parents are both realistically available, able to modify instinctual ways of interacting, if such be needed.

In following up our cases at the Hanna Perkins Therapeutic Nursery School and Kindergarten (R. Furman and A. Katan, 1969), we were struck with how well the gains acquired in treatment by way of the parent had persisted with our successful cases. At first we thought this was due either to the nature of the child's conflicts or to the basic soundness of the treatment approach. In time we became aware of yet another factor, the parents' maturation during the prelatency years of work that enabled them to bring to the children in their latency a relatively stress-free period in which to consolidate their gains, make further modifications in their identifications, both ego and superego. Parents successful in the work are relieved and impressed with what they have accomplished, learn to listen to and respect their child, and let things be talked out when necessary. These are some of the prerequisites of a constructive latency.

Two contrasting examples of problem management in latency may be helpful here. In one instance a child became aware of a parent's dishonesty over minor financial matters, a most unfortunate neurotic symptom with which the child began to identify. The parent could recognize what was occurring and discussed the problem fully with the child, acknowledging his own problem, the distress it brought him, and expressing his wish that the child would not have the same unfortunate difficulty. That child's problem subsided entirely. In another instance, one parent of a child in analysis had difficulty with alcohol which the entire family totally denied, despite the child's witnessing many episodes of drunken, out-of-control behavior. The parent was quite unable to acknowledge the problem, much less discuss it with the child, and this contribution to the child's lack of control could never be mastered in the analysis.

Latency is a time when deficient or unhelpful ego identifications can come to the fore and can be observed if they are not denied—the example given earlier of the difficulty with homework being a case in point. Even if their roots lie much earlier, sometimes much can be done if they can be addressed, their origin accepted and discussed. This work can be difficult for single parents, however. In cases of bereavement an idealization of the lost parent may be difficult for a surviving parent to avoid or to help a child put right. In cases of separation or divorce or a child raised out of wedlock, it can be difficult for the responsible parent to discuss the absent parent without rancor. These difficulties, however, are not insuperable; they can be and frequently are overcome.

Adolescence

The psychological processes active during adolescence are as intricate and complex as they are important and crucial. Perhaps only the period of the resolution of the oedipal phase is as important for future mental health. One aspect of adolescence, of course, involves a recrudescence of the forces operative at the end of the phallic–oedipal phase. Each therapist will have his own most favored or useful way of conceptualizing what occurs during adolescence, and it should not be surprising if child analysts from Cleveland lean heavily on Anny Katan's formulation (1937).

In her paper that introduced the concept of object removal, Katan started with the return of the oedipal strivings in adolescence, noting that the personality had but two options available in managing these to avoid incest: defenses against the drives or a change in object for the drives. Although asceticism is often a temporary phenomenon of this developmental period, health requires that one must fail in the struggle against the drives. Attention then focuses on a change in the object of the drives, the process of object removal. This has two components: a removal of the libidinal investment in the internal representative of the infantile object; a displacement of a particular and unique kind of energy freed from the old object to enable its reinvestment in a new object outside the family. This combination of decathexis and displacement serves well for the positive oedipal strivings, the libidinal attachment to the parent of the opposite sex. It has further been proposed (R. Furman, 1988) that decathexis operates with the negative oedipal libidinal or homosexual strivings and with the aggressive urges accompanying the libidinal ones, but displacement of these would lead to a homosexual object choice and uncontrolled aggression. Although both are seen often as temporary phenomena, they do not represent adaptive resolution. The suggestion has been made, the hypothesis offered, that following decathexis, in lieu of displacement, the homosexual and aggressive strivings are contained or managed by a combination of identification and the processes inherent in neutralization and sublimation.

This thinking helps to understand the great flood of instinct with which the adolescent is faced as well as the painful loneliness of this age period, the result of withdrawal of the instinctual investment in the internal representatives of the parents. This thinking emphasizes the role of the ego in the developmental conflicts of this phase in managing the identifications as well as the economic considerations inherent in drive fusion, neutralization, and sublimation. Also to the fore come the neutralized, reality-based relationships with the parents, since withdrawal of the instinctual investment in the early objects will be able to proceed in proportion as the other aspects of investments remain. Without them it can feel to the adolescent that the withdrawal of the instinctual investment has in effect destroyed the inner representative of the parent.

If the developmental tasks of adolescence are viewed in this fashion, it becomes easier to understand how marginal adjustments in latency no longer suffice and how these adjustments fall apart and fail in adolescence. This is particularly true of the difficulties encountered by the child of the single-parent home that have been addressed in this paper. To the extent identificatory processes are modeled on the early, instinctualized identifications of the phallic–narcissistic phase, it will be difficult and unhelpful to utilize them in adolescence. To the extent that the processes of fusion of aggression, neutralization, and sublimation have been inadequate in the past they will have difficulty with assisting the adolescent in mastery. To the extent that the ego has had a deficit of integrative capacity and neutralized energy available for its tasks, there will now be problems. It is almost as if the developmental requirements of successful adolescent development were peculiarly designed to expose the difficulties inherent in a basically phallic–narcissistic personality orientation.

With other phases the attempt has been made to emphasize what still can be done to deal with arrests or regressions that go back to the phallic–narcissistic level. In adolescence it is much more necessary to say that prevention is the most important approach to these problems because they often present enormous difficulties even in a treatment setting. Adolescents stand the best chance of dealing with their developmental conflicts when their positive investments in themselves and others are already healthily in place. Their attempts at this time to receive such loving investment from without, almost regardless of source, too often seem regressive in nature and, to the extent such loving is an attempt to fill an old void, will have to be rejected as infantilizing and antidevelopmental. It is not that adolescents do not require an inordinate amount of patient loving, which of course they do. It is just that the time is past when such can be reparative. They very much need stable objects for identification at this time, crucially so, although there are times when these are superficially rejected. Adolescents are very attuned to the problems inherent in parental exhortation to do as I say, not as I do. At this point they are very much more apt to do as the parents have done.

In conclusion, we wish to underline what has been implicit throughout this chapter, that the effects of the one-parent family on the child's personality development are potentially most serious when they impinge upon him or her during the earliest years of life and when he has few, if any, experiences of a positive relationship with both parents. However, total or partial loss of a viable relationship with either parent at later stages threatens to revive early fixation points in the prephallic and phallic–narcissistic phases because the narcissistic hurts and intensified aggression cause regression.

References

Daunton, E. (1969), Diagnosis. In: *The Therapeutic Nursery School*, eds. R.A. Furman & A. Katan. New York: International Universities Press, pp. 204–214.

Edgcumbe, R., & Burgner, M. (1975), The phallic–narcissistic phase: A differentiation between preoedipal and oedipal aspects of phallic development. *The Psychoanalytic Study of the Child*, 30:161–180. New Haven, CT: Yale University Press.

Freud, S. (1915), Mourning and melancholia. *Standard Edition*, 14:237–258. London: Hogarth Press, 1957.

Furman, E. (1969), Observations on entry to nursery school. *Bull. Philadelphia Assn. Psychoanal.*, 19(3):133–152.

———(1974), *A Child's Parent Dies*. New Haven, CT: Yale University Press.

———(1978), Use of the nursery school for evaluation. In: *Child Analysis and Therapy*, ed. J. Glenn. New York: Jason Aronson, pp. 128–159.

———(1980a), Early latency—normal and pathological aspects. In: *The Course*

of Life: Psychoanalytic Contributions Toward Understanding Personality Development, Vol. 2., eds. S. I. Greenspan & G. H. Pollock. Washington DC: NIMH, U.S. Dept. of Health & Human Services, pp. 1–32.

———(1980b), Transference and externalization in latency. *The Psychoanalytic Study of the Child*, 35:267–284. New Haven, CT: Yale University Press.

———(1981), Treatment-via-the-parent: A case of bereavement. *J. Child Psychother.*, 7:89–102.

———(1983), Something is better than nothing. Contribution to the scientific forum on fantasy and reality in the organization of the oedipal situation. *Bull. Hampstead Clin.*, 6(2):168–171.

———(1985), On fusion, integration and feeling good. *The Psychoanalytic Study of the Child*, 40:81–110. New Haven, CT: Yale University Press.

———(1987), The early father–child relationship. In: *Helping Young Children Grow*, ed. E. Furman. Madison, CT: International Universities Press, pp. 21–34.

Furman, R. A. (1980), Some vicissitudes of the transition into latency. In: *The Course of Life: Psychoanalytic Contributions Toward Understanding Personality Development*, Vol.2, ed. S. I. Greenspan & G. H. Pollock. Washington DC: NIMH, U.S. Dept. of Health & Human Services, pp. 33–43.

———(1986),The father–child relationship. In: *What Nursery School Teachers Ask Us About: Psychoanalytic Consultants in Preschool*, ed. E. Furman. New York: International Universities Press. pp. 49–62.

———(1988), Object removal revisited. Paper read at the Scientific Symposium on the occasion of the 20th anniversary of the Cleveland Center for Research in Child Development, Cleveland, May 1986. *Internat. Rev. Psycho-Anal.*, 15:165–176.

———Katan, A. (1969), *The Therapeutic Nursery School*. New York: International Universities Press.

Jacobson, E. (1954), Contribution to the metapsychology of psychotic identifications. *J. Amer. Psychoanal. Assn.*, 2:239–262.

Katan, A. (1937), The role of "displacement" in agoraphobia. *Internat. J. Psycho-Anal.*, 32:1–10, 1951.

Maynard, R. C. (1985), Young people seek family-core values. *The Plain Dealer* (Cleveland, OH), July 11: 23 A.

Meiss, M. (1952), The oedipal problem of a fatherless child. *The Psychoanalytic Study of the Child*, 7:216–229. New York: International Universities Press.

Neubauer, P. B. (1960), The one-parent child and his oedipal development. *The Psychoanalytic Study of the Child*, 15:286–309. New York: International Universities Press.

Reich, A. (1954), Early identifications as archaic elements in the superego. *J. Amer. Psychoanal. Assn.*, 2:218–310.

Rosenfeld, S. K., & Sprince, M. P. (1965), Some thoughts on the technical handling of borderline children. *The Psychoanalytic Study of the Child*, 20:495–517. New York: International Universities Press.

6

The Place of Object Loss in Normal Development

FRED PINE, PH.D.

Loss is pervasive in the normal developmental process. I am not here referring to those adventitious losses that affect us all at one or another point in our lives—the early death of a parent or friend, a parental divorce or one's own, a childhood hospitalization—but rather to losses that are inherent in the developmental process, part and parcel of it. That these losses do not simply eventuate in despair alerts us to expect to find other aspects of the developmental process—balancing and compensatory—that are built in as well. Here, as everywhere in human functioning, evolution and culture seem to have provided us with endless potential both for stress and for adaptation. I shall here describe a number of such losses, selecting those that I believe to be more or less universal and affectively powerful. I shall comment on some of their interrelations and, when I can, on what they can teach us about reactions to adventitious losses as well. I shall begin in midstream, with object loss in adolescence, because it is richly suggestive regarding features of normal developmental loss, and then move in both directions—to the childhood and the adult periods.

159

Adolescence

In her article on children's reactions to the death of parents, "How is Mourning Possible?," Wolfenstein (1966) answered her title question by suggesting that full mourning for a parent who dies can only be achieved when the death has occurred after the offspring's childhood and adolescence, and thus after the normal course of adolescent mourning. The normal developmental events of adolescence involve a mourning process as the parents of childhood are slowly decathected in the adolescent's press toward new, nonincestuous object ties. This view of adolescence as, in part, a mourning process is relatively widespread; but the conception of the preparatory function that it serves for mourning of love objects who die, and the notion that full mourning cannot be achieved prior to this normal developmental mourning, are Wolfenstein's distinctive contributions in that paper.

Other chapters in this book look at the impact of one or another adventitious loss—those that are not inherent in the developmental process. Some of the features that characterize the normal developmental losses are at times present in the adventitious losses as well, and serve as modifiers of them. There is no doubt that object losses of the kinds discussed elsewhere in this book have significant impact upon development. Often sudden, and therefore catching the person unprepared, often total, final as losses—though even if more gradual and less total—they are more often than not acute disturbers of the normal developmental process. But they do not fall on unprepared ground. Just as normal adolescent loss can prepare the ground for later mourning, other normal developmental losses already gone through, linked intimately therefore to the age of the person, set the preparedness (or unpreparedness), the structural tools, if you will, for dealing with the adventitious losses; and the accumulation of life experiences and bodily events, organized into inner meanings, into fantasies, provide the intrapsychic, dynamic significance of the real-life losses.

Normal object loss in adolescence involves the loss of the parents of childhood; that is, of the inner possibilities of using the later parents in the same ways that they were used earlier.

The adolescent is pushed away from the parents equally by the inner demands of defense against early pregenital dependent ties and against the reactivated oedipal constellation (not to mention the parallel defense processes in the parents). At the same time, he or she is pulled away from the parents by the attractiveness of the world (i.e., by the possibilities for explorations, sublimation, and displacement that the adolescent, with expanded motor, cognitive, and relational capacities has available in the extrafamilial surround), and these forces gradually diminish the intensity of the adolescent's tie to the parents. That this process is not free of conflict is indicated by the characteristic, periodic depression of the adolescent period and the equally characteristic periods of regression to the old childhood–parental ties and modes of relating. To call this process one of mourning is to indicate the work of de-attachment that goes on, the emotional pain of that work, and the ultimate substantial freeing of the tie, as in mourning after a death, so that new ties can be made and life can go on.

The features that characterize this developmentally required object loss in adolescence can be identified more precisely (Wolfenstein, 1966, 1969). First, and of major significance, it is extended over time; the workings of the process take place all through the adolescent period. As a corollary to this, the de-attachment process takes place according to the growing adolescent's own inner timetable. Though driven, so to speak, by defense needs, he or she can also be relatively active in the process. Renunciation, an active intrapsychic process, supplements loss, a passive one. Forward steps, regressions, and reprogressions are all possible, as are trial actions, object displacements in fantasy before those in reality, object displacements to the "extended familylike peer group" before those to individuals "outside," and the like. A second equally significant feature of the adolescent object loss is that there is a pull as well as a push; there are new gratifying relationships to be found while old ones, gratifying but disturbing, ambivalently held, are given up. In short, the cost–benefit ratio is not totally one-sided. Object finding runs parallel to object loss. And third, and again equally significant, the adolescent object loss is accompanied by object retention. What is given up is the particular place the parent held in the gratification system of the offspring's mental life. In aiding the adolescent to achieve this, the nonintrusive, continuing emotional availability of the parent serves as a facilitator of the gradual de-attachment. But in any event, the permanent object concept is stabilized by the period of adolescence, and therefore the inner concept of the actual parent is not given up. And not only does the inner object concept remain, but ongoing relationships with the parents continue, albeit in aim-inhibited ways. To illustrate, Anthony (1970) writes that a "relationship then becomes possible in which two adults (the parent and the grown child), linked by mutual happy memories, find to their surprise (not knowing the strength of the identification processes) that they have many interests in common and discover a new mature pleasure in each other as people" (p. 320). Is there then "object loss?" Indeed there is, and the emotional pain midway through the adolescent process testifies to it. At the end, the parent can no longer hold the primary libidinal place in the life of the offspring. But the loss process is of a very special kind—of long duration in the occurrence and therefore following the adolescent's inner timetables, offering important compensatory and alternative object ties, and in the long run, involving continued (aim-inhibited) relationship with the primary objects as well as retention of the permanent (inner) object concept.

These special features of the normal process of object loss in adolescence are not always absent in the case of adventitious losses—death, illness and hospitalization, divorce, placement— and later I shall illustrate, briefly, some of the ways in which their presence may modify the impact of one or another loss.

Childhood

The other great and intense experience of loss in the normal developmental process of the preadult period is attendant upon the growing awareness of separateness in the normal separation–individuation process. I am of course referring here to the contributions that Mahler (1972) and Mahler, Pine, and Bergman (1975) have made to our understanding of development. We do not assume that the child is born with differentiated concepts of self and other. These must be learned, and their learning does not come easily to the infant who has had blissful experiences of melting, as though undifferentiated, into the mother's breast or body during feeding and falling asleep.[1] The learning follows a course in which there is an early period of beginning differentiation, in the second half of the first year, that in turn gives way to the so-called practicing period. The latter is a time of elated motor mastery during which the toddler seems relatively less concerned with the mother's comings and goings than he or she was earlier or will be (again) later; motor behavior appears to absorb all attention. But then the motor feats settle in, they fall into place as functional tools of the child, and the still very young child rediscovers its mother; that is, once again *she* absorbs the child's attention. But awareness of differentiation is now much further along, learning having taken place all through the practicing period. And so the toddler arrives at eighteen months or so more aware of differentiation, not yet emotionally ready for it, and enters what Mahler refers to as the "rapprochement" period, a time of low mood (because of the sense of loss of the fusion with mother) and of efforts to deny that loss (by stubborn efforts to coerce mother to act as an extension of the child). All in all it is a critical developmental period for the resolution of issues of fusion/omnipotence and differentiation/loss. The continued emotional availability of the mother and her maintenance of an optimal distance facilitates the process of differentiation and of continued object contact. The crystallization of the affect of sadness at this time, as a phase specific event, has been beautifully described by Mahler (1966) in her important paper on moods, and is testament to the experience of loss.

Considerations regarding object constancy are, as in the adolescent process, highly relevant in understanding the developmental pathway through early loss of the undifferentiated

---

[1]Recent research detailing the differentiated perceptual and cognitive capacities of the infant does not rule out the presence of these affectively intense moments of "merger" experience which have an important organizing impact upon aspects of mental life (Pine, 1985, chapter 4; Pine, 1986).

other—though the considerations at this early period are of a very different sort from those in the adolescent period. For, we believe, the child in the rapprochement period does not have a fully reliable internal representation of the constant object. While Piaget (1937) has demonstrated that the eighteen-month-old child has more or less developed a capacity to hold the image of the affectively neutral object (i.e., acts as though he has a concept of its permanence even in its absence), additional factors come into play regarding the libidinal object, the primary caretaker, usually the mother. These factors are at least threefold, and all involve intense affective processes leading to (at least moments of) instability of the internal representation of the libidinal object. First, intense periods of longing, of need, create an object demand that is not satisfied through or capable or regulation by the stable thought of the love object. Second, at other times, and indeed related to unsatisfied longing, the representation of the mother is so buffeted by violent and angry feelings that its stability, once again, is disrupted (McDevitt, 1975). And third, more clearly in cases of disturbed development but also in the mix of progression and regression that characterizes even optimal development, defense against the clear representation of the differentiated object in itself is likely when urges toward fusion are prominent—either momentarily or through massive fixation or regression.

On the other hand, one of the great developmental achievements accompanying the gradual awareness of differentiation, and indeed compensating for the experience of loss, is precisely the development of a well-differentiated, unified, internal representation of the love object that is stable over time (Pine, 1985). To be able to achieve comfort from the internal object representation rather than from the actual love object in the flesh is an immense developmental gain. It not only protects the child from absolute dependence upon the physical presence of the mother, which cannot be sustained in any event, but it does this with no loss of the child's developing autonomy, rather, indeed, a potential gain. By carrying an image of the mother inside, not only a "picture," but a set of expectations of her behavior, an expectable relationship, the child is free to rove autonomously, not dependent upon the mother's physical presence to stabilize functioning. The internal object representation permits a greater closeness than the reality object can at many times provide, with no sacrifice of the autonomy that the child has already achieved through its developing locomotor independence and capacity to delay gratification. By the end of the third year, most children achieve this capacity to take comfort from the internal libidinal object representation to a considerable degree. But in fact this does not settle the developmental issue. People vary all through life in their relative dependence upon actual contact with the reality object for comfort and pleasure; they vary in complementary fashion in their capacity to take comfort from the internal memory or image of the love object.

Thus far, then, the adolescent period and the earliest years of life contain *age specific*, *universal* (or at least spread throughout our culture), and *intense* normal developmental experiences of loss: the early period entailing loss of symbiotic union (and accompanied by increasing awareness of self–other differentiation and the growth of object relationship and inner object constancy, both replacing self–other union), and the later (adolescent) period entailing renunciation of the tie to the infantile love objects (with a progressively committed turn to new extrafamilial object ties).

What of the childhood period: childhood proper, the elementary school years, the so-called latency period? As I see it, there is no loss experience comparable to those of the early years or adolescence. Losses abound: leaving home for the entry into school, the turnover of teachers each year, a first summer trip or camping experience without the parents, friends who move away, the relative loss of parental attention with the birth of a sibling, and, of course, the ongoing variations in the emotional availability or unavailability of the parents. Any one of these, or others, may have a profound impact upon the life of any particular child. And they are all "normal" events (I have not listed deaths, divorces, hospitalization, for example). But it is my impression that there is no single experience of loss, characteristic of the midchildhood years, that approximates the universality and intensity of the losses in very early childhood and in adolescence that I have already described.

In fact one of the central features of the childhood period seems to me to be the child's sense of the timelessness of his life as it is lived in the family. I am not here speaking of children of chaotic, disorganized families in chaotic and disorganized surroundings, where a sense of unpredictability, or the predictably unpredictable, may be pervasive. But in normal childhood there is a sense that the trip to school, the family dinner, the relationship between the mother and father, and between self and parents, the feel of one's room, of one's bed, afterschool play, snacks at the local candystore, rules and games and contests, are all forever, unchanging, expectable. This is in contrast to the adolescent experience of awareness of alternative life paths and the growing awareness of the (inner and external) expectation that one leave the home behind and set out on one's own. Losses of various sorts abound in childhood, as I have already said, but I believe that, normally, they fall on a soil of inner object constancy and of secure object relatedness in which they can ordinarily be well absorbed. Indeed, as miniexperiences of loss they add to the crystallization of the reality of loss, to the repertoire of ways of dealing with it, to the child's general preparedness.

Now it is certainly true that for some children these miniexperiences of loss, these normal loss experiences of childhood, may have profound effects, may be well beyond the child's coping capacity, and may stimulate anxiety, regression, and/or symptom formation. But here it is my impression that this is distinctly not due to age-general features of the loss but to idiosyncratic features of the individual child. For some this is based on old, unresolved symbiotic ties or instability of the inner object representation. In other instances, what appears on the surface to be a problem of separation and object loss turns out to be a manifestation of an unconscious conflict involving aggression, rivalry, or the like—in short a disguised impulse–defense conflict—which cannot be understood without a more complex inner view of fantasy and unconscious meaning.

Until now I have been explicitly presenting a description of the losses that are part of the normal developmental process, but I have been implicitly laying the ground for understanding the varying impacts of adventitious losses as well. For a close-up look at any one of them reveals that some of the same considerations that I have been describing for normal losses— the gradualness of the process and its fit with the child's inner timetable, the retention of aspects of the relationship to the "lost" object, the continuance of emotional availability of the parents, the availability of alternative love objects, and the stability of object constancy, can each apply to particular adventitious losses as well and permit us a more differentiated view of their impacts.

Thus, recently I came to know (through a consultation) a nine-year-old boy whose father had moved to a geographically distant city for work reasons, had been there for about two years, and saw his son about twice monthly when one or the other traveled to visit. The boy missed his father intensely (for specific historical reasons that I shall not go into) but the experience of loss was modified not only by the continued contact but, and this is what I wish to emphasize, by the boy's ongoing inner sense of relatedness to the father (object constancy). He told me about this in a very adultlike way, saying he might not see his father for a whole month but he "knew inside" that when he saw him again it would be just like it always was to be with him. Lest you think this is because of the continued loving climate of the parental interrelationship, I have to add that this was not so, because the parents were actually quite embattled and this was a form of trial separation. The boy's achievement of an ongoing sense of relatedness to his father was truly an inner achievement which lasted in spite of distinct coolness tending toward hostility that the mother (whom he lived with) felt toward the father.

Or an example from another domain: in her work on the reactions of children and adolescents to the death of a parent, Wolfenstein (1966) points out that the availability of alternative objects, preferably who are there before the death and continue as meaningful substitutes, can modulate the impact of a death to some extent. Implicit in this is also the suggestion that a more gradually occurring death allows for anticipation, shifts of attachment, and in general allows for preparatory work to go on. But these features are familiar ones. The gradualness of the process and the availability of alternative objects (here through displacement) are features that modulate the normal adolescent mourning process as well.

And just one more brief example: Some time ago an adult analytic patient made clear to me that his mother's illness when he was a child, where the child (the patient) could only stand at the doorway to his mother's room but not enter, made for an intense experience of loss. The very presence of the mother aroused a longing that could then not be satisfied and that therefore heightened the feeling of loss. The issues here were essentially ones of emotional availability, not really geographic availability, and they are of general import. It was precisely because of this mother's ongoing emotional unavailability, even prior to her illness, that the doorway-to-bed separation was so painful (as we came to understand it), symbolizing not actual loss, but that state of unavailability, "so near and yet so far."

Adulthood

Turning now to losses in the adult period, I shall describe four, each of which I believe, like those already described, are more or less universal and inherent in the developmental process, and are affectively powerful, though their intensity often appears as a background mood because of the slow-wave development of each of these losses during the long course of adulthood. The "object" lost in the first two that I shall describe is the self, or rather, a part of the self. The several losses to be described come in no particular sequence (with the possible exception of the last one), being spread throughout adulthood in the slow-wave development to which I have already referred.

First, then, is the loss of omnipotentiality. If in adolescence we can imagine all that we might become, endless in its possibilities, and suffer the anxiety of uncertainty, in adulthood we come to be aware of all that we might have been, and suffer a resignation to actuality. This, I believe, has no one-to-one relationship to actual achievement in life, in social, familial, occupational, or other spheres. The awareness of limitation, of roads not taken, of choices not made and no longer makeable, of wishes not realized or long since abandoned, of the inevitable gap between hope and actuality in one's own life, is an inevitable byproduct of the human capacity to hope, dream, and anticipate a future, on the one hand, and to perceive, judge, and assess reality on the other. The tension between these two is one piece of human existence.

We can conceptualize what happens in terms of a final modification of the ego ideal. From this perspective, we can think of a developmental line from infantile narcissism and omnipotence ("I am the world; my wishes are its commands"), to the belief in the omnipotence of the parents and identification with that omnipotence, to disillusionment with parental perfection and postponement of the ideal state into the future (or displacement of it into illusion). Then comes the adult awareness of limitation, of things never to be realized. Or we can conceptualize what happens in terms of a final step in the delay of gratification and of bowing to the reality principle. From this perspective, the capacity to delay and the hope of ultimate satisfaction gradually transform into a recognition of limitation, of the permanence of nonsatisfaction in one region of wish or another.

I do not wish to paint a totally gloomy picture, and will in fact now add color to it. For it is in the nature of the normal developmental process that background harmonies alter major themes. Evolution, or culture, or human resiliency seems to make it so. So, first, this again is a gradual process. This loss of a part of the self (ego ideal and wish) is not all or none. While we cannot say it takes place at the person's own timetable (like the adolescent's relative withdrawal of investment in the parents of childhood), still it occurs only gradually, over a long time span, now in this area and now in that. Nor is the loss all or none in another respect: areas of limitation are balanced by those of fulfillment. Nor is the loss once and for all: moments of awareness of limitation, of background loss, and dissatisfaction and depression, are offset by moments (almost inevitably recurring) of pleasure, satisfaction, and optimism. So the long time duration (permitting the development of coping mechanisms) and the presence of compensatory features (areas of satisfaction) set the context in which knocks to the ego ideal and the current self-assessment are weathered.

A second loss in the adult period, also a loss of an aspect of the self as object, is of optimal body function or appearance. This is most sharply and powerfully delineated for women, with the clear biological clock of the childbearing period and the clock's running out, eventuating in menopause. But, though clearest there, this loss is omnipresent and the impact of one or another aspect of loss is dependent upon the place that that feature had held in the mental life of the particular person: changes in the face seen in the mirror—lines on the skin, graying of hair. There are changes in physical agility, strength, or endurance, inwardly noted changes in metabolism—food requirements and weight phenomena, sleep requirements— and the progressive accumulation of minor ailments barely noted at first, that progressively become a whole groundswell.

Clearly the time of onset of such losses varies widely, as does the site of their impact. The relative loss of endurance in a young professional athlete, or changes in the skin of a young/ old model will obviously have a special relevance, but we each have areas which are of special relevance to us, dependent upon the site of our body narcissism, the place of our bodies in our sense of self, the role of actual body function in our ongoing lives, and the nature of the specific alteration in body function or appearance. Direct alterations in sexual function are of widespread concern, though, of course, the meanings (in fantasy) of loss of any specific function may serve as a representation of sexual or other alteration for any one individual.

A critical feature here is timing. Neugarten (1970), in discussing menopause and having discovered that it is not a "crisis" in the lives of many or most women, argues that crisis is a function of things occurring out of their expected place in the timetable of life. Thus, early debilitating illness or loss of body function will create an inner psychological demand for adaptation, with considerable ongoing stress, in ways quite different from those occurring more in the expectable timetable. In a similar way, for example, the precociously menstrual girl, first by far among her friends, or the one with long delayed menstrual onset, faces a very different inner demand for adaptation than does the girl on the more normal cycle. The impact of that loss of self that is stimulated by changes in body function and appearance is related to timing, site, and degree of alteration, and its place in the fantasy and actuality systems of the particular individual. But the losses, and the coming to terms with them, are universal.

A third loss in the adult period is that progressive loss of one's own children that begins with the very birth of the child. This is the other side of those losses, in the separation–individuation phase and in adolescence, of the parent by the child. But for the parent, it is not phase-specific. Certainly there are potential times of sharp impact: for the mother, at birth, as the child separates from her body and the narcissistic self-containment of the late phase of pregnancy comes to an abrupt end, to be replaced by the care of an other who is sometimes not easy to care for, with a will of its own. Or again for the mother, usually, the impact is sharp at school entry, when the all-day care of the child is suddenly lost and the mother is left with time alone, and when other adults (teachers) become significant to the child who is now shared with others. In late adolescence, the now mostly grown child moves out, to college or a place of his or her own, producing an "empty nest" at the parental home. These are points of potentially sharp impact of the loss experience. But each person responds differently to the different potential losses (Mahler, Pine, and Bergman, 1970); for example, some responding to the differentiating infant's greater willfulness as a loss, and some responding with relief to the end of the period of total dependence and the growing sense of relating to an *other*. But whether it is the held baby's capacity now to pull away from the holding mother's body to crane its neck looking around a room, or the toddler's busy preoccupation with the world out there, or the "no" that proclaims individuality and separateness, or the entry into school, or the early adolescent's renewed privacy and new secrecy stimulated by the resurgence of sexuality, or the late adolescent's turn to other primary objects outside the home, or the physical move away—whichever of these, or others, or all, are critical to the particular loss experiences of particular parents, in one way or another, through one or another of them—the loss experience is universal and, ordinarily, affectively powerful.

But, as for the adolescent described earlier, aspects of loss are matched by aspects of retained actual relationship, inner relatedness, and object constancy in all their manifestations. Aspects of loss are balanced by aspects of gain: repossession of one's own body by the postnursing mother; repossession of one's own time and life rhythm with the progressive move of the child into its own life; and development of a relationship to an other, an independent person, tied with the bonds of shared history and mutual identification. Clearly this process is by no means always beatific in its course or outcome; I have tried to describe its major outlines. Always these are shaped by individual need, by individual fantasy and pathology, within the limits of individual adaptive flexibility.

And finally there is a fourth area of loss in the adult period, the loss of peers through death and the preparation for one's own death, the final step in loss of body function and the loss of self that goes with it. From what I've seen of the deaths I have observed and been part of, close-up—those that are on timetable, in the aged, following the "rules" of normal development, not the crisis-interruptive deaths of the young or middle aged—it seems clear that the deaths of peers serve as preparation for one's own death. The loss of body function in the debilitative illnesses creates a profound sense of loss of the self as experienced and yet, amazingly, character finds a way of handling the situation, ideally or not, such that self and character consistency are to a large degree retained. Continuity of self is preserved, even at the price of "optimal" (i.e., purely objective) adaptation to the illness. And additionally, the loss of function, like the loss of peers through death, prepares the ground for a readiness for death. Denial, fright, despair are all there, potentially or actually, but I have been impressed by the preparedness and deep acceptance, even under the residual denial. Indeed, what choice is there?

In summary, the normal developmental process is filled with built-in experiences of object loss—of parental and child objects and of self as object. Clearly it is inherent in the human condition, loss being but the reverse side of the coin of attachment, the price we pay for the tension between related-ness and individuality. But, within the developmental process, these losses are seldom one-sided. When they occur on timetable (which is what makes them part of normal development), they are accompanied by object retention or object replacement, by personal growth, or by adaptive possibilities that temper their effect. But they only temper the effect; the background of loss is evident throughout development.

References

Anthony, E. J. (1970), The reactions of parents to adolescents and to their behavior. In: *Parenthood: Its Psychology and Psychopathology*, ed. E. J. Anthony & T. Benedek. Boston: Little, Brown, pp. 307–324.

Mahler, M. S. (1966), Notes on the development of basic moods: The depressive affect. In: *Psychoanalysis: A General Psychology*, ed. R. M. Loewenstein, L. M. Newman, M. Schur, & A. J. Solnit. New York: International Universities Press, pp. 152–168.

———(1972), On the first three subphases of the separation–individuation process. *Internat. J. Psycho-Anal.*, 53:333–338.

———Pine, F., & Bergman, A. (1970), The mother's reaction to her toddler's drive for individuation. In: *Parenthood: Its Psychology and Psychopathology*, ed. E. J. Anthony & T. Benedek. Boston: Little, Brown, pp. 257–274.

——— ——— ———(1975), *The Psychological Birth of the Human Infant*. New York: Basic Books.

McDevitt, J. B. (1975), Separation–individuation and object constancy. *J. Amer. Psychoanal. Assn.*, 23:713–742.

Neugarten, B. L. (1970), Dynamics of transition of middle age to old age: Adaptation and the life cycle. *J. Geriat. Psychiat.*, 4:71–87.

Piaget, J. (1937), *The Construction of Reality in the Child*. New York: Basic Books, 1954.

Pine, F. (1985), *Developmental Theory and Clinical Process*. New Haven, CT: Yale University Press.

——— (1986), The "symbiotic phase" in the light of current infancy research. *Bull. Menn. Clin.*, 50:564–569.

Wolfenstein, M. (1966), How is mourning possible? *The Psychoanalytic Study of the Child*, 21:93–123. New York: International Universities Press.

——— (1969), Loss, rage, and repetition. *The Psychoanalytic Study of the Child*, 24:432–460. New York: International Universities Press.

7

The Significance of Loss and
Mourning in the Older Adult:
Clinical and Research Findings

JEROME GRUNES, M.D.
WENDY WASSON, PH.D.

The concept of loss of the object is a significant one in psychoanalytic theory. Sigmund Freud (1917) distinguished between conscious loss through death, which signaled the beginning of the painful work of mourning, and the unconscious loss characteristic of those who fell ill with melancholia or what we now call the depressive states. The idea of unconscious loss had profound implications for the development of the structural theory (particularly the concept of the superego), for the notion of ambivalence, narcissism, and symptom formation. We can make a case that all psychopathology can be viewed as responses to unconscious loss, whether due to the feared loss of the object, of the object's love, or of the love of our superego. Individuals respond to such threats, not only by becoming ill

The authors would like to acknowledge the assistance of Drs. David Gutmann, Jordan Jacobwitz, and Brian P. Griffin in this work.

but with a variety of ego and character defenses as well as the use of other coping devices.

In order to describe depression in late life and those aspects of personality that seem to guard against the incursions of psychopathology, we shall describe some of the investigations undertaken at the Older Adult Program of the Institute of Psychiatry at Northwestern Medical School. These studies have focused on those older patients who have fallen ill for the first time in later life. Such a sample has permitted us to study the "stressors" of the latter half of life and their relationships to earlier trauma. Intensive diagnostic assessments, including projective psychological tests as well as psychotherapeutic treatment, have enabled us to develop hypotheses regarding normal as well as pathological aging. These studies suggest that certain structures composed of fantasies about ourselves constitute our central myths and may be essential for our well-being. These structured fantasies which serve as protectors of the integrity of the self are subject to attack by stressors of later life. The overturning of such soothing, regulatory, and self-reparative processes may lead to regression and the emergence of symptoms of anxiety and depression.

We shall now turn to one study at Northwestern, which sheds some light on the characteristics of older depressed patients. The case records of 116 outpatients ranging in age from fifty-five to ninety-three years were examined. Seventy-nine percent of this group were diagnosed as depressed and/or suffering from anxiety states. It is clear that the affective disorders constitute a vast majority of the elderly seen for the first time as psychiatric patients in later life whether as inpatients or outpatients. However, the precipitants of psychopathology differed for men and women in the sample, with 47 percent of the women responding to interpersonal losses while only in 12 percent of the men could such precipitants be implicated. About four out of five men responded that work problems (including retirement) were the precipitants. Physical illnesses were about twice as prevalent in women than men in the onset of psychopathology. Men also were more likely than women to seek treatment because of marital problems (eleven to one). Childlessness was present in 43 percent of the men and in 33 percent of the women. In terms of past trauma and childhood loss before the age of sixteen, 40 percent of the men and 81 percent of the women had histories of death of one or both parents, separation from parents, and trauma including child abuse, death of siblings, parental alcoholism or psychiatric disorders, divorce and severe childhood illnesses.

The prevalence of childlessness and early loss and trauma was significantly elevated when compared to that of a comparable group of community-dwelling elderly. While these findings will require closer scrutiny and interpretation, we can say that early separation through death or divorce seems to predispose individuals to later life pathology, especially women. Also, the absence of children and of the parenting function needs closer study. While we have studied childless women, we were surprised at the even greater percentage of childless men in this sample. Finally, there may be some important differences between the depressive dynamics of older men and women. This later observation is supported by two additional studies, which have investigated groups of older depressed men and women in more detail.

We will begin by reviewing our initial study of outpatient and hospitalized men with the diagnosis of depression. The patients ranged in age from the forties to the seventies. Groupings based on history and psychodynamics were elicited. One category included men of the youngest group. They presented with symptoms of agitated depression. Problems at work which heretofore had been quiescent were present, and even more important than these was a conflictual relationship with a newly assertive wife who was viewed as unsupportive. This group of men viewed their wife's development toward independence in the postparental years as a kind of "dismissal." "It's like she fired me from my job," one of the depressed men exclaimed. Besides sharing similarities in symptoms and presenting complaints, these men shared parallel histories. Usually, they were the youngest child of aging parents. The father was seen as absent or weak, and the mother as strong and competent. Sometimes these men held mother responsible for the castration of the father. Their failure to separate from the mother had a variety of consequences, including heightened dependency on maternal figures, coupled with a tendency to view them as dangerous and threatening toward men. There was also a reliance on outer structures for direction and control, as well as a strong feminine (unconscious) identification. The retention of the maternal bond through a dependency liaison with a nurturing wife lead to a stable adult and parental period. In the postparental years, these men tended to move into the niche left by their grown children and in effect replaced the now departed children as the object of the wife's concern and affection. As this dependent and passive role is ego syntonic, the men were not troubled by this development. It was only with the reaction of the wife toward autonomy and self-sufficiency and the rejection of her heretofore maternal role and loss of interest in being the indulgent mother to her husband that the breakdown toward depression in the husband began. In some cases studied, the men who have such dependent vulnerabilities managed to stave off a depression by shifting their maternal transferences toward their grown daughters. In such instances, the illness occurred when the daughter would leave home, usually to marry. This subgroup of men tended to develop somatic illnesses as depressive equivalents.

A second group of casualties preserved the maternal bond inwardly while denying the feminine identification. They present themselves to the external world as "hypermacho." The masculine world of work provides them with the opportunity to enact their defensive stance. It also provides them with the "fathers" they require in the form of patrons, mentors, and employers. Work serves them as a predictable source of control and self-esteem. They tend to marry nurturing, nonassertive women. The depletions that occur in the workplace, the loss of unlimited possibilities for achievement, threaten the defensive bulwark which had been erected against the more feminine aspects of self. When the wife in the postparental years no longer performs the function as the externalized feminine aspect of her husband's self, the man experiences her as castrating. This is heightened by the awareness of a more emotional and maternal aspect of the self which heretofore had been repudiated. An agitated depression with panic states (a version of homosexual panic) emerges. Suicidal attempts are often present. One method of denying this sexual bimodality is for the male to seek new sources of oral supplies in the form of alcoholism.

These are but two possible outcomes of early unresolved problems regarding separation from the mother in men which become manifest in midlife. The emergence of psychopathology in these men seems to support the "cross-over hypothesis," which states that in the postparental period men begin to experience their more passive–feminine aspects, while women seem to become more "masculine," striving, and ambitious. Does this in fact hold true for women?

A study of depressed women has shed some light on this question and led us to other insights about the "stressors" of later life. Wasson (1986) has intensively studied thirty-one women, sixty years and older with self-defined depressive states. She used twenty-five case reports of community-dwelling women as a normal control. Recurring themes in the histories and projective testing of these women led to hypotheses about late onset depression in women. Three groupings were sorted out. Type A were women who became depressed in response to feeling frustrated and disappointed in the postparental years. Discontented and unfulfilled, she often attributed blame to her unresponsive and needy husband or children. Having always cared for others, she consciously, but more often preconsciously, wanted others to care for her. Resentment and disappointment would be her responses in the postparental years when others turned to her. Confronting her in later life was the loss of the sustaining fantasy that nurturance, appreciation, and admiration shown toward her would finally be realized. Such structured fantasies could be viewed historically as compensating for feelings of deprivation in earlier life. The loss of this myth of being finally loved and valued led to the pathology.

The fact that these women report feeling greater anger and irritation in late life may support the "cross-over hypothesis," where women move from a more passive to an assertive stance. However, their inability to manage this aggression constructively may lead to their sense of feeling stuck and resentful.

However, Type B were widows whose sense of self has been dependent on their husbands. Not only had he served as a source of comfort and soothing but he also had been the organizer and regulator of the woman's activities. The narcissistic object choice of these women make mourning impossible. The men had been *selfobjects* in Kohut's term. Inconsolable, they were unable to cope with the loss, and while they do not deny the death, they nonetheless repeat the view that all would be well if only the husband returned. In reality, this resembles a hallucinatory wish fulfillment, and what is transient in normal mourning becomes almost permanent for such widows. With such losses of their sustaining fantasies of being cared for and protected, these older women feel that something which had been theirs is now missing.

In Type C we find a group of women, usually older than the previous ones, who experience a profound loss of self-esteem in response to physical illnesses (particularly of the motoric apparatus) which interfere with their autonomy. While other losses (such as the death of a spouse) are taken in stride, the assaults on the body which render them dependent on others precipitate a crushing of a self-esteem which had been built on fantasies of the self as strong, reliant, and competent.

Each of these typologies of depression in older women suggest specific psychotherapies. With Type A, an interpretative psychotherapy can bring to consciousness the wished-for fantasies, and resolution within the framework of the treatment is possible. Type B is resistant to any insight and requires a substitute for the lost husband in the form of an organizer and regulator of activities and self-esteem. The revival of past memories is painful and resisted. The focus must be in the here and now. Treatment tends to be interminable, involve ongoing sporadic contact, or become unnecessary only when the patient feels that she has found an adequate replacement. Type C responds well to psychotherapy which involves a life review. The capacity of the older woman, in concert with the therapist, to hold on to a potent image of herself and her past may allow an acceptance of current limitations. This kind of treatment puts special burdens on the therapist and is discussed in a paper by Grunes (1981).

While the two prototypes of depression among men and the three among women are helpful in distinguishing common paths in the forest of late life psychopathology, we do not consider them to exhaust the list. In general, however, we have been impressed by the central position of specific organized fantasies as they relate to old problems and their resolutions. These constructs exert powerful effects in the personality and help resist regressions to psychic illnesses. The loss of these structures due to specific life events or developmental stresses lead to illnesses of a depressive and anxious nature.

At this point, it would be helpful to review what we know of symptom formation, using Freud's topographical model. Manifest regression is set in motion in response to the subjective experience of loss, where fantasies of a soothing, reparative nature are brought into play. This process aids the return of "normalcy." However, regression proper may occur as well, particularly for those patients who have histories of psychic trauma and early losses, or constitutional predilections. In regression proper, memory traces of preoedipal and oedipal objects are activated together with the conflicts and resolutions which have led to neurotic symptomatology.

Thus, one may see activated ideas, such as "I lost Mommy because I was vanquished, bad, unlovable." As painful as these neurotic formulations are, they are solutions which protect the self from further regression to an almost unimaginable state of helplessness, nothingness, and meaninglessness where all representations of objects in the unconscious are lost. Freud highlighted the essential paradox, that in being so preoccupied with the lost object, the depressed individual is in fact holding onto the object, albeit unconsciously. In grieving there is the *fear* that everything is lost and the self cannot survive. In depression, there is the underlying *conviction* that everything is lost and the self cannot survive. This dreaded situation cannot be acknowledged and must be defended against.

Let us now leave theories of symptom formation and focus on the structured fantasies that appear valuable in preserving the self in stressful periods of development. Fantasies about ourselves (e.g., I am omnicompetent, my past privations ensure further rewards, or I am childlike and can always find a strong, protecting other) are potentially problematic, but oppose tendencies toward deeper regressions to painful anxieties of loss of other and self. Such protective fantasies vary from simple wish fulfillments to profound and deeply held views of the self which are not subject to reality testing. Clinical examples of this hypothesis are offered in Wasson's paper on depressed women (1986).

In middle to late life, many of these fantasies may be undermined with the increased awareness of loss and mortality. The assault upon these fantasies can be a precipitant for psychological stress in susceptible individuals, and may result in psychopathology. Jaques (1965) considered this process to be the underlying dynamic of the midlife crisis, wherein one's vulnerability is recognized and experienced; the resolution of the midlife crisis occurs when the idealized self as object is mourned.

However, the aged person may not repair or "work through" losses in the same way as in middle age. Incomplete mourning seems to be the lot for many elderly. An eighty-year-old woman, telephoning for an appointment, said that she was suffering from the loss of her great love. When seen at her first appointment, it was discovered that her husband–lover had passed away ten years before but that the painful aspects of his loss were as fresh as if he had recently died. An attractive woman, she had sought out substitutes but found that she could not invest in another man despite her participation and enjoyment of physical closeness and sexual relationships. She found herself in a state of limbo, unable to give up the lost object totally or to invest in her own self. The latter narcissistic state would, she feared, be permanent, and if she accepted the reality of her husband's death, she feared that she could not enter another relationship nor sustain another loss, or she would herself die. To avoid the potential for loss, she thought of dating younger men but the shame that would come from her daughters' disapproval dissuaded her from active pursuits in this direction. In the course of treatment we discovered that her capacity to mourn had been "used up." In the preceding five years, she had lost through death five of her siblings. Like a character in Greek tragedy, she felt cursed by the gods. This was further enhanced by the terminal illness of a male friend with whom she had traveled and had had a satisfactory sexual relationship, though not a loving one.

At the onset of this woman's treatment, two questions arose. Are we as human beings limited in our capacity to mourn, and is the prototype of mourning characteristic of younger and middle-aged adults different in older people? To the former question, we would suggest that the work of mourning can be traumatic not only because of ambivalence toward the lost object but also because of its energy requirements, which may be excessive in later life. It would also appear that mourning proceeds differently in the second half of life and that its incompleteness is part of the process itself. The affirmation of life over death which Freud regards as the necessary precursor for accepting the reality of loss is less strong and dependable in age. Life is not always triumphant, as witnessed by the number of older people who die following the loss of a loved object. For in the aged, mourning no less than depression can be lethal, interfering as it may with basic biological needs. Both mourning and depression have physiological components. Inanition, sleeplessness, general hypometabolism, nutritional deficiencies, electrolyte imbalance, and increased susceptability to infection can lead to morbidity and even mortality.

As we look back on the subject of loss and mourning in the elderly, we conclude tentatively that external losses may or may not set off processes that result in either mourning or depression. From the five studies of anxious depressions in late life, we can speculate that early trauma through loss can predispose the older individual to derailments in the sense of self, when developmental shifts occur. In late life, fantasies which have protected the individual from slights and loss may be assaulted by the inherent problems of aging.

Yet, mourning, particularly in the old, may never be complete. The affirmation of life over death needed to accept the reality of the loss of a loved object cannot be assumed to occur axiomatically. In addition, the energy expenditure during the mourning process may be an excessive burden even when substitute objects are available.

Depression in later life needs to be further explored, since many of our metapsychological formulations are based on younger individuals. We need further clinical evidence for the applicability of such theoretical postulates for the aged.

References

Freud, S. (1917), Mourning and melancholia. *Standard Edition*, 14:237–258. London: Hogarth Press, 1957.

Grunes, J. (1981), Reminiscences, repression and empathy: A psychotherapeutic approach to the impaired elderly. In: *The Course of Life: Psychoanalytic Contributions Toward Understanding Personality Development*, Vol. 3, ed. S. Greenspan & G. Pollock. Washington, DC: NIMH, Dept. Health & Human Services, pp. 545–548.

Jaques, E. (1965), Death and the mid-life crisis. *Internat. J. Psycho-Anal.*, 46:502–514.

Wasson, W. (1986), Depression in older women (unpublished).

Part III

Clinical Contributions

8

Personality Change through Life Experience. III: Two Creative Types of Response to Object Loss

MILTON VIEDERMAN, M.D.

The experience of loss, one of the most powerful human experiences, has generated an extensive psychiatric and psychoanalytic literature. Beginning with Freud (1917) and elaborated by Lindemann (1944), numerous studies have examined normal and pathological bereavement (Clayton, Desmarais, and Winokur, 1968; Clayton, 1972; Parkes and Weiss, 1983). Recent interest has been generated by the accumulation of new data revealing that bereavement may have profound physiological effects and may lead to both physical and psychiatric illness (Maddison and Viola; 1968, Klerman and Izen, 1977). Moreover, recent evidence suggests that bereavement may be a lifelong process (Zisook, Schuchter, and Schuckit, 1985).

The overwhelming emphasis in such studies is on the distress generated by loss, which is seen not only as a painful psychological reaction to bereavement "but also as a duty to the dead" (Parkes and Weiss, 1983). Almost ignored, however, are the much less common but dramatic instances of loss and bereavement as crisis situations leading to growth and personality change. Kolb (personal communication) describes an instance in which a chronic, severely psychotic, institutionalized man insisted that when his father died, he would become well and would be discharged from the hospital. This prediction came true. Loss in this situation was experienced as a release from bondage. It is my intent in this chapter to present two cases that illustrate this phenomenon and to discuss their theoretical implications.

The idea that positive change is possible in the context of loss is poorly developed in the literature. Freud (1923) described identification with the lost object as a response to loss and indicated that the ego, in part, is the product of the accretions that stem from such identifications. Parkes and Weiss (1983) discussed the recovery process in bereavement, emphasizing change over time that involves coming to terms with the reality of loss.

> Those who recover from bereavement do not return to being the same people they had been before their marriages or before their spouses' deaths. Nor do they forget the past and start a new life. Rather, they recognize that change has taken place, accept it, examine how their basic assumptions about themselves and their world must be changed and go on from there. . . . Three distinct tasks in recovery are: First, that the loss be accepted intellectually; second, that the loss be accepted emotionally; and third, that the individual's model of self and outer world change to match the new reality [pp. 155–156].

This statement encapsulates the authors' view that this new identity is formed in response to the changed reality. However, it does not reflect a significant reworking of intrapsychic conflict. Pollock (1961), who has written extensively on mourning from a psychoanalytic point of view, focuses on how the requirement to adapt to a changed reality leads to intrapsychic change. He refers to the possibility that the outcome of the mourning process may be a reinvestment in an ideal but does not elaborate upon this notion. Cath and Herzog (1982), in a chapter on the death of the father, make a number of references to issues that are pertinent to this theme. They discuss the universal fantasy that individuals at the end of the journey of life will greet the forgiving good father. They point out the change in perspective on life that occurs with each loss and the increased richness of experience that each loss evokes, based upon the experience of the past and "blended with every past goodbye."[1] Cath and Herzog note not only that fantasied expectations can no longer be gratified, but also the sense that loss of a parent may obviate the last chance to earn respect or to pay back what has been given. The authors comment upon positive gains that may accrue from loss. They note that some grieving men, having assessed both sides of a dilemma (ambivalence) during the dying of their father, and after the death, have been stimulated to even greater heights of creativity and achievement. They seem relieved from an internal bondage and subservience. This theme will be elaborated below.

Vaillant (1984), in an interesting paper entitled "Loss as a Metaphor for Attachment," examines loss from a point of view of the possibility of personality development and growth. He describes clearly how the integration of previously split good and bad maternal objects can occur in the context of loss, thereby resulting in the establishment of a predominantly good internalized maternal object that leads to enhanced self-esteem and self-worth. He describes cases from the Grant study (Vaillant, 1977) in which individuals who effectively accomplish such integrations become more object related, creative, and effective in their professional and personal lives.

Clinical Cases

The following two case histories will be presented to illustrate two distinctly different modes of growth and personality change as a product of loss.

---

[1]A forty-year-old mother who had recently experienced a stillbirth described this well when she stated that the loss had brought her to realize that life is like a long railroad journey with people getting on and off the train at different times. She realized for the first time in her life that "everyone is fundamentally alone." This experience led to an altered relationship with her mother upon whom she had previously been quite dependent. Although there was considerable sadness as she discussed the sense of aloneness, she remained intensely related to other people.

Case Example 1

Mr. G. was a thirty-year-old homosexual man who appeared for consultation in the context of a crisis precipitated by his mother's impending death with esophageal carcinoma. He had a strong feeling that he had to do something for her, say something to her, work something out with her, but he was not clear as to what this was.

The patient was a slightly effeminate man who was articulate, psychologically minded, and expressive. He wept effusively throughout the four sessions that spanned the one-and-one-half months that preceded his mother's death and was strongly motivated to examine the sources of his conflict with his mother. He had just returned from a visit to her and was extremely distraught. He felt that he would "explode, fragment and be unable to pull [himself] back together again." A veil of secrecy had surrounded her diagnosis and progressive deterioration. Neither she nor the family had discussed her current predicament. He emphasized repeatedly his extremely loving relationship with his parents and his good fortune in having such parents. It became apparent that although there were many positive features in the relationship, it had been a highly idealized one. In his own words, his parents were "perfect parents for a perfect child." Yet there was a note of sarcasm as he described how his parents had "found him a psychoanalyst," when in college he had revealed to them for the first time that he was homosexual. When I speculated that it must have been a heavy burden to be a perfect child, the patient exploded with rage toward his parents as he became aware for the first time of his long-standing feeling that they had never accepted his homosexuality and that he had never met their expectations that he be the man that they wanted him to be. He had been a late child in a second marriage for both of them. It was only at his father's insistence that the mother had become pregnant again when she was thirty-five. Both of the parents had had children from a previous marriage. The patient remembered his discomfort at "never having measured up" to the masculinity of his stepbrother, sixteen years his senior. He had always been "feminine," interested in playing with dolls and had particularly enjoyed being with his mother and sharing in her household activities. It was in college that he became convinced of his homosexuality. This had resulted in considerable family turmoil. When the acute crisis was over, he believed that he "had forgiven them," though in retrospect he realized that his parents never asked about the man with whom he had lived for four years and would never invite him to their house as they did with his other married siblings. I pointed out that his mother's impending death had confronted him with an awareness that this would be the last chance to obtain her acceptance. The patient burst forth with tears of rage which I connected to his fear of exploding and fragmenting. I further suggested that his fear of facing his anger toward his parents had to do with his sense that this would destroy the positive and caring aspects of the relationship which seemed to exist. He responded by describing his puzzlement at the rage he had felt toward his maternal grandfather only now to recognize that he attributed his mother's attitude toward his homosexuality to the grandfather.

The second session took place after an interim visit to his parents' home in a distant city. Although he felt considerably better, the visit had been a painful one and he was concerned about not having discussed his mother's impending death with her. He described vividly an episode in which his mother had slept through the night, missed the pain medication that he was carefully administering to her and had awakened in great pain and quite shaken. For the first time he realized that their roles had been reversed, that he was taking care of her just as she had taken care of him even in adulthood. He felt panic about the disruption of the dependent relationship as he faced loss. The next day she was feeling better and indicated that she had wondered whether she would live through the night. Unexpressed rage was generated at the thought that she had not spoken to him of this, that she had not said that she would be leaving, that she would have abandoned him without a word. His intolerance of the demand for strength and independence that her death would place upon him had a clearly infantile narcissistic quality, suggesting a young child's separation from his mother.

The patient revealed that he had been examining his own life and had realized that his relationship with his lover was designed to convince his parents that he was in a marriage, though in fact this relationship had been unsatisfactory for him. He awakened one night, looked at his lover's face, and saw it transformed into the face of his mother. It became clear to him that in his relationship with this man he had effected a reversal, for the lover was weak and dependent, just as he had continued to be with his mother. Moreover, he was invested in his lover's idealization of him and their relationship as a reenactment of his relationship with his mother.

In the third session he was more calm and less tearful. He recognized the fantasy of a conflict in the family between his mother's desire to protect him and his father's desire to confront him with the realities of the world. The mother's view had prevailed and he experienced her presence as a "protective umbrella" from the realities of life. He realized that what he called his gay life-style was an escape from responsibility and reality. The thought of having children was anathema to him, for he could not tolerate the thought of young children dependent upon him. It became clear to him that the consultation itself was an attempt to find a surrogate parent to protect him from the harsh realities of life. He continued to be troubled by the need to have a dialogue with the mother, but he was quite unclear as to its nature. I suggested that he would work something out for himself.

The fourth session revealed that important changes had occurred in the interim after another visit home. While he was on the plane he decided that he would terminate the "passionless" relationship with his lover. In the two years prior to his having established a relationship with this man, he had had a passionate relationship with a young undergraduate that was tumultuous and painful. He had realized that this man, five years his junior, could not commit himself to a permanent relationship and the patient had interrupted it before an expected abandonment. In this relationship too, he had played the role of the idealized figure. In contrast to this tumultuous experience, the current relationship was one of safety and security, but devoid of passion. The lover was dependent, even-tempered, and acquiescent and there was no manifest conflict. He realized that in this relationship he was reproducing the relationship of his parents, who had substituted security for passion in their second marriage although each had been in a passionate previous marriage. During the trip he had had an important experience with his mother. The patient had spent a night at his mother's bedside "talking her down" during a delirious episode. The next day she felt very relieved, and as he was putting her back to bed she said "give me a hug you good old boy." He went on to say that she had started to say "good little boy," but realized that he was not little any more. The patient, with great feeling, told her that she was saying goodbye to him and was finally accepting him as a grown-up. For the first time he felt accepted as an adult and responsible man.

We decided that no therapy was indicated at this point, but that he was free to consult me in the future. This, in part, was predicated on my view that his regressive vulnerability might press him to continue to seek a maternal surrogate.

About one month later I received a note from him indicating that his mother had died, and that although it had been extremely painful, he was handling it well. A subsequent note close to three months later revealed that he was living alone and beginning a new relationship with his first lover.

Discussion

The crisis of the mother's death confronted this patient with the reemergence of unconscious, unresolved conflicts related to his continuing dependency upon his mother, his sense that he was a little boy, and his constant wish and need to live up to his parents' expectations by maintaining an unsatisfying idealized relationship which was fantasied as a marriage that might be acceptable to them. Rage toward his parents had been repressed for fear that it would damage the positive and loving aspects of the relationship. As the anger emerged, I acknowledged the loving aspect of his ambivalence so as to increase his tolerance for what was so fearful to him and to permit him to experience both sides of his ambivalence. The crisis situation generated by the impending death forced the patient to work

out these conflicts by confronting his mother, thereby modify-
ing his view of her perception of him with a subsequent change
in his self perception (self-representation). In this situation
action in the world occurring after insight consolidated the
inner change and led to subsequent confirmatory action that
permitted him to give up an unsatisfying relationship that
reproduced his parents' marriage. (Note: See Viederman
[1987, in press] for the description of a model designed to
understand the role of action in personality change through life
experience.)

My interpretive stance was designed to avoid actualizing the
development of a dependent transference relationship that the
patient sought by conveying confidence that he would work
things out for himself. He may have experienced this unconsciously as gratification of a paternal transference for he saw his
father's attitude, in contrast to his mother's, as one encouraging
independence. This is reminiscent of Loewald's view of an
aspect of the therapeutic action of psychoanalysis in which the
analyst, like the good parent, develops a perception of the
individual stamp and direction of the analysand–child's development which then acts subtly as indication of the possibilities
for growth (Loewald, 1960).

Case Example 2

Mr. R. was a forty-six-year-old married father of two referred
by an internist who had been treating him for mild hyperten-
sion. In his letter of referral, the internist indicated that he had
become concerned about the patient's mental state during a
routine visit when he appeared depressed and unhappy, seemingly in the context of "ambivalent feelings about his father who
had died six months before." He was described in the letter as
an "artistic, philosophic man, who by nature is a solitary
person." Considerable urging by the internist had been necessary to have the patient seek psychiatric consultation, since he
was convinced that he could work things out on his own. The
consultation of three sessions occurred over the course of a
month.

Mr. R. was a somewhat obese, intelligent, articulate, and

introspective man who was obsessional in style, but revealed considerable warmth and capacity for relatedness. Though tense and controlling in the initial part of the interview, he gradually relaxed as I clarified some of the issues that evolved during the consultation. There was evidence of a mild depression with some suicidal ideation. It rapidly became apparent that the patient's depression reflected a crisis that involved conflict about his marriage and a search for a new expression of himself.

His current dilemma emerged quite clearly during the first session.

The patient had been in an unhappy marriage for eighteen years. There was little communication with his wife and although she had recently suggested a separation, he recognized that he had great difficulty in separating because of hesitancy about leaving his adolescent children. The marriage had been joyless since its inception and was devoid of sexual gratification. His wife, "a very decent, but somewhat cold woman," had lost her mother when she was one-and-a-half years of age and her father when she was twelve. Although he had lived with his parents until he left home as a young adult, communication with them had been limited and he recognized that his marriage had been like the marriage of two orphans who desperately needed to seek one another out. The patient had attempted to compensate for the barrenness and dullness of his marriage by painting, and although this had afforded occasional relief, he had abandoned this six years before. His work as a minor administrator in the city government had been moderately gratifying, but not especially fulfilling for a man of his intellectual capacity.

The patient was one of several children, born to a working class family in Puerto Rico. His father, a carpenter, was an insensitive and, at times, abusive man, who had denigrated the patient's intellectual and artistic aspirations. His mother was a submissive and masochistic woman who seemed to the patient to be a distant and unimportant figure in his life. The patient had married shortly after escaping the family to come to New York. He had a number of close male friends but felt chronically dissatisfied with life.

A visit to his father shortly before his death due to cancer six months before had evoked in him a strong sense of personal dissatisfaction and nonfulfillment in his own life, particularly as he compared it with the experience of his father who had similar dissatisfactions. Yet at that time he felt paralyzed about changing his life.

In the months preceding his father's death, he had encountered a Eurasian woman, half Japanese, who had appeared to be extremely sensitive and intelligent. Shortly after their encounter, she had telephoned to ask for advice about her professional situation. Their first lunch together was extremely satisfying as she spoke in a surprisingly personal way about her own unhappiness in marriage. When he renewed the relationship after his father's death, a strong sense of mutual understanding developed between the two and he began to experience himself as the man he had always sensed he could be but had not been. They met after work, talked intensely and vigorously, and became totally immersed with one another in a loving and passionate though unconsummated relationship. The intensity of love and experience of passion was new to him. Once again he became involved in artistic pursuits. He described with some amusement how he had shown one of his collages to a friend without indicating its origin. This friend, an architect, was quite entranced by it, expressed his opinion that it was a work that revealed considerable talent and commented that it had a decided Japanese quality. His lover, who had harbored aspirations to be a writer, began to write. During this first session, as the material was revealed, I commented on his view of his father's sense of failure in marriage and in life. He became reflective as I suggested that the anticipated pain associated with leaving his children had something to do with his description of his own father as inadequate and cruel.

In the second of the three sessions, the patient described an excellent weekend that he had spent with his woman friend at another friend's apartment. Retarded ejaculation that had been a regular problem in his sexual relationship with his nonorgastic wife had resolved partially and he had discussed the sexual problem with his friend, something that he had never been able to do with his wife. His return home had confronted him with the leaden quality of the marital relationship.

He recounted two dreams: the first, a repetitive one that had occurred throughout his adult life; the second, a dream that had occurred more recently, after the father's death, but immediately before the consultation. The dreams were a source of fascination and pleasure as he described and discussed them.

> I'm walking up a hill with a sense that there are many people alongside of me. On the ground there are small objects of great fascination and color, including stones and bones of old animals, as if the whole residue of the world were there. This group of people seems to be in the process of setting out to discover something. When I reached the top of the hill, I discover that there is no longer anyone with me and I am amazed at a magnificent and immense parthenon with columns as high as the World Trade Center. This is a stark desert place. Yet, in front of me is the sea, full of animals; sharks, whales and full of violence. I am awed by the scene and yet strangely I feel a tremendous peace. Finally I decide to descend the hill.

> I am looking for my father in Puerto Rico in a small bungalow. I assume that he is present in one of them, though I do not know which it is. I enter one and discover him. He is in bed and ill. There is an important communication between us. At the head of the bed is a woman dressed in white. I have sexual intercourse with her in the presence of my father who accepts this knowingly. I look at him with a smile of complicity and in our mutual sense of understanding there is a powerful sense of satisfaction.

The patient spontaneously commented on the dreams. He recognized that he has been in quest for something throughout his life. He noted that the search for beauty and art is full of pitfalls and dangers. The violence of the first dream is associated with sadism, which his father manifested in punishing him by forcing him to kneel down on ragged tin cans. He remembered that his father would often walk through the town with him as a child and point out the horrors of life, sometimes taking him to the slaughter house (the bones) to show him the dead animals and to "teach him about the brutality of the world." Never did he have a sense that his father understood him, yet he felt that in some primitive way his father was attempting to teach him something about life. It was apparent that the mastery of violent rage was an important element in the dream.

The second dream was more of a puzzle to him. The sense of complicity with his father and the experience of strong release that occurred in the dream was something that had never occurred in any real transaction with his father that he could remember. Nonetheless, the dream symbolized for him a release from the paralyzing constriction that characterized his marriage.

In the third session the patient appeared somewhat hesitant and constricted as he began. He had decided not to consider therapy at this point and he intimated some vague distrust of me (that I inferred was related to a negative paternal transference). He was pleased that his wife and children were moving into a new apartment. This gave him a sense that they would be better taken care of. Especially relieving was a conversation he had with his fourteen-year-old daughter who had been angry with him. After he confronted her, they embraced and took a long walk. He revealed his determination to leave the marriage. The session ended with the theme of reconciliation and calm.

I was informed by his internist two months later that he did leave the marriage. Currently he is living alone but has experienced an increased zest for life.

Discussion

This man had always experienced himself as an alien in a family that was not attuned to his intelligence and artistic sensibility. His mother was a worn, suffering, distant, and unhappy woman who seemed to figure little in his current thoughts and feelings. His father, who had a powerful negative influence on his life, was uncomprehending of the special qualities that made him different from other members of the family. The relationship with the father was unambivalently hostile, though there were moments when his father in a rather perverse way seemed to attempt to educate him to his own paranoid view of the world as ungiving and malevolent. The reconciliation and complicity that he wishfully experienced in the dream apparently did not reflect his real experience with his father as far as he could recall. A desperate flight from the primary family had led him to a joyless marriage of "orphans" that reproduced the marriage of his parents. His father's death released him to find a love relationship which was accompanied by renewed artistic interest.

The first dream strongly suggests a lifelong yearning to experience the richness of the world, replete with both beauty and peace, but not without attendant dangers. It suggests a wishful fantasy that in this pursuit he would find power and beauty at the summit, but only in leaving father (the group) behind. The mastery of rage was important. There was no evidence of mourning the father or suggestion of a hypomanic flight. The second dream seemed primarily wishful and releasing and manifestly represented overcoming an oedipal inhibition.

The patient approached the consultation in a state of crisis and uncertainty, with unconscious wishes for resolution that became apparent in the second dream. My interpretation of his identification with his father in a failed marriage and my focus on his fear of hurting his children as his father had hurt him liberated him and permitted him to spend a highly gratifying weekend with his new friend. This led to his presentation in the second session of dreams that encapsulated his sense of being different from his father and his wish for freedom from the father. He then consolidated his new relationship and began a dialogue with his daughter that came as a great relief. Interpretation and insight had led to action and an inner change that was catalyzed by the support of a therapist (Viederman, 1987).

Discussion

Personality change as referred to in this chapter will be conceptualized as a change in the representational world (Sandler and Rosenblatt, 1962) with associated change in object relationships. It is important to distinguish the representational world which includes representations of the self, objects, ideal self, and ideal objects with associated conscious and unconscious fantasies from object relationships. Unlike object relationships which can be observed and described, representations are inferential structures that stem from the observation of behavior and the revelation of fantasy. These two realms are in a constant dynamic relationship. Experience, along with wishful and fearful fantasy, shape our representations of objects and self, and inversely, representations shape our perceptions and behaviors as manifested in object relationships. The representational world is a structured though modifiable template of reality that permits an efficient interaction with the external world of objects by utilizing sets of expectations built in part on the accretions of experience. Under favorable circumstances these representations are not very distorted by traumatic and conflictual antecedents and are a path to reasonable adaptation to the world.

There is a tendency to blur the boundaries between these separate conceptual realms. Vaillant (1984), in the paper alluded to above, speaks of internalization as the process that results in creative response to loss. The implication here, incorrect in my view, is that the individual takes in some image of the lost object in a way that fortifies him, makes him more complete, worthy, loving, and creative. This conceptualization suggests a psychic mechanism, when in fact it is a fantasy. Indeed this much resembles the meaning attached to the cannibalistic rituals of the natives of the South Pacific, who, in devouring the brains or hearts of their vanquished enemies, believe they are incorporating their wisdom or courage.

It is my intent in these case descriptions to demonstrate how, in moments of crisis, experience with objects (object relationships) can lead to radical change in internal representations. Under usual circumstances, representations viewed as structures (psychic organizations with a slow rate of change) are crystallized and can be modified only slowly, a fairly consistent observation in psychoanalytic work. Indeed, in relatively healthy people, the enduring quality of these structures, carefully built over time, makes them useful for they permit a confrontation with reality in which preexisting experience is rapidly mobilized as new situations are encountered. Yet, in situations of crisis, radical transformations can occur in the context of transactions with these objects (i.e., in the context of object relationships). In these situations of crisis two possible situations may occur. (1) Actual transactions with an important object may lead to a changed perception of the attitude to this object with consequent change in representation of object and of self (the first case). (2) Wishful expectations of a change in an object relationship not at all reflected in reality, as revealed in the second patient's dream, may lead to change in self representation under special circumstances, in this case the therapeutic encounter. In the first case, it was the change in reality that led to inner change; in the second, powerful forces for change mobilized by loss and supported by the environment (the therapeutic situation) led to action which then consolidated change in the inner world. It is to be emphasized that the rapidity of change in each of the cases was facilitated by a crisis generated by the reality of the death of a parent.

Although Vaillant's (1984) conception of internalization as an instrument of creative change in response to loss is blurred, his conception of the integration of good and bad object representations is useful and applicable to the first patient discussed above. This patient had repressed his representation of the mother as hostile and unapproving in order to maintain his idealization of her and of the relationship that undoubtedly had important authentic loving components. His capacity to confront the hateful component of the selfobject representational configuration permitted him to integrate the good and bad maternal representations; in Vaillant's terms, to undo splitting. One might view this alternately as an unmasking of the repressed hostile component of an ambivalent relationship since his other relationships did not seem to be characterized by splitting, and there was no evidence of alternation of good and bad representations as described by Kernberg (1975) with borderline patients. However, it is important to note that the unconscious hostile component was defended against by repression and idealization. This is not a typical ambivalent relationship in which there is awareness of both loving and hostile elements.

One might characterize this patient's state in approaching the mother's death as a pathological anticipatory grief response.[2]

----

[2]It is my view that uncomplicated grief can be distinguished from pathological grief responses that take the form of depression, although there is some controversy about this in the literature. The failure to discriminate

Had he not worked through the conflicts described, there is reason to believe that a pathological grief response such as a severe depression would have ensued as was described by Freud (1917) in "Mourning and Melancholia." What differentiates the evolution of the first case from the usual course of an incipient pathological grief response is the fact that the patient had a strong need to confront his mother. Hence, an important part of the resolution could be catalyzed by a real transaction with the mother before her death.

The second case is quite different. The father's death occurred in the context of a conscious unambivalently hostile relationship and led the patient to face his unhappy marriage and to take action. There was little evidence of the usual pain of mourning. The origin of the benevolent representation in the dream is obscure.[3] One might infer that some aspects of his

---

normal grief from depression or pathological grief is a reflection of two factors: (1) that the clinical indicators of grief cannot be viewed simply as either present or absent, but must be considered from the point of view of intensity; and (2) that the diagnosis requires inferences about a total clinical picture rather than a simple summation of symptoms. With regard to the first factor, it is important to note that neither depression nor pathological grief reactions exist in absolutely pure form. The degree of latent conflict will determine to what degree there is a depressive cast to what is otherwise a normal grief response. The elements that are useful in differentiating grief from depression include: the general absence of guilt, or guilt of omission rather than commission; the absence of shame or substantial diminution in self-esteem, with a continuing basic sense of being good, worthwhile, and so on; the capacity to distinguish between the feeling states of sadness and depression; the cognitive awareness of ultimate hope for the future even though the feeling state may be one of hopelessness and pessimism; rapid fluctuations of mood with the capacity to laugh and joke at certain moments alternating with waves of sadness which overcome the individual at other times; the absence of significant active suicidal ideation and the absence of psychomotor retardation. Also important diagnostically is the empathic response generated by the grieving person which contrasts with the heaviness or irritation that one often experiences in the presence of a depressed person. Intensity of feeling, duration, and vegetative signs do not distinguish the two. These criteria are reliable guides in distinguishing normal grief from pathological grief responses.

[3]This second dream occurred after the death of the father but before the institution of the consultation, and hence could not have represented a benevolent representation of the therapist. Moreover, it is unlikely that it represented a hopeful expectation of the encounter since the patient was reluctant to come and a slightly negative tone pervaded the consultation.

father's behavior, even aspects that on the surface appear sadistic, were in some measure experienced as loving, for they might be interpreted as attempts by the father to educate him to the reality of a world which he, the father, experienced as cruel and difficult. This is echoed in the first dream, which has a predominant feeling tone of fascination and peace in spite of its violence and destructiveness. The patient associated the group in the manifest content of the dream with his father whom he accompanied to the slaughterhouse (animal bones) on trips through town. It is therefore possible but unlikely that positive feelings regarding the relationship with his father may have been evoked in the dream. We must recognize that in listening to a patient's descriptions we are dealing with psychic and not veridical reality.

Although one cannot eliminate the possibility that there were other positive surrogate paternal figures in this man's life, the tone of the description of his early life suggested the absence of supportive parental figures. It seems more likely that the image in the dream was a wishful fantasy constructed at a moment of need and possibility. What permitted this man to construct such a fantasy and to use it as he did is unclear. The fact that the dream occurred in the setting of a bedside commission is of particular interest in light of the observation of Parkes and Weiss (1983) that bedside commissions of dying people maintain particular power. That the patient's second dream was constructed as such a bedside commission is of particular interest.

Indeed it is a hostile, critical, punitive, and controlling relationship with the father that the patient described. It is to be emphasized that a permanent loss leads to an unmodifiable change in our world and ultimately in our fantasies as they relate to the lost object, although obviously internalized representations do not simply disappear with death. "We cannot anticipate doing things with the person ever again or even hear what he thinks or feels about anything" (Hofer, 1984). In predominantly benevolent relationships much pain accompanies the process of mourning. But in this patient's relationship with his father, characterized as it was by a predominantly hostile voice with no evident positive valence of ambivalence, not to hear ever again what the father thinks or feels about the patient, his marriage, his sexuality, came as a powerful release from bondage. Can superego constraints so readily be dissolved in the context of the reality loss of the father because of the predominance and the conscious nature of the hostility? In other words, was the patient's confinement in his marriage a superego constraint, tonically supported by the living presence of the father observing and criticizing the patient? The patient's inhibition would seem to have reflected an unconscious oedipal constraint dissolved by the father's death.

The unalloyed hostile relationship had a powerful, inhibiting influence during the lifetime of the father. It is interesting to note that an important aspect of the patient's inhibition beyond sexual object choice was an inhibition about leaving his wife, something his father could not do. One might also consider that the father's death, the abandonment by the parent, tolerated well and freely, freed the patient to overcome his inhibition about leaving his wife and especially his children (for whom he would remain a caring parent even in separation, unlike his own father).

The Undoing of Identifications as an Instrument of Change in the Context of Object Loss

An aspect of change that was evident in the experience of both patients included a marked modification in existent love relationships that previously had reflected an identification with parents. The second patient broke away from a sterile marriage that resembled the marriage of his parents. The first patient realized that in choosing his homosexual partner, he was reproducing the passionless second marriage of his mother. He also had identified with his mother on another level by choosing partners in both of his homosexual relationships who encouraged him to play the role of the idealized nurturing object as his mother had been to him. This identification also had a function of defense, for by maintaining this stance of power, strength, and capacity to nurture others, he had repressed his own fearful sense of weakness, impotence, and unconscious dependence upon her. This unconscious representation of himself as weak was confirmed by his conscious awareness that being a homosexual afforded a secondary gain, that of avoiding a responsible role as a parent to real children, a role which he was fearful of assuming. The mother's impending death confronted him with the breakdown of an elaborate defensive fantasy of an ideal parent–child relationship that would go on forever and assure his own immortality as a beloved child. In reversing roles with the mother and becoming a nurturant figure to her in reality on her deathbed, he crystallized a new representation of himself, as a mature homosexual adult acceptable to her and capable of caring for himself and constructing his life. His decision to leave the homosexual relationship in which he was engaged and to live alone was a product of his new self-perception and, indeed, had been implemented by the time of a fifth meeting two months after the mother's death, at which time he had reestablished a relationship with his first lover and was experiencing a normal mourning reaction.

Freud (1917) elaborated the theory that identifications precede object choice and follow object loss. In general, the accretions that are products of these identifications enrich the ego and are reflected in personal growth. In the two patients described above, the inverse was true. Object loss led to personality change and growth by an undoing of previous identifications with the lost object that had been inhibiting and had prevented personal growth.

The Regressive Model of Pathological Grief Responses

Horowitz, Wilner, Marmor, and Krupnick (1980) utilized a dynamic-regressive model in differentiating between normal grief and pathological grief responses. Normal grief involves the painful separation and relinquishment of the cathexis to an adult object that has been lost. In contrast, pathological grief responses involve the regressive reevocation of early selfobject constellations that are conflicted. The existence of these conflicts had been muted by the nature of an adult object relationship until the loss occurs.[4] Horowitz et al.(1980) state:

[4]For the first patient, to whom this discussion applies, the original object and the adult object were one and the same, not the usual case described by Horowitz and colleagues.

The essential point is that recent internalization of ambivalent attitudes toward attributes of the lost person is not the major reason for states of pathological grief. Although these new identifications and attitude formations are important processes, a major cause of pathological grief appears to be the reemergence of earlier self-images and role relationship models. These were established before the loss, but were held in check by a more positive relationship . . . [with the adult object] [p. 1159].

Horowitz and his co-authors emphasize that the relationship with the lost person tends to mute underlying regressive anxiety about neediness, lovability, and worthiness. Hence, before the death and by virtue of the relationship with the other person, the individual can feel strong, worthy, and lovable in the context of the sustenance generated by the relationship. With loss, however, there is a regressive reactivation of the unconscious conflicted infantile relationship. Horowitz et al. categorize the various constellations that he observed in the responses of these individuals to loss. His categories were: (1) a frighteningly sad response to loss in which the loss evokes a state in which the individual feels "weak, abandoned, and needy . . . in desperate hope of rescue, with intense fear that such rescue will not occur" (p. 1160); (2) rage states, in which the loss is experienced as an attack upon the self or a product of the evil destructiveness of the survivor; (3) deflated states in which the loss undermines self-worth; and (4) states of apathy and numbness that Horowitz relates to Schmale and Engel's (1975) description of conservation–withdrawal.

This conceptualization of regressive reactivation of a conflicted repressed selfobject constellation is well illustrated by the first patient described. However, this occurred in the context of an anticipatory grief response rather than in reaction to loss. Of particular interest is the fact that the conflicts which emerged in the context of anticipated loss were worked out in an actual transaction with a mother who was about to die. This patient revealed elements of Horowitz's first and second categories, for not only did he experience panic and fear that he would be unable to care for himself, but also rage at the abandoning mother.

Of special importance is the substantial change that this patient underwent in the context of loss. Horowitz and his colleagues make brief reference to internalization, by which they mean that the self takes on the role which the lost object performed in order to compensate for the sense of inadequacy and deficiency. The examination of this case suggests that one can more precisely define the dynamic changes as changes in the representational world.

Psychobiology and Bereavement

This section represents an excursion into the psychobiology of grief suggested by observation of the first patient. The phenomenology of his pathological anticipatory grief response and its underlying conflictual constellation, based upon a dependency relationship with the mother reevoked by the threat of loss, has much in common with the reaction of a young child to a separation from the mother.

In this light, it is interesting to examine Hofer's recent discussion of bereavement in an imaginative paper "Relationships as Regulators: A Psychobiologic Perspective on Bereavement" (1984). Hofer, like Horowitz et al. (1980), presents a psychodynamic regressive model, but it is important to note that unlike Horowitz and his colleagues he applies this to a normal grief response. Hofer outlines two potentially separable aspects of the bereavement process, each having a relationship to the phenomenology of infant separation responses elaborated by Bowlby (1980) and others: the first, the acute "protest" phase, lasting minutes to hours; and the second, the chronic "despair" phase, lasting hours to days. The acute phase in adult bereavement in characterized by agitation, crying, shifts from aimless activity to inactivity, and a preoccupation with the image of the deceased. The second is characterized by decreased social interaction, cognitive difficulty with impaired concentration and attention, sadness and/or depression, restlessness, and decreased appetite. Hofer proposes that each of these phases has distinct physiological concomitants that parallel phases of infant separation. The first phase in infant separation is associated with physiologic and metabolic disturbance involving increased heart rate, and cortisol and catecholamine secretion. The second phase delineated in studies of infant animals subjected to separation involve physiological changes which affect the metabolic, cardiovascular, endocrine, and immune systems. In the second phase of separation these changes are transduced by different maternal regulators, such as the absence of milk, body warmth, tactile and oral stimulation, as well as the absence of what he calls social entrainment of biological rhythms (implying that the biological rhythms of the infant are disrupted in absence of the tonic support of the mother's biological rhythms). Hence, in this second phase, each of the experiential phenomena (i.e., absence of body warmth, milk, etc.) transduces specific physiological dysfunctions and has specific psychological and behavioral concomitants.

The following statement has particular pertinence to the examination of bereavement in adults.

> Might these same sorts of regulating actions . . . [those of infants and experimental animals] . . . be going on in close human social relationships such that bereavement also produces a set of withdrawal responses? This reaction could be possible when one of two persons who have been living very closely together dies . . . [the second phase] . . . However, what about the situation in which the two grew up together, but now see each other only occasionally, living many hundreds of miles apart, and the death is announced over the telephone. Do the chronic background symptoms of bereavement occur to the same degree in this case, in which loss is not one of actual interaction (as in second phase of bereavement) but of hopes, expectations, and memories? I know of no studies on this question, but it would certainly be interesting if the acute waves of distress occurred to the same degree in this situation of "bereavement at a distance" but the chronic background symptoms were much less pronounced. Evidence on this point would give us an idea of the relative importance of the withdrawal of sensorimotor aspects of a relationship in the acute and the chronic symptoms of bereavement [Hofer, 1984, pp. 191–192].

Hofer goes on to suggest that since man is a symbol-using animal, the internal representations of objects in the absence of direct contact may serve as regulators of the first phase, but not in the second. These representations may permit temporary separations in the developing infant without full-scale bereavement responses. Indeed, this is the basis for the concept of libidinal object constancy, that which first permits the infant to tolerate brief separations from his mother.

> Therefore, the inner experience of our relationship with another person, the memories, the expectations, and the way we bring our perceptions of their reactions and responses into our everyday life through fantasy, are at least as important to consider as the actual interpersonal interactions themselves [Hofer, 1984, p. 192].

Hofer emphasizes that a symbolic loss will have a separate and different effect than a loss that involves, in addition, the deprivation of everyday physical contact. Here I would like to add an additional element to Hofer's speculation. Is it not possible that in a situation of adult loss with two individuals living apart that two situations may prevail? The first is one in which the relationship with the lost object does not have a predominantly unconscious conflictual base. Here a normal grief response will ensue involving only the first phase described by Hofer. In the second case, exemplified by the first patient, the loss evokes previously repressed conflict activating selfobject representations with powerful attachment needs as existed in the earliest mother–child interaction, thereby leading to a pathological grief response in which elements of the second phase play a part. Indeed the first patient's expressive behavior had qualities strongly reminiscent of childhood separation.

Hofer's own animal experiments may suggest that pathological grief involves modifications similar to the second phase of separation that are regressively activated (Hofer, 1982). In one such experiment, Hofer determined that rats subjected to early separation developed gastric ulcers when stressed by having them restrained in slings as adults. This phenomenon was accompanied by a disturbance in thermoregulation which involved a fall in body temperature in the restrained rats. If, during restraint, the temperature was artificially maintained, then they did not develop gastric ulcers. This lability of temperature regulation accompanied separation in the infant animals, but could be prevented by placing milk in their stomachs at certain regular intervals at the time of separation. Hence it was the absence of gastric filling with milk that was a transducer of disturbances in temperature regulation and this vulnerability was regressively activated by restraint in the adult.

In a similar way, it seems quite possible that disturbances in early mothering, or more accurately mother–child interaction, may create vulnerabilities in two spheres—physiological and psychological—that are activated in adult life at the time of loss, though they had been previously concealed by defensive operations on a psychological level and remain quiescent on a physiological level. These physiological disturbances would be activated and then accompany pathological grief responses in the adult at the time of loss. In this regard, it is conceivable that the variable patterns observed in current studies of psychoimmunologic and psychoendocrinologic responses to loss may be flawed by the failure to distinguish between normal and pathological grief. It may be that only during pathological grief is the organism vulnerable to physiological change that may lead to physical illness.

Summary

Two cases have been presented to demonstrate personality change as a product of object loss.

The first case involved a crisis situation in which there was a regressive reactivation of previous conflict with a mother who was about to die. This led to an anticipatory pathological grief response. Of particular interest was the patient's use of a brief psychotherapeutic encounter to examine the conflicts in this relationship in order to facilitate a real interaction with the mother. This led to change in their relationship and changes in his representational world.

The second case illustrates how the loss of a predominantly malevolent and hostile paternal object did not lead to mourning, but rather to a release from oedipal inhibition. In each situation, identifications with the lost object were undone. The first patient had characteristics phenomenologically and psychodynamically similar to what Hofer has described as the second phase of infant separation. The implications for research in the psychobiology of grief are explored.

There may be practical implications in the study of these patients. The first patient experienced a pathological grief response. The opportunity to work this out psychotherapeutically in an anticipatory way before the mother's death may have implications for preventive psychiatry.

The second patient presents an interesting question that demands further exploration; namely, how a predominantly hostile relationship continues to influence behavior and how an actual loss may be releasing and lead to changes in object relationships and in the representational world.

References

Bowlby, J. (1980), *Attachment and Loss*, Vol. 3. New York:Basic Books.

Cath, S. H., & Herzog, J. M.(1982), The dying and death of a father. In: *Father and Child*, ed. S. H. Cath, A. R. Gurwitt, & J. M. Ross. Boston: Little, Brown, pp. 339–353.

Clayton, P. J. (1972), The depression of widowhood. *Brit. J. Psychiat.*, 120:71–78.

———Desmarais, L., & Winokur, G. (1968), A study of normal bereavement. *Amer. J. Psychiat.*, 125:168–178.

Freud, S. (1917), Mourning and melancholia. *Standard Edition*, 14:237–258. London: Hogarth Press, 1961.

———(1923), The ego and the id. *Standard Edition*, 19:12–66. London: Hogarth Press, 1958.

Hofer, M. (1982), Some thoughts on "The Transduction of Experience" from a developmental perspective. *Psychosom. Med.*, 44:19–28.

———(1984), Relationships and regulators: A psychobiologic perspective on bereavement. *Psychosom. Med.*, 46:183–198.

Horowitz, M., Wilner, N., Marmor, C., & Krupnick, J. (1980), Pathological grief and the activation of latent self-images. *Amer. J. Psychiat.*, 137/(10):1157–1162.

Kernberg, O. (1975), *Borderline Conditions and Pathological Narcissism*. New York: Jason Aronson.

Klerman, G. L., & Izen, J. E. (1977), The effects of bereavement and grief on physical health and well-being. *Adv. Psychosom. Med.*, 9:66–104.

Lindemann, E. (1944), The symptomatology and management of acute grief. *Amer. J. Psychiat.*, 101:144–149.

Loewald, H. (1960), On the therapeutic action of psychoanalysis. *Internat. J. Psycho-Anal.*, 41:16–33.

Maddison, D. C., & Viola, A. (1968), The health of widows in the year following bereavement. *J. Psychosom. Res.*, 12:297–306.

Parkes, C. M., & Weiss, R. S. (1983), *Recovery from Bereavement*. New York: Basic Books.

Pollock, G. H. (1961), Mourning and adaptation. *Internat. J. Psycho-Anal.*, 42:341–361.

Sandler, J., & Rosenblatt, B. (1962), The concept of the representational world. *The Psychoanalytic Study of the Child*, 17:128–145. New York: International Universities Press.

Schmale, A., & Engel, G. (1975), The role of conservation-withdrawal in depressive reactions. In: *Depression and Human Existence*, eds. E. J. Anthony & T. Benedek. Boston: Little, Brown, pp. 183–198.

Vaillant, G. E. (1977), *Adaptation to Life*. Boston: Little, Brown.

———(1984), Loss as a metaphor for attachment. Kardiner Memorial Lecture, New York.

Viederman, M. (1987), Personality change through life experience. I: A model. *Psychiatry*, 49:204–217.

———(in press), Personality change through life experiences. II: The role of ego ideal, personality and events. In: *Psychoanalysis—The Second Century*, ed. A. Cooper. New Haven, CT: Yale University Press.

Zisook, S., Schuchter, S., & Schuckit, M. (1985), Unresolved grief among psychiatric patients. *Psychosomatics*, 26:497–503.

9

The "Parent Loss" of Empathic Failures and the Model Symbolic Restitution of Eating Disorders

David W. Krueger, M.D.

Introduction

I have described previously the findings of a Parent Loss Research Group studying the developmental consequences of parent loss by death or continuous separation in childhood (Krueger, 1979, 1983, 1984). The cumulative evidence from this data is that the meaning, impact, and consequences of parent loss on emotional development and resultant adulthood psychopathology is determined by several factors. Chief among these are the phase-sensitive developmental issues (i.e., when in developmental time the loss occurred); the unique interpretation by the child of the loss (the "personal myth" developed, including perception and fantasy of cause and effect); the availability of ongoing empathic selfobject relationships, and the sex of the child vis-à-vis the sex of the lost parent. Specific issues arise in the treatment of adults as a derivative of earlier parent loss, and must be considered as they relate to developmental diagnosis, therapeutic alliance, transference, countertransference, mourning, and termination (Krueger, 1978; Krueger, 1989).

I spoke initially of the parent loss patient, who, as a consequence of the loss of a parent, is subject to subsequent difficulty in forming intimate attachments in adult life, difficulty in establishing a therapeutic alliance, and particular types of transference phenomena. Pioneering work in the area of understanding parent loss psychodynamics has been done by Pollock (1961) and Fleming (1972), and their work reminds us how the loss of a parent may also become a nucleus around which elements of conflict and developmental arrest become organized. The loss *event* is important as well as the loss *process*. The loss process entails the chain of events preceding, set in motion by, and subsequent to the loss. The loss itself may represent and bring into sharp focus earlier deprivation as well.

The actual loss due to death or continuous separation of a parent during development imposes an actual trauma with resultant intrapsychic organization, which frequently provides a sensitizing precursor for any subsequent experiences of loss. Certain subsequent experiences of loss in adult life (significant others, health, physical disability) resonate with this sensitivity predisposing toward depression and other overdetermined symptoms (Servoss and Krueger, 1984).

These concepts, based on trauma and object relationships, extend also to the relationship between early parent loss and narcissistic pathology. The actual loss of a parent between the ages of two and four (age two being when there is sufficient self and other differentiation to experience the loss of another as a distinct object) profoundly affects narcissistic development and object relationships (Krueger, 1983). Idealization and restitution fantasies involving the lost parent are predominant. These children develop fantasies centering around the theme of an eventual return of the lost parent. Daydreams are embroidered with idealization and fantasies that the real parent is gifted, wealthy, famous, or aristocratic. Being unable to register or comprehend the concept of permanent or absolute loss at this time, the child imposes restitutive fantasies and maintains an idealized image of the parent whom he or she hopes will return.

These preoedipal losses become emotionally organized around narcissistic issues and fear of abandonment.

Empathic Failure as Loss

My thesis is that certain empathic failures have results similar to actual loss of a parent. These empathic failures—experienced as the loss of emotional connectedness and bonding with a parent—are experienced as emotional loss just as "real" as an actual physical loss of a parent by separation or death. The empathic loss (failures) also involves similar attempts of restitution and reunion.

I will first present a summary of the empathic matrix and process in which body self and psychological self are formed and integrated. These empathic failures beginning in preoedipal, even preverbal, time have a profound impact on subsequent development. To illustrate the developmental impact of empathic failure upon both body and psychological self, I will focus consistently on patients with eating disorders. Those individuals who present with bulimia and anorexia nervosa demonstrate in a most vivid and extreme manner the crucial developmental arrests leading to pathological narcissism, as well as the process and content of restitutive efforts to create what was missing in their development and currently in their self functioning. Clinical vignettes will illustrate issues along a developmental continuum which result in the common denominator of eating disorders as an attempted restitution for earliest failed empathy (self regulation) to later replacement of a missing object (loss of a parent as a distinct object).

Body Self and Psychological Self Development

Freud (1923) indicated that the ego is "first and foremost a body ego." Freud (1923) defined body image as the aggregate deposit of internalized images which encompass the self representation and internalized representations of love objects.

The accurate mirroring by the parents of the sensations and feelings arising from *inside* the developing infant and toddler form the core of a body self and awareness that crystallizes into a body image. This body image is the foundation of the emerging development of a self image.

The first awareness of the infant is an awareness of being reflected in the mother's eyes, of physical sensations and body presence as outlined by the mother's hands. Vocalizations and eye-to-eye contact resonate with the affective state of the infant, and vice versa, so that the pair are intimately in tune with each other. This mirroring function by the mother not only reinforces and affirms, but forms. By the mirroring being consistent and accurate, a body self is created out of chaos through the presence of the empathic mother.

For the infant, reality is the infant's body as defined by the mother's response, as she is viewed as an accurate mirror of the infant. The accuracy of mirroring is thus crucial.

The developmental task is the formation of a stable, integrated, cohesive mental representation of one's body—a core body image: what is inside, what is outside, and clear, distinct boundaries between the two. This creation of an individual internal space occurs simultaneously with the evolving psychological self.

The failure to achieve an accurately delineated body boundary and differentiated internal awareness of the body self results in difficulty in subsequent development of the psychological self. Subsequent limitations occur in the ability to symbolize, to fantasize, and to be insightful.

Under most ordinary circumstances, there is parallel development of body self and psychological self: the dual awareness of establishing body boundaries and delineating internal body states is coherent and consistent, and is integrated with the parallel development of affective, cognitive, and motoric maturation. In normal development, this unity is a natural synthesis. In pathological states, the individual components and nuclei of development are not integrated, and thus call attention to each of the component elements. It is from this pathological distortion that we are clinically confronted with the fundamental need for developmental integration of body self and psychological self. It is this process which helps us see what a basic container and foundation the body self is for the overall sense of self. When the body self does not develop in an intact and coherent way, the sense of self correspondingly cannot develop, as it has no secure container or core. Some symptomatology, especially psychosomatic symptomatology (in which I would include eating disorders), indicate various loci of these pathological nuclei, and at one level are an attempted restitution for missing developmental experiences.

If the sensations, movements, and affects generated by the infant are not met and affirmed to some significant and accurate extent, or if they are supplanted by the mother's own needs and internal state projected onto the baby, the infant must comply. Although these empathic failures may occur in varying forms throughout development, an initial and significant failure of development of a distinct body image results in an inability to recognize an internal focus of sensation as an internal point of reference. The nucleus of this pathological process is in the earliest phase of the formation of the nascent sense of self: in the autistic and symbiotic stages of life (i.e., in the first weeks and months of life) before separation–individuation begins.

Developmental Deficit as Loss

The earliest body image and subsequent self images are the response to the empathic reflections of significant others in the external world. The mental representations which are formed are then affected by the process and nature of interactions, as well as by an interruption of that process. The experience of another individual as a selfobject, most predominant in early development, concurs with the experience of the loss of that selfobject as loss of continuity of both body self and psychological self.

The empathic nonpresence or inconsistency of the mother in preverbal and early verbal time is a type of loss experience with specific pathological results. There are basically three categories of disruptive events in the establishment of body self resulting in disrupted narcissistic development (Krueger, 1989):

1. Empathic unavailability (i.e., nonresponse) of parents
2. Parental overintrusiveness
3. Parental inconsistency or selectivity of response

Empathic Unavailability and Nonresponse

From infancy onward, these mothers have not been able to connect and resonate accurately with internal experiences of the infant. Body boundaries may have not been consistently outlined by caress, touch, or secure holding. As they become older, these individuals experience their body self and image as overly large, disproportionate, and misshapen. Their projective drawings and mental images of their bodies are distorted, without shape, and excessively large (Krueger, 1989). Examples of empathic unavailability and nonresponse include bulimics and borderline personality disorders.

Overly Intrusive Parents

These mothers remain in a mergerlike state with their infant/child/adolescent/adult, disallowing separateness and growth to an autonomous self. The body self and image is experienced by these individuals as easily invaded. The body boundaries in projective drawings are *indistinct* and *blurred* (Krueger, 1989). They experience their bodies as separate from themselves, and carefully guard their body integrity. They may attempt to establish their body and self boundary and distinctness in rudimentary ways: refusing to eat, exercising in order to feel real, or stimulating their skin in various ways. Anorexics and other overly dependent characters are examples.

Inconsistency or Selectivity of Response

The response by the mother to only selective stimuli from the infant affirms a *selective* reality. Consider, for example, the mother who ignores emotional stimuli, and responds only to physical needs and physical pain. This interaction establishes the preception and experience of the child to be affirmed and organized around pain and illness. The body image drawings from this group tend to focus on or emphasize the center of pain and pathology. Various psychosomatic illness propensities result (Basch, 1985).

An absence of accurate, empathic mirroring of the entire presence of the infant, including affective state, body boundaries, and internal body experiences, may lead to the need to tune out or extinguish internal reality, resulting in the lack of internal awareness and the distortion of ego development. Concurrently, the body boundary may not be developmentally distinguished, resulting in the combined failure of both lines of development: a failed development of cohesive recognition and distinction of internal states, along with the failure in development of specific and distinct body boundaries (Lichtenberg, 1978; Krueger, 1989). Psychopathological manifestations are later created in an attempt at restitution of the emptiness experienced due to this early deficit. These attempts include an inordinate need for and fear of physical contact such as hypersexuality without intimacy, wrist-slashing in order to feel real and distinguish boundaries, or eating disorders. Eating disorders highlight the basic body functions of eating and elimination, and concomitant symptomatology may emphasize one or more components of the *internal* body function such as the use of laxatives, diuretics, binging, or vomiting, or the focus on external body boundaries such as wearing loose clothes, inordinate exercise and weight-lifting in order to establish firm body outline, and excessive focus on body image and "fat."

Parent loss as well as empathic loss in this early developmental (preoedipal) phase can be equally pathogenic. The individual's attempt to restore the selfobject functioning, whatever the nature of the loss, is made through the creation of symbolic restitutions. Food has already been established as the first object of transition from mother to infant.

The Developmental Pathology and Symbolic Restitution in
Eating Disorders

In the treatment of over 400 eating disordered patients in both inpatient and outpatient settings[1] two findings are consistent. First, the body image of each patient is developmentally disrupted: blurred, distorted, indistinct, or incomplete.[2] It has been well demonstrated that patients with eating disorders have a sense of estrangement from their bodies, insensitivity to body sensation, and blurred body boundaries (Stroker, Goldberg, Green, and Saxon, 1979). Second, they have an early preoedipal and even preverbal developmental arrest which includes a lack of internal body boundaries, distinct body image, and cohesive sense of self. Additionally, each individual showed definitive developmental improvement (i.e., more than just symptomatic improvement) when aspects of body self (including body image) were addressed and integrated in treatment along with aspects of the psychological self (Krueger, 1989).

Patients who present with anorexia nervosa and bulimia have a painfully inadequate means to regulate themselves internally. Many cannot even distinguish basic bodily sensations, including hunger. They do not experience the distinctness of their bodies or their body boundaries. Lacking an internal evocative image of their body or sense of self, they necessarily rely on external feedback and referents, such as other people, to mirror their worth and adequacy. This deficient self-regulation results in rapid oscillations between grandiosity and self-depreciation, and a pervasive reliance on external cues.

The individual's absence of a cohesive sense of self originated in the failure to develop a cohesive, distinct, and accurate body image. Subsequent failure to negotiate separation and individ-

---

[1]The inpatient setting is a nine-person, multidisciplinary treatment team comprising the Eating Disorders Treatment Program which I direct. The treatment efforts are psychoanalytically informed and developmentally organized, integrating both verbal and nonverbal treatment modalities in a self psychological approach. The outpatient work is psychotherapy or psychoanalysis.

[2]The body image assessment is via description, projective drawings, videotape feedback, and Expressive Arts Sensorimotor assessment.

uation stems from an early nucleus of arrested development, encountered when the nascent sense of self emerges from the mirroring experiences with the mother during the first weeks and months of life, extending and changing forms throughout development. Later developmental issues include the failure to have oedipal issues to manifest or to resolve thoroughly, and the regressive retreat at pubescence away from sexual and separation–individuation issues.

In such individuals, these preverbal and early verbal experiences fail to acknowledge and confirm a separate body self from the mother, and result in a blurred, vague, unformed, or distorted body image.

This indistinctness of body boundaries is related to the blurring of emotional boundaries when they experience closeness with another individual. Emotionally, where one ends and the other begins becomes uncertain.

Improvement in body image is a prerequisite for recovery from more pronounced eating disordered and narcissistic pathology (Krueger, 1989). The body self and the body image is a basic foundation for a psychological sense of self, and is most profoundly and vividly illustrated in patients whose lexicon is emotional symptomatology and whose language is their bodies.

They rely on other people for their supply of affirmation, enhancement, function, and esteem, and are attempting to find a way to internalize this source. While feeling like a fraud, there is conformity to what other people expect and an attempt to mold themselves to these expectations. There is a sensitivity to others and their wishes and moods to such an extent that they feel no separate existence: Words and actions may be split off from feelings. Many activities stem from wanting to be seen and affirmed by others. In some patients, the activity of excruciating exercise, running or swimming, may appear objectively to be for the purpose of losing weight or fitness, but is often experienced by these individuals as a way to *experience* themselves and their bodies—to feel *real*. One patient said: "There are times when I *have* to exercise—if I don't, then I would just fade away—blend into everyone else around me."

These and other self-stimulating behaviors are aimed at countering the anguish of emptiness, anger, boredom, or deadness internally. The anorexic experiences deprivation and converts passive to active by imposing the deprivation (of food) herself, and establishes an artificial boundary by saying "No" to food proffered by parents. The bulimic attempts to fill her emptiness with the fullness of food, then purges herself of her disappointment and anger over the fact that a symbol is only a symbol.

These individuals experience external stimuli as impingements—a feeling that their body, indeed their self organization, is easily invaded, influenced, exploited, and overwhelmed by external forces (especially important people).

They have little or no recognition of an internal center of initiative or reference. They have struggled for their entire lives to be perfect in the eyes of others—to please, or make themselves over to gain some sense of recognition, identity, effectiveness, and control.

The following vignette will illustrate how anorexia is designed in part to elicit countertransferences: a way of forcing others to respond actively when empathic response and connectedness have failed. To force others to get her to eat provides something specific to oppose externally, yet *insure* the presence of another, in reality or fantasy, who is concerned and caretaking. The anorexic symptomatology can be viewed as a behavior motivated to establish her distinctness from her parents while at the same time demonstrating her dependent needs for them. Additionally, it is her effort of control: to focus concretely that which is otherwise incomprehensible.

Vignette 1: A Twenty-One-Year-Old Woman with Anorexia Nervosa in a Middle Phase of Psychoanalysis

Pt. My body grew up without me. I never got any affirmation that I liked myself. I shut myself off to try to focus on pleasing my parents. It was hard for me to see any good I do naturally. I had to have someone tell me what to do and became that. It's still difficult to form my own ideas. I feel very alone now when I'm self-sufficient and make my own decisions. It's frightening.

A. And it's confusing to yearn for and to fear the same thing.

Pt. And especially what you said yesterday—to want oneness and connectedness, yet detest it too and want my separateness.

When I didn't eat, everyone—my family—including the therapists I'd seen before coming to you, all wanted me to eat, and saw it as a problem—like a flaw or defect.

A. It must have been confusing and hurtful at a time when you were experiencing it as a particular accomplishment.

Pt. The only real one of my life. But a destructive one.

A. Yet you described how your *intent* wasn't destructive, even if the *result* was.

Pt. My intent was to be separate and to be my own person—to have control of my life. If you'd tried to force or control my eating when I came to you, it'd have been just like my parents. If you'd tried to reward me for eating, I wouldn't have found my own direction and motivation from inside me.

(pause)

I realize how I've tried to be so perfect—to try to please others. I didn't even know myself. To feel connected to others I'd go along with anything they wanted—to go along with the crowd. I'd never do anything to be threatening or assertive.

A. Yet you've also described how much you want to feel special, distinct.

Pt. Whenever I do, I feel criticized. Like my mother is telling me all the things I'm doing wrong or not good enough.

A. It's as if your mother is always there—an image you're always creating.

Pt. She definitely haunts me. It's like I have to live up to her expectations twenty-four hours a day. I feel like I'm sneaking food even when no one is around. She's always there.

A. For you to defy.

Pt. Yes.

A. At least you're never alone that way.

Pt. Well, she's not physically present. It is her image in my mind. I see what you mean. It's hard to think about giving that up—it's been there for so long, like she's always with me. Telling me what to do. And I oppose much of it. It takes a lot of energy.

A. It must.

Pt. It sounds frightening at first to tell her goodbye and to create my own standards to live up to.

With a lack of internal referents, the patient is more inclined to compensate and focus on something explicit, concrete, and external which can be controlled—an explicit metaphor with emotional meaning for what is missing internally. Her attempt is to restore or replace something missing internally by a very precise external symbol. Food becomes a quintessential metaphor to represent the giving, loving, nurturing selfobject who has been lost or has never been present consistently and empathically.

An eating binge actually supplies the symbol of what is missing—the restitutive effort which creates the momentary illusion for the bulimic of having anything and everything that she wants. The anorexic uses food as a vehicle in the process of deprivation, to restrain her awareness of needing others, as if she is completely need-free, even of physical nurturance. By self-imposing a deprivation, she creates an active mastery over an experience that she had previously experienced passively at the hands of others.

There are many such behaviors which are regarded as impulsive, addictive, or compulsively unrelenting which are designed to evoke or establish a boundary or a selfobject regulatory function. A binge may be used to fill a sense of emptiness and despair, to feel better, to anesthetize oneself from the painful awareness of nonconnectedness with another or with one's self.

Vignette 2: Separation–Individuation Issues

One patient described how she became bulimic when she was age thirteen. At that time, her parents began having serious struggles of their own. With this withdrawal of her parents into their own problems and needs, a thinly veiled abandonment depression was crystallized in this already depleted young girl. She was already on the brink of symptomatic difficulty with the new surge of urges that were part of her pubescence, the bodily changes she was experiencing, and the enhanced social pressure in her school.

This experienced loss of connectedness with her parents coincided with the onset of a reparative effort at fantasied connectedness via the binge use of food. She could magically construct her parents in her mind as she would take in food, be completely in control of the presence of a nurturing object. Concomitantly, she could also, by thrusting her behavior into her parents' view, elicit certain and predictable (although negative) responses from them in a way that insured their engagement and presence rather than withdrawal.

The following sequence was reconstructed from our work.

When her parents did not respond immediately and exactly as she wanted—as an extension of her desire and interest—she became enraged. She was thus confronted with her separateness, distinctness, and disconnectedness from them and others.

She would at first refuse food,[3] pushing it back at the table, in effect saying: "I don't need food or anyone else" (i.e., I have no dependency needs), and "I'm pushing back the anger I am full of." She later binged, which created the illusion of being nurtured and given to—as if she could have anything and everything she wanted—like the magic of childhood restored. It focused her pain on her distended stomach, and she became relatively more comfortable being full of food rather than feeling full of anger (or of feeling empty). Additionally, the binge reestablished connectedness with her parents, as she imagined her mother and father watching critically.

She also became aware, as I asked for more detail, that during the binge, her focus was always on what she could have *next*, never what she had at the moment. The anticipation of

---

[3]In *every* one of the over 400 eating disorder individuals we have seen, each began with an initial episode of anorexia, however brief. This is developmentally consistent, as the developmental step of saying "No" to parents is re-created: "No" in effect says, "I am not an extension of you—your body, your desire, or your wish. This is where you end and I begin."

what she could eat next kept the illusion of satisfaction seemingly only a bite away. She reflected, "It's like I'm looking for something, but never finding it. The food isn't it."

In "looking for the answer," she maintained the hope that the answer (just the right food) magically will be only one step away. The food chosen was always a "taboo" food (sweets), which enacted her assumption that she was bad for eating in the way she did.

Her purge seemed to have the purpose of getting rid of her fullness of anger *and* of her need for anyone or anything external. She would then ask her parents to let her do something which she knew would be refused, such as to stay out until 1:00 A.M. When they refused, she became angry. This did two things: she herself created a scenario in which she was told "no" and knew she would be told "no." But this time *she* created it—she was in charge of where, when, and how it occurred. It allowed her to focus her anger at her parents, and again become the victim— but *predictably*, and *by her own hand*.

By empathically examining this sequence—the *internal* as well as external scenarios—she came to recognize other related issues; for example, her fear of asserting herself. If she asserted herself and someone didn't respond exactly as she wanted them to, she experienced it as a rejection. She recognized other fears of rejection. Someone saying "no" to her was a confrontation of her distinctness and separateness—something she both desired and feared.

These events, and the onset of her bulimia, appeared at the developmental juncture of the recognition of her parents as distinct entities from her, the objectification of parents as people, as people with problems who are all too human in their own way. This disillusionment added in a traumatic way to her already compromised connectedness with her parents and her own fragile sense of self.

Vignette 3: Traumatic Loss and Attempted Restitution

Anne, a twenty-four-year-old nurse, presented with a fourteen-year history of bulimia. She had binged and purged to the point of erosion of tooth enamel, amenorrhea, and impairment of work functioning.

As we examined in detail the scenario of a binge, Anne indicated that her favorite binge item was chocolate chip cookies. She would eat two to three bags of these cookies as she came home from work each afternoon, when she was alone at home. In examining the emotional significance of such a specific food item and the history of food in her family, Anne's associations were of her father giving her chocolate chip cookies. When he would return home after being away for some time, he would bring her chocolate chip cookies, and they would sit and talk of what had occurred during their separation.

Anne then recalled that her bulimic episodes began at age ten, immediately after her father died, with a binge on chocolate chip cookies.

She had been able to create the illusion of his presence with each binge, with the transient fullness and satisfaction of his presence—precisely at times when she was confronted with his absence and her aloneness by her empty house.

The Family System

These dynamics also operate at a systemic level in order to reinvolve a member of the family who becomes preoccupied, emotionally absent, or otherwise disengaged. Various efforts, including impulsive acts, often precipitously engage the response of disengaged other(s) (Boszormenyi-Nagy and Spark, 1973; Lansky, 1981).

Anecdotally, I have seen several cases in which a girl developed severe anorexia nervosa, in part as an unconscious attempt to keep her parents together at a time of impending divorce. Some instances have even been conscious efforts. The anorexia provided such a mutual concern and focus for the parents, that they became united in an effort to save their daughter.

There has also been an unusually high incidence of at least one parent of anorexic girls who is significantly older than parents of nonanorexic peers—often by a decade or two. There is an equally high incidence of anorexic girls with one parent having a severe physical condition or terminal illness. These situations create in the girl a fear of loss of her parent. These fears of loss by death or separation seem especially great to the girl who is developmentally arrested and unprepared for autonomous functioning. Her illness, then, is a specific attempt to not grow up, to not have her parents get old and die. She may attempt to magically freeze the march of biological time by not beginning pubescence. Or the older adolescent or young adult may attempt to retreat to a "safer" time—before she blossomed into a young woman. (The body image drawings of these girls and young women at the time of presentation for treatment show a prepubescent, asexual figure, often small and helpless-looking.)

The daughter's illness also has a specific effect on the family system: rather than being anxious about their own impending separation/aging/loss/death, the parents have an external focus—their sick daughter. Her condition is a specific, delineated external focus, which, contrary to theirs, can seemingly be controlled.

Summary

All of these descriptions have a common theme of the narcissistic vulnerability of certain individuals with early developmental arrest that is combined with a precipitant of an interrupted emotional availability of a significant person (Mahler, 1971). This change in the availability or relationship of a significant selfobject results in an internal experience of hurt/anger/disorganization and the attempt to control something specific and concrete, which then directly has an effect of regulating both the body self and psychological self experiences via an attempted restitution of the selfobject.

Such actions which involve restitutive and organizing efforts are to restore some perception of body boundary and integrity, as well as to connect with a lost (empathically disconnected) selfobject. This connectedness is to establish a sense of completeness and organization within that restructured but fragile body and self-selfobject boundary.

A fragile self attempts reorganization by actions, which have the intent of creating or of reestablishing a disrupted self-selfobject bond. This attempted compensation for a porous, vague, or ineffective body and ego boundary must not be lost as a central issue in therapy (Krueger, 1989). Often the symptomatic results of such an adaptation (e.g., the aspects of bulimia or anorexia) become the center of therapeutic focus rather than the intent and initiating sequence of such action. Thus, it is most useful to initially and empathically examine her experience and her attempted adaptation rather than approach it from the side of the pathological result.

The subjective experience of many of these patients is of feeling hopelessly lost, empty, and losing form. The selfobject had been functioning, prior to the narcissistic injury, as a referent and regulator to maintain form and boundary functions. With the loss via withdrawal or unavailability of that selfobject, the patient precipitously experiences the loss of form. When the boundary-regulating and internally regulating function of the selfobject is withdrawn or unavailable, the patient has to rely only on her own vague or unformed boundaries and internal regulation. These vague and indistinct body boundaries do not serve as an adequate vessel for a solid, cohesive, consistent sense of self.

Every new step toward autonomy holds the threat of loss. The search for replacements in the lifelong mourning process of separation ties us to the continuous search for symbols (Rizzuto, Peterson, and Reed, 1981). As differentiation takes place, what is internalized in normal development is an increasing capacity to represent the absent object: to internalize it, to imbue it with affect, to form and transform it.

A process has been described which precipitates narcissistic injury in a person who has developmental deficits of certain empathic developmental experiences due to the emotional or physical unconnectedness with a parent. The fantasies and actions of the symptom sequence serve as restitutive efforts (directed at the body as well as the psyche) to create an illusion of a present, empathic parent(s).

The process of narcissistic vulnerability, disorganization, and restitutive attempts must be examined from both intrapsychic and interpersonal perspectives.

References

Basch, M. (1985), Discussion on clinical presentations. Presented at the Eighth Annual Conference on The Psychology of Self, New York.

Boszormenyi-Nagy, I., & Spark, G. (1973), *Invisible Loyalties*. New York: Harper & Row.

Fleming, J. (1972), Early object deprivation and transference phenomena: The working alliance. *Psychoanal. Quart.*, 41:23–32.

Freud, S. (1923), The ego and the id. *Standard Edition*, 19:12–66. London: Hogarth Press, 1963.

Krueger, D. (1978), Psychotherapy of adult patients with problems of parental loss in childhood. *Curr. Concepts Psychiat.*, 4:2–11.

———(1979), Anxiety as it relates to success phobia: Developmental considerations. Paper presented at American Psychoanalytic Association Meeting, New York.

———(1983), Childhood parent loss: Developmental impact and adult psychopathology. *Amer. J. Psychother.*, 37:582–592.

———(1984), *Success and the Fear of Success in Women*. New York: The Free Press.

———(1989), *Body and Self: The Developmental and Clinical Role of Body Image in Treatment of Disorders of the Self*. New York: Brunner/Mazel.

Lansky, M. (1981), Treatment of the narcissistically vulnerable couple. In: *Family Therapy and Major Psychopathology*, ed. M. Lansky. New York: Grune & Stratton.

Lichtenberg, J. (1978), The testing of reality from the standpoint of the body self. *J. Amer. Psychoanal. Assn.*, 26:357–385.

Mahler, M. (1971), A study of the separation–individuation process and its possible application to the borderline phenomena in the psychoanalytic situation. *The Psychoanalytic Study of the Child*, 26:403–424. New York: Quadrangle.

Pollock, G. (1961), Mourning and adaptation. *Internat. J. Psycho-Anal.*, 42: 341–353.

Rizzuto, A., Peterson, M., & Reed, M. (1981), The pathological sense of self in anorexia nervosa. *Psychiat. Clin. N. Amer.*, 4:471–487.

Servoss, A., & Krueger, D. (1984), Normal versus pathological grief and mourning: Some precursors. In: *Emotional Rehabilitation of Physical Trauma and Disability*, ed. D. Krueger. New York: SP Medical & Scientific Books.

Stroker, M., Goldberg, I., Green, J., & Saxon, J. (1979), Body image disturbances in anorexia nervosa during the acute and recuperations period. *Psychosom. Med.*, 9:695–701.

10

Parental Loss through Divorce: Dimensions of the Loss Experience

REBECCA LOHR, M.S.W.
MORTON CHETHIK, M.S.W.

Children who lose a parent through death experience a clear, unmistakeable, and permanent loss that has acute effects as well as a long-term impact on the course of development. Loss through death constitutes a traumatic event in the lives of both children and adults. For children, in addition, the death of a close relative constitutes what Nagera (1970) has referred to as a "developmental interference." Loss of a parent through divorce has also begun to be viewed both as a traumatic event in the lives of children and parents, and, in addition, can become for children a "developmental interference" (Chethik and Kalter, 1980). While the loss of a parent through divorce may or may not be a total loss, depending upon the emotional and geographical availability of both parents, there is inevitably a loss. What is the nature of the loss that the child experiences? This chapter describes the nature of the grieving process as it relates to children whose parents have divorced and reviews the specific impact of this kind of loss at different developmental stages. Certain dimensions of the loss experienced through parental divorce are explored: (1) loss of the parental unit, and (2) partial loss of the parental objects. Some of the long-term effects of loss through divorce are described.

The Nature of Grieving Loss through Divorce

The most common affect that children experience in response to separation and divorce is that of sadness and grief (Chethik and Kalter, unpublished). Longitudinal studies (Wallerstein, 1985) have reported that the feelings of sadness persist over time and are related to the perception of loss of a parent (most often the father) and the intact family unit. While the loss of the parent through divorce may be only a partial loss, the child experiences a significant loss in relation to the parent who leaves the family and in many cases, at least temporarily, an emotional loss of the remaining parent who retreats from the parenting functions and is unavailable to assist the child in the grieving process and reorganizing the family system (Chethik, Plunkett, Colfer, and Lohr, 1984).

A major task for the child is to experience the grief and pain associated with loss and to incorporate it into developmental progress. How capable, cognitively and affectively, is the child of grieving the loss associated with parental divorce? Anthony (1974) describes the sense of abandonment as always existing, even in the best managed divorces, and grieving may persist for some time. Anthony suggests that "the child should not be dissuaded from mourning what he has lost, and he may even need to be helped to mourn" (p. 469). Bowlby (1960) emphasized that young children not only grieve but that they often do so for longer than was sometimes supposed. He used the term *mourning* to cover a variety of reactions to loss. In the intervening years, considerable controversy developed over his use of the term *mourning* in relation to young children, and in a later paper (Bowlby and Parker, 1970), he used the word *grieving* to denote the whole range of processes that are brought into action when a loss is sustained. While the word *mourning* carries with it the concept of recognition of permanence and finality, *grieving* (as used by Tessman, 1978) denotes the "affective state of sadness, pain and desolation when unrequited longing for

the absent person is paramount; it may occur without perception or acceptance of the loss as permanent" (p. 133). Utilizing
this definition of grieving, all children whose parents divorce
have to go through a process of grieving the loss of the intact
family unit and the loss, to varying degrees, of the absent
parent (Mendell, 1983). Even in situations when children have
access to both parents on a regular, ongoing basis through joint
custody and shared possession arrangements, grieving has
been observed.

Most authors (Bowlby and Parker, 1970; Anthony, 1974) agree
that for children to mourn a loss, assistance from a trusted
person on whom they can depend for emotional support is
needed in order to deal with painful affects.

Reactions Specific to Different Developmental Stages

The work of Wallerstein and Kelly (1980) has made significant
contributions to our understanding of children's reactions to
divorce at different developmental stages and how children
have dealt with the divorce experience at one, five, and ten
years later. The pervasive theme is that of an acute, and often
persisting, sense of loss, while clear patterns emerge in terms of
the ego's capacity to deal with loss, and the meaning of the loss
experienced at different developmental stages. They noted
(1975) that responses to parental separation expressed in the
two-and-a-half- to three-and-three-quarter-year-old youngsters
in their study were similar to those described by A. Freud and
Burlingham (1943), and others, following separation of children from primary caretakers. Symptoms were noted in all
children of the youngest group even though all but one had
experienced no disruption in maternal or environmental continuity. The most enduring symptom was pervasive neediness.
In the three-and-three-quarter to four-and-three-quarter age
group, the child's self-esteem and self-image appeared burdened and the sense of external order in the world was
disrupted. In youngsters who evidenced poor adjustment,
depressive reactions and developmental inhibitions were observed. The five- to six-year-olds had greater capacity to
express their sadness, their longings for their fathers, and their

wishes to restore the family. In more vulnerable children, interferences in resolution of oedipal issues and delayed entrance into latency were seen. The most striking response in early latency age children to parental separation and divorce was reported to be their pervasive sadness (Kelly and Wallerstein, 1976). They were acutely aware of their suffering and unable to utilize age-appropriate defenses such as denial, or seek relief in more autonomous actions available to older children. Children who were in older latency were seen as less immobilized by their suffering and attempted to master their feelings about the painful disruption through activity and play (Wallerstein and Kelly, 1976). Adolescents already developmentally in the process of disengaging from parents and mourning their lost childhoods react with exacerbated feelings of loss and mourning (Wallerstein and Kelly, 1974).

Our clinical work has included a number of sibling pairs who were reacting to the same divorce event from the vantage point of different ages, sexes, and developmental stages. The following case illustrates how understanding the child's internal perception of the divorce process is a central aspect of understanding the child's experience of parental loss through divorce.

Clinical Example 1

Jimmy, age ten, and Sherry, age six, were brought for evaluation by their parents who were in the process of divorcing. They had joint custody and shared possession of the children, with four days of the week spent with the father and three days with the mother. Both parents were extremely sensitive to the children's feelings and reactions to the separation and pending divorce and had provided excellent parenting for them. Mrs. D.'s manifest reason for requesting an evaluation was that the children wanted someone to talk to about their feelings in regard to the parental separation. The more latent reason which surfaced was her fear that her decision to divorce had irreparably damaged her children and she was experiencing considerable guilt and anxiety around the decision and its impact. Mr. D. was clearly in pain about his wife's decision, and while he consciously accepted it, he was very wishful that it would not occur and was perhaps leading the children to feel that a reconciliation might be possible, despite Mrs. D.'s insistence that it was not. Mrs. D. was concerned that Sherry was feeling confused by her father's messages, making it more difficult for her to accept the painful reality of the family disruption. There was no history of quarreling or fighting between the parents. The children had been told that mother was moving out of the family home as the parents could not make each other happy. This revelation came as a shock to the children who had felt cared for and happy within the family.

Following the separation, the parents maintained warm interactions with the children and attempted to maintain an amicable relationship with each other in front of the children, despite undercurrents of pain and resentment. Upon further exploration during the evaluation, mother's unhappiness surfaced as an intense feeling that her artistic abilities had never been fully supported or encouraged by her husband, while he perceived that explanation as a rationalization and externalization of her conflicts and inhibitions around artistic expression. Her own individual therapy had not resolved this issue, and she was committed to pursue the divorce action.

While both children reacted with painful feelings to the loss of their secure family life, there were very unique and specific reactions that reflected their age, sex, and developmental stage.

Jimmy, according to both parents, was very attached to and strongly identified with his father. He had difficulty talking about his feelings in general and the divorce in particular. He told his mother he preferred "not to think about the divorce." Rather, he wanted to spend time with his friends playing sports and reading. His major resentment was that in splitting time between his father's home and his mother's apartment, his baseball practice schedule and Boy Scout activities were disrupted. Further, he wanted the week to be split evenly and felt the four day/three day split was not "fair." Jimmy was very attuned to his father's pain over the separation, and empathic with his sense of loss when it was time for the children to go to their mother's. Similarly, in sessions, Jimmy described how sad his sister was, and acknowledged that he did not like to think about the divorce because it made him feel sad. He spoke nostalgically about the many good times and trips his family had together, and drew a picture of the four of them as a family unit. While he did not voice angry, aggressive feelings, they were expressed in displacement in stories about war games and in fantasies about punching kids at school who were more aggressive and bigger than himself. His competitive feelings were well sublimated in his academic pursuits and ambitions to become a scientist or astronaut some day.

Sherry had become symptomatic immediately after being told that her mother was moving out of the home. She appeared withdrawn and depressed at school, and refused to eat because she was afraid she would throw up. The acute symptoms persisted for three weeks and were responded to with sensitivity by her teacher and parents. In addition to talking with her about her sad feelings, her mother had packed special notes in her lunch pail every day, and they drew special pictures for each other to keep. Sherry had seemed bewildered and confused by her mother's decision to leave, asking questions like, "How does love stop?" implying that if mother stopped loving father, she could stop loving her, too. She beseeched her mother to "make it all better" and voiced that her pain was so great that she thought she might die. She talked with both parents about her "secret wish" that they would be reconciled. When with her father, she handled acute feelings of loss and separation by crawling into his bed each night and calling her mother every morning. Her guilt around the oedipal feelings and pleasure of being alone with her father also aroused anxiety that she may have caused her mother to move out, and she expressed protective and intense loving feelings toward her mother. Her anger toward her mother was strongly defended against by turning it against herself. She repetitively asked her mother, "Will I be all right?"

Sherry's recently achieved developmental status of latency age was more severely disrupted by the parental separation than was Jimmy's more solid task orientation of midlatency. Her defenses against loss and abandonment could not protect her sufficiently from sad and angry feelings, and symptoms emerged in the form of an eating disturbance and depressive affect. Jimmy, on the other hand, was able to sublimate his feelings in intellectual pursuits and fantasies of adult success that contributed to a greater sense of mastery in dealing with his sadness.

Dimensions of Loss Experienced

Loss of the Parental Unit

There are varying degrees of actual loss of the parental object at the time of separation and divorce as far as the young child is concerned, but inevitably the ongoing bond between the parents is significantly altered and the family unit that included both parents no longer exists. In our clinical work, we have been impressed with the significant loss that the child experiences of the family itself and the way in which the family as a social and psychological unit has developed and functioned over time. More than half of the children in Wallerstein's (1984) ten-year follow-up of children who were preschoolers at the time of divorce spoke wistfully of life in an intact family and revealed persistent reconciliation fantasies. Children appear to carry with them a compelling internal image of the family that they have, or feel that they have, lost.

The admixture of reality, memory, and fantasy varies, dependent upon the child's actual experience within the family prior to the disruption and the internal representations that develop over time. Very young children, for example, who have spent little or no time in the two-parent family constellation will express a wish for the family unit. Older children, confronted with a changed external reality, have to revise their concepts of the roles of mothers and fathers and their perception of permanence in relationships. Divorce brings cognitive dissonance and inconsistency to the child's world (Hess and Camara, 1979). The family system embodies not only the two parents, but also family rituals, activities, patterns, values, and extended family relationships, all of which are altered in the divorce process and contribute to the child's sense of loss of continuity of the family. Further, economic restructuring and changes in residence are very common changes that occur following divorce for both mothers and fathers. As mothers are often dependent upon their ex-spouse for child support, they tend to be most affected in terms of economic stability and predictability of income, which can then contribute to a sense of insecurity and unpredictability for both mothers and children.

One of the most commonly observed means for coping with the sense of loss of the parental unit is the child's wish to have the parents reconcile. In an earlier work (Lohr, Chethik, Press, and Solyom, 1981), we distinguished between reunion fantasies that are typical of children who have been bereaved by the death of a parent, and reconciliation fantasies that are persistent and compelling in children who have experienced parental divorce. The reconciliation fantasy is used in this context to denote "the child's wish for a continuation of the parental ties to one another as well as to the self" (p. 123). While reconciliation fantasies are rarely described as part of a presenting problem for children, the fantasy often emerges in play, drawings, fantasy, and associations. When children of divorce are asked to draw a picture of their family, they often include both parents long after a divorce has been finalized. The family depicted is typically an idealized version in which all members end up happily under one roof. For children, also, even a conflictual relationship with a parent and family feels preferable to an unknown future, as it provides continuity and predictability. This is not to say the child's best interests would necessarily be served by having parents remain together, but it is important to realize the intensity of the child's wish not to experience a disruption of the family unit.

Lohr et al. (1981) described the transitory reconciliation fantasy as a normal response to an unsettling traumatic event that may stress the ego of the child beyond what can be incorporated into a sense of reality. Denial in fantasy is a natural and normal defense for young children because of their low tolerance for painful events and affects (Nagera, 1970), but it can also be observed in older children, adolescents, and even adults. Children's denial of the reality of parental separation and divorce can be fueled by a parent's similar defenses and fantasies, particularly during the early stages of the divorce process. In our clinical work, we have often observed that children hold onto a persistently powerful fantasy of reconciliation. Major determinants in the persistence of these fantasies and their interference in developing ego functions can be both external and internal. Strong bonds and attachments between marriage partners do not sever readily on an unconscious level and persist long after a conscious decision to divorce has been made. Unresolved parental attachments fuel a child's wishes for parents to reunite, and we have observed that the parents' inability to come to terms with a spouse's decision to divorce is often mirrored in the child's clinging to the internal image of the intact family. An environmental stimulus, such as a geographical move, remarriage of a parent, or birth of a half-sibling can reactivate old and inadequately resolved reconciliation wishes.

There are internal determinants of reconciliation fantasies as well. Feelings of guilt and responsibility for parental divorce, particularly strong in preschool children (Wallerstein and Kelly, 1976), can contribute significantly to the maintenance of reconciliation fantasies over time. The young child may reason that his guilt over fantasized wrongdoing would be expiated if the child could reunite the parents. One six-year-old boy poignantly referred to his boisterous behavior as causing his parents' quarrels to erupt; thus, he felt, if he could only by his overly conscientious behavior bring them back together again, his guilt would be absolved. His inability to effect reconciliation left him feeling helpless with impotent rage and despair as he could not undo the damage he felt in fantasy he had wrought. During the oedipal phase, and into newly experienced latency, young boys are particularly likely to experience guilt over becoming the oedipal victor (Neubauer, 1960). The reconciliation or reunion fantasy also serves to keep the parental object in the picture as a resource for identification and internalization.

Loss of the Parental Object

Divorce involves the partial loss of a parental relationship, usually with the father, and with great frequency, the diminished affective and sometimes physical availability of the mother. Both parents often experience diminished capacities to function in parental roles during the first year following divorce, with a reestablishing of a healthier equilibrium by the end of the second year. The loss of the noncustodial parent, albeit circumscribed, is a permanent one that results in disruptions of established ties, internal functions that had been served by the day to day relationship with the absent parent, and the established parenting patterns and rituals. The partial availability of the absent parent following divorce contributes to a significant difference between the child's coping with affects and impulses in reaction to divorce as compared with the absolute unavailability of the parental object after death. For while the child whose parent dies may maintain denial in fantasy of the finality of death, and have fantasies about being reunited with the deceased parent, there is little environmental support for maintaining that psychic state. The potential availability of the parent after divorce fuels the child's optimism that the absent parent may continue as a significant object in terms of ongoing developmental functions as well as the hope for parental reconciliation. Anthony (1974) points out that the loss complex is radically different in the case of death and divorce, but in either case "the image is distorted, and therefore healthy identification is impaired" (p. 473). Continuing availability of the absent parent following divorce can serve to aid the child in testing out perceptions and fantasies in relation to the self and the parent; for example, the child's fantasy that he or she is to blame for the divorce may become reinforced if there is no ongoing contact between the child and parent following divorce that would allow for the reworking of that interpretation. The frequency and extent of contact with the noncustodial parent seems of less import than the quality, consistency and predictability of contact. The live-in parent can help mitigate the negative sequelae to divorce by allowing the necessary mourning of the lost family unit to occur, and by reestablishing a family structure that continues to meet the developmental needs of the child.

The absence of the father, and living in a single-parent household, has significant implications for development of a positive sense of masculinity and femininity (Kalter and Chethik, unpublished). There has been general agreement in the literature about the negative effect father absence has on sons in terms of inadequately consolidated superego functions, deficient impulse control, poor social adjustment and school performance, and problems in masculine identification (Biller, 1981). Adverse effects have been noted as more marked and enduring for boys than for girls in the aftermath of divorce (Hetherington, Cox, and Cox, 1978). More recent work has evidenced interference of father absence in daughters' development of a sense of femininity and self-esteem and separation-related conflicts between mothers and daughters (Kalter, Riemer, Brickman, and Chen, 1985). For both boys and girls, problems in sexual identification appear more prevalent when contact with parents of both sexes is limited. The sense of distance and loss seems to exist even when there is ongoing contact with the absent parent as the day-to-day opportunity for the child to affirm a sense of identification with the absent parent is missing.

For boys, developing a positive identification with the absent father may be complicated by the mother's communication, conscious or unconscious, that her son embodies the negative characteristics of his father or that she does not want her son to grow up to be like his father toward whom she may retain predominantly hostile, angry feelings (Chethik, Dolin, Davies, Lohr, and Darrow, 1986).

The resolution of ambivalence toward primary love objects is more complex for both parents and children after divorce. As a part of disengaging from the ex-spouse, parents often need to see them as all bad and to suppress good feelings because of the sadness evoked by pleasant memories. Children may identify with a parent's need to see the other parent in only a negative light, or may maintain an essentially positive view of the absent parent who, as the non-in-house parent, becomes indulgent and does not set limits. Many children express more negative affects and impulses toward the in-house parent (usually the mother) and preserve the more precarious relationship with the absent parent through idealization, and perhaps, identification with select attributes of the lost object. In the two-parent family, children experience love and hate feelings toward both parents. After divorce, many children split the ambivalence, with one parent becoming the object toward whom most negative feelings are experienced, while the absent parent is the recipient of positive feelings. This paradigm is reinforced in single-parent families where the mother becomes the sole disciplinarian and the father is the supplier of weekend treats. Even when the father repeatedly disappoints a child, the child often has to preserve the image of the relationship through denial of shortcomings and idealization. In that way, the fantasy of the all-giving parent can be preserved and the child defends against acute, and often repeated, feelings of disappointment and rejection. Difficulties in resolution of ambivalence toward primary objects can contribute to problems in establishing intimacy and commitment in future relationships (Kalter and Chethik, unpublished).

Clinical Example 2: Loss of the Parental Unit and In-House Father

Rich, a five-year-old youngster, anticipated entering kindergarten in September with the energy, exuberance, and eagerness to learn that is delightfully characteristic of many children of his age. The family events that occurred over the three summer months preceding his entry into kindergarten dramatically shook and altered his secure view of himself and the world around him.

Rich's father had moved out of the family home "suddenly" at the beginning of the summer with the ambiguous explanation that he was moving into an apartment six blocks away and did not know if or when he would return to the family. During the next two months, visits had initially been several times weekly between father, Rich, and his three-year-old sister. These visits had been reduced to once a week and every other weekend at Mrs. T.'s attorney's suggestion because "frequent visits were too stressful for Mrs. T." By August, Rich was adamantly refusing to have contact with his father, and mother had been advised not to "force" Rich to visit with him. Mrs. T. sought evaluation with the expressed concern that Rich was refusing to go to kindergarten, was nocturnally enuretic, and vacillated between acute, intense angry feelings and warm, loving interactions with her. Further exploration revealed that Rich had regressed from a happy, active youngster to a whiny, clinging, dependent child who often shared his mother's bed and complained frequently of physical symptoms.

The psychologist who performed intelligence and projective testing noted that Rich had difficulty separating from his mother and demonstrated a high level of anxiety. He functioned in the high average to superior range of intelligence; however, he was self-deprecatory in every way. In projective testing, his responses suggested extreme concern about what he viewed as a traumatic event. Each of his stories would begin benignly and then the phrase "suddenly" would appear. When he reached the picture that is usually seen as depicting a father figure, he said, "I don't want to do no more." Throughout the stories there was fear of impending danger. He drew a person whom he described as "a boy, dressed up like a monster, but he is really a little boy and he feels dumb." Why? "The boy gets all mad and breaks his glasses he drank out of." When asked what makes him mad, he replied, "His Dad goes to work and he doesn't have any friends to play with." There was overwhelming evidence in this and subsequent clinical evaluation sessions that Rich had experienced a real trauma in the breakup of his family. He exhibited acute separation anxiety and held himself to blame for his parents' difficulties and his father's departure.

Evaluation of the parents revealed that Rich's mother was also overwhelmed with grief and sadness, and was not accepting the finality of the father's decision to separate. The parents had not planned to have children, as the father had two sons by an earlier marriage and the mother had had a son as a single mother. However, they had been happy when she became pregnant. Mrs. T. had a close, enmeshed relationship with her parents. Her father had become seriously ill and died during her pregnancy with Rich. She felt unable to grieve until after delivery and did not mourn her father's death until after Rich's birth. Rich attained all developmental milestones early, and responded to his sister's birth when he was two years old by moving into a single bed as "a big boy." Rich was very attached to his half-brother who was thirteen years older.

Work with Mother

Mrs. T. was very resistant to bringing her son for treatment. She was embarrassed and ashamed to sit in the lobby, as she felt that mothers whose children needed psychiatric treatment were uncaring, insensitive mothers. She felt tremendously guilty about Rich's needing help, perceiving it as a stigma, a badge of failed motherhood. She felt the divorce was punishment for her "past sins" and that she was helpless to redeem herself. The only way she envisioned being able to help Rich was to get his father back, a demand that Rich often made of her— "Just go and ask him and he will come back to us." Rich's plaintive cries echoed her own, and also voiced her unconscious wish for the therapist to get the father to return. The reunion and reconciliation fantasies ran strong and deep in this as in many divorced families.

A central theme in the work with Mrs. T. was Rich's ongoing need for contact with his father, while simultaneously enabling her to disengage from her own relationship with her ex-husband. Initially, she protested the recommendation that visitations continue between Rich and his father. She often perceived Mr. T. as providing inadequate supervision of Rich during visits; further, Rich was often quite upset and angry when he returned home. She typically attributed his upset feelings to problems going on in Mr. T.'s household. She felt "dumped on" that Mr. T. never was the target of Rich's anger, while she, who sat up with him when he had a fever of 102 degrees and provided most of the caretaking, was frequently the object of Rich's wrath. Much supportive work was done with her around how Rich felt safer expressing anger toward her as the parent he saw every day, while he experienced the relationship with his father, also his rival, as more tenuous. She wanted Rich to be as angry at his father as she was, and had difficulty with his ongoing attachment to him. We worked on the painful feelings she had about not being able to have an ongoing pleasurable relationship with Rich's father as Rich had, and there was a part of her that wanted to deprive them of their closeness in retaliation for her own feelings of loss. She had sufficient ego strength, however, to differentiate her own feelings and needs from Rich's, which served to support a more stable relationship between Rich and his father.

Mrs. T. had to cope with a number of real stressors that are not uncommon for parents in the two years immediately after divorce: a move from the family home and full-time employment. These were perceived as demeaning experiences and she vacillated between anger and depression over her losses in economic security and social position. The loss of the family home was particularly stressful for her as, after the divorce was finalized, Mr. T. moved back into the home with his new wife and her children. Mrs. T.'s feelings about being displaced and replaced were acute and real.

Relationships with grandparents often become more problematic after divorce, with old conflicts resurfacing and intensifying. For Mrs. T., her inability to complete the separation process from her mother had contributed significantly to her marital problems, and after the divorce, regressive, hostile dependency versus autonomous functioning emerged as a central issue for her. Her wishes that her mother would die and let her live her own life evoked tremendous guilt, compounded by her mother's chronic, and at times, acute heart condition. She was able to do some work on this longstanding issue, resulting in less guilt over her impulses to separate from her mother. Thus, the divorce precipitated both a painful crisis and an opportunity to rework old developmental issues.

Mrs. T. obtained emotional and social support from a divorce group sponsored by her church. Members from the group helped her move and offered listening ears when needed. The intensity of their anger toward ex-spouses was initially difficult for Mrs. T. to hear. Defensive denial, avoidance, and reaction formation against her aggression were prominent features that were explored in individual sessions and allowed Mrs. T. to recognize her anger around feelings of rejection and abandonment.

Work with Father

Mr. T. was actively responsible for bringing Rich to his sessions for a period of six months, but resisted treatment himself. He conveyed unwillingness to talk about his feelings and guarded-ness about his new marital relationship. Individual sessions with him were infrequent and usually at the therapist's request. His interaction with Rich, however, appeared warm and empathic. The parent guidance sessions focused largely on the impor-tance of his maintaining an active role in his son's life and separating his resentment toward Rich's mother because of her continuing demands on him from his relationship with Rich. His avoidance of issues was gently confronted in order to foster more direct, active, and less passive means of dealing with conflict.

Therapy with the Child

The early months of treatment focused on separation issues. Rich was often sick and his mother would cancel his sessions. When they did come in, he experienced difficulty separating from his mother and staying in the sessions alone. He com-plained about being hungry, tired, thirsty, and wanted to return to his mother to be soothed and cared for. He talked about how much he missed his mom when he was at school and he wanted to go home to be with her but, "I know that I can't." Simulta-neously, there were sessions in which he was eager to learn to play games like Battleship and was intent on winning, experi-encing pleasure when he did. However, his wins were often followed by self-injury such as slamming the car door on his finger on the way into the hospital. A common theme of treatment involved his wishes to indulge himself, which were then accompanied by disastrous consequences. He drew an apple tree filled with red, luscious apples, telling a story of a boy who ate too many of the forbidden fruit and died. Stories often revolved around water imagery in which there were sharks that became attacking and ferocious, maiming people and eating the smaller fish in the sea. During this time he was wetting his bed frequently and spending the rest of the night in his mother's bed. He often resisted going to school, and illnesses became a means of remaining home with his mother.

His mother, in dealing with her own feelings of loss, often turned to Rich as her "little man." Rich expressed his anger toward his father indirectly, displacing it onto his big brother, Terry, who had gone off to college leaving him behind. Terry was gigantic and strong, a mighty protector, and Rich was angered at being left behind, little and helpless. He experienced marked sadness during his first Christmas after the divorce that his father was not there, and anger at his mother who had taken the children east. He portrayed his mother as an omnipotent, controlling female who was destructive and coercive. He subsequently built a sturdy He-man castle, the sturdiest, most indestructible castle in the world, of which he was king. This more powerful, phallic position initially had a defensive quality, but eventually changed over to a period of extraordinarily creative play with Legos. Excitement pervaded the sessions as he talked about heat and fires, and firemen had to be called in to put out the fires. A fireman had to be present all the time to keep fires from getting out of control. He occasionally referred to his father helping him build something or to clothing his father had given him.

Around the time of his sixth birthday, he was actively working on the theme of wanting to be special with the therapist and receive special gifts. There was visible sadness and aggression expressed when his wishes were not gratified. He played out competitive themes between lions and panthers who engaged in ferocious battles, spaceships with huge powerful lasers, supermen who showed Herculean strength. Sometimes he would get so "hot" that he felt something would explode. He occasionally would grab his crotch and say he had to find ways of cooling things down. He would then send the car through the car wash making loud swooshing sounds. He revealed secretively that one night while a baby-sitter was there he had lit a match and almost burned himself. He was frightened that if he got too hot, too excited that he might hurt himself or be left (fear of abandonment and loss, and castration anxiety). In one session, with enormous excitement he built a race track and had two racing cars in a heated race, the winner of which would receive a grand prize, "a big fat pig." It was possible then to interpret that he felt his dad's leaving had something to do with his own competitive strivings and his excitement about being with his mother, "the big fat pig." While we knew that he wanted to win the big prize, he also wanted the racing car (his father) to stay in the race. This play was followed by a period of competition juxtaposed with body damage and self-recriminations that were interpretable. In school, he was experiencing a tremendous amount of pleasure, functioning at a very high level, and was quite successful in his academic achievements.

At this point, Rich's mother obtained a full-time job, and his father agreed to bring Rich for his appointments. Rich was beginning to accept the permanence of the parental divorce, and while not happy about it, he accepted that his father had moved back into the family home, while his mother, his sister, and himself had moved to his grandmother's house. However, for months he refused to acknowledge that dad was sharing his home with his girlfriend and her children and eventually remarried. He refused to call his new stepmother by name and when asked about her, he said, "They're just friends." The father, too, had difficulty talking with Rich about his remarriage. Only gradually was Rich able to reveal in play his curiosity about their relationship, his jealousy of his father's new wife and children, and how left out he felt.

Work with the father focused on helping him find words and means of discussing these changes with Rich. After the remarriage, Rich also had to begin to relinquish the fantasy that his mother, or himself, could just go to get dad and bring him home again. With his father bringing him, Rich initially had difficulty settling down into the sessions and used extensive denial and avoidance in dealing with fantasy material. His play, however, became more overtly competitive and exhibitionistic. He wanted to be the biggest, brightest, and best and win out over all. He wanted to crush the big man, and talked of going into his mother's bed because he was fearful of sleeping in the top bunk (he might fall out and hurt himself). He became more directly angry and disappointed with his father, and would complain that his father never bought him the right kind of potato chips, or that the father's stepson got to stay with father all of the time. He developed puppet shows in which two men were fighting over the land, one killed the other, and became the victor. He enthusiastically engaged in competitive games of cards and Battleship, having to assure by various means that he would be victorious. He began to delight in his phallic prowess, such as roller skating skills and playground activities.

As we prepared for the therapist's upcoming vacation, separation themes again surfaced in play, as well as angry derogation toward the therapist. He did not see why he had to come to therapy, it was not helping him anyway, and "you don't even look like a psychiatrist, you're dumb." He went to see the film *Gremlins* and was upset and tearful during and after the movie. He said that Gremlin's brother killed the mother because she had not given him as many toys as she had given Gremlin, so Gremlin ended up both the winner and the loser. Then he became fearful that the therapist would not return and he began to demand that she tell him where she was going on vacation and with whom. His fantasy was that she was going off and having a joyful time with her own family and children.

After the vacation interruption, father called to say that Rich was doing well and did not want to return to therapy. The therapist said that while it was important to listen to Rich's feelings, this was a decision that the parents and therapist should make together. It was pointed out that Rich had many feelings about being left, which he characteristically preferred to avoid and deny, and that termination needed to occur in a planful, not a precipitous manner. (We have observed that many divorced families repeat the pattern of the departure from the marriage in the treatment situation.)

In this case, father was unilaterally going to disrupt the treatment relationship without notice, and Rich, as he had done after the divorce, was choosing to avoid feelings that were frightening to him. His father agreed to bring Rich for one session if Rich would agree. Rich presented the same symptoms in that session as he had done a year previously. He refused to be seen alone, could not separate from his father who came into the session initially, and when his father left, he went running after him. He angrily voiced that he did not want to see or talk to the therapist again. The therapist said to both the father and Rich that it must be very frightening to have such intense feelings and to have to talk about them, and the belief that if they were not talked about they would go away. She drew the parallel between the current situation and Rich's refusal to see his father after the parental separation.

Mr. T. colluded with Rich's avoidance and denial, saying that Rich was fine during vacation and that the only problem was in his coming to therapy. That soon appeared not to be the case—Rich began to refuse to go to school and when angry, he said he wanted to kill himself. The parents agreed that he should return to treatment. Rich, too, said he wished to return, but was embarrassed and ashamed of his anger at the therapist. Upon his return, displaying a pseudo-adult manner, he was apologetic for his past "misbehavior." He appeared enormously relieved as we spoke of how angry kids could feel when important people in their lives leave them, how hard it is to talk about feeling left behind, and how it was understandable that a kid would rather not come in from play to deal with sad, angry feelings. That the therapist did not retaliate and was still available to continue the therapy was very reassuring to him.

When the therapist moved from one office to another, Rich was told in advance that we would be meeting in a new office but that there would still be the same toys and that the time would not change. He was curious and anxious and wanted immediately to check out where the new office was. He was initially excited, saying there would be more space to play kickball. After the move occurred, however, he was less enthused; the new office was not that much bigger, there were still constraints on how active he could be, and he missed the old office. As we talked about how this move was a replay of his earlier experiences around the family's disruption and moves, he gradually became more comfortable in the new office. He labeled a drawer as his own and put his special toys in it. He would always seek assurance that his Lego houses remained intact, and that no one would demolish them.

After a four-week period during which Rich did not see his father (he had pneumonia), Rich seemed overtly happy and relieved when contact with him resumed. One hour was preoccupied with making a man out of clay. Then, at the end of the hour, with much agitation, he dismembered the man, threw the body on the floor, stomped on it, picked it up, and rolled it into a ball. He threw the ball with all of his might against the wall, saying "I hate him." When he rejoined his father, he gave him a big hug. Father later reported that Rich had not shown anger toward him but had become very anxious when his father was fifteen minutes late to pick him up, calling him every few minutes to be assured that he was coming. His father further mentioned that on one trip to a session, Rich cried as he talked about his brother Terry returning to college because then he would not be able to see him for four weeks. In his sessions, he also spoke of his sadness, but mentioned that someday he would be going to college.

During termination, Rich decided that he wanted to draw a special picture to leave for the therapist to remember him by. With colors that he thought the therapist liked, he drew a large airplane and a small airplane flying off into the sunset.

Status on Termination

Rich was described as the star pupil in his first grade, an eager learner and a creative youngster. His father described him as communicative with both himself and his stepmother, no longer excluding her from secret communications just with his father. He was playful with his stepbrother of the same age and accepting of his place in their home. He was usually eager to go visit with his father, but still evidenced some fear and anxiety that his father might not appear to pick him up. He remained more angry with his mother, while rarely overtly angry with his father. He showed evidence of masculine identification with his older stepbrother and father, and love, intermingled with anger, toward his mother. A developmental foundation in latency was emerging, evidenced by pleasure in academic pursuits and enjoyment of competitive sports. He related well to other children, although preferring to be the boss or the leader or always needing to win in his interactions with them. He slept in his own bed with occasional bed wetting. Areas of continuing concern were his tendency to turn his aggression against himself, to remain vulnerable to threats to his narcissistic equilibrium through loss of objects or loss of self-esteem when unsuccessful, and at times his attempts to play his parents off against each other in shows of his own omnipotence.

Mrs. T. stabilized within two years after the divorce and had a much more solid sense of herself. She maintained a job successfully and regained a level of financial security. At last contact, she had developed a sustained relationship with a man to whom Rich reacted with a predictable amount of rivalry and anger at losing his position as oedipal victor. Although on the manifest level Mr. T. seemed to have settled into his remarriage, his guardedness in discussing that relationship was suggestive of more underlying problems.

Discussion

This case illustrated the profound effect that parental separation had on a youngster whose development appeared to be progressing along the expected continuum. The loss of the parental unit, the partial loss of the paternal object, and the temporary affective unavailability of the maternal object burdened his ego beyond its capacity to cope and he became overtly symptomatic. He regressed in the face of these losses to earlier forms of behavior and clung ambivalently to his mother as the remaining parent. While Rich did not, in an absolute sense, lose his father as a significant person in his life, he was no longer a central figure in the family configuration and thus took on a diminished function in terms of being available to Rich in stemming the tide of the regression and resolution of oedipal issues. Rich's denial of the reality of the parental separation was expressed in the form of compelling reconciliation wishes. The loss of the family was deeply felt by both mother and son, and their fantasies of reuniting with the father were mutually reinforced. Rich became, in many senses, "the man of the house" (Tooley, 1976) and the "oedipal victor" (Neubauer, 1960). The loss, thus, took on particular meaning reflective of his oedipal age and stage at the time the event occurred.

Long-Term Effects of Parental Loss through Divorce

In both clinical and nonclinical populations, the long-term effects of loss through divorce have been studied. One of the complex problems in understanding the effect of parental loss through divorce on the course of development is in distinguishing specifically the impact of divorce from other stressors that may affect development over the life span. In a comparison of survey responses of two large-scale representative samples of the American adult population, the first in 1957 and the second in 1976, Kulka and Weingarten (1979) found surprisingly few differences on global measures of adjustment in a comparison of adults from divorced backgrounds with those from intact families of origin. It was their impression, however, that experiencing a parental divorce serves as "a marker event or an organizing framework . . . and that, while its overt consequences are few, it still exerts an influence in subtle ways through its effects on an individual's pattern of responding to, evaluating, and ordering life roles" (p. 58). They found modest support for the salience of parental separation and divorce during adulthood on adult adaptation, with adults who had experienced parental divorce more likely to report having felt an impending nervous breakdown, high psychological anxiety, and marital problems. Coming from a nonintact family of origin had more negative impact on the psychological well-being of men than of women.

The most significant long-term effects have been noted in the development of intimacy and commitment in heterosexual relationships. Kalter et al. (1985) reports in a study of young adult college women whose parents had divorced (a population that was brighter, more academically successful, and better off financially than the average) that they were "significantly less sanguine about the future and uncertain about ultimately being in a marriage that will last" (p. 542). In a ten-year follow-up study of forty young adults currently nineteen to twenty-nine years of age, Wallerstein (1985) reports that overall the young adults were in agreement with each other that they had sustained an important loss and experienced intensified anxiety about the hazards of love and commitment. They found little emotional comfort in the high incidence of divorce in their society and 66 percent expressed conscious fear of marriage despite their wish to marry. Twenty-six percent were intensely fearful of repeating their parents' mistakes in their own relationships, and an additional 40 percent were moderately worried.

From a clinical perspective, adolescents and adults in treatment often express intense affects of sadness and grief about parental divorces that occurred many years previously. The intensity of the longstanding affects and the ongoing impact of the experience on perceptions of the self, as well as anticipations and fears in object relationships, has been compelling. The unconscious compulsion to repeat past experiences in future relationships has seemed to propel young women, in particular, into either intense, frequent relationships which result in repeated experiences of loss and rejection and/or avoidance of intimacy and closeness in heterosexual relationships (Hetherington, 1972).

Summary

We have asked, "Why is it so traumatic for a child to experience a parental loss through divorce and what is the nature of the loss?" The child has to grieve over not only the acute sense of loss experienced at the time of the divorce and thereafter, but also over the ways in which the parents have altered their availability in assisting the child to meet and resolve subsequent developmental tasks. The loss of the parental and family unit is a permanent one that is often defended against with temporary or persistent reconciliation fantasies. The loss of the parental object may be partial and permanent, as occurs most often with the father, or acute and temporary, as when the mother is emotionally inaccessible during the divorce process. In order to grieve over the losses experienced, the child needs parental objects and other trusted adults to tolerate and cope with the acute painful affects at the time of the divorce. Ongoing, consistent relationships with both parents after divorce can, to the extent possible, enable the child to have access to those parental functions that meet the ongoing developmental needs of identification, development of positive sense of self and sexual identity, and resolution of ambivalence. The impact of the losses experienced over time may be seen later in recalled affects of sadness and grief and impairment in heterosexual relationships.

References

Anthony, E. J. (1974), Children at risk from divorce: A review. In: *The Child in his Family*, Vol. 3, eds. E. J. Anthony & C. Koupernek. New York: John Wiley & Sons.

Biller, H. B. (1981), Father absence, divorce and personality development. In: *The Role of the Father in Child Development*, 2nd ed., ed. M. E. Lamb. New York: John Wiley & Sons, pp. 489–552.

Bowlby, J. (1960), Grief and mourning in infancy and early childhood. *The Psychoanalytic Study of the Child*, 15:9–52. New York: International Universities Press.

———Parker, C. M. (1970), Separation and loss within the family. In: *The Child in his Family*, Vol. 1, eds. E. J. Anthony & C. Koupernek. New York: John Wiley & Sons.

Chethik, M., Dolin, N., Davies, D., Lohr, R., & Darrow, S. (1986), Children and divorce: The "negative" identification. *J. Divorce*, 10:121–138.

———Kalter, N. (1980), Developmental arrest following divorce: the role of the therapist as developmental facilitator. *J. Amer. Acad. Child Psychiat.*, 19:281–288.

——— ———(unpublished), Treatment of children and parents of divorce: A trauma-focused perspective.

———Plunkett, J., Colfer, M., & Lohr, R. (1984), Divorce: The parenting function and narcissistic conflict. *J. Prevent. Psychiat.*, 2:455–471.

Freud, A., & Burlingham, D. (1943), *War and Children*. New York: International Universities Press.

Hess, R., & Camara, F. (1979), Post-divorce family relationships as mediating factors in the consequences of divorce for children. *J. Social Iss.*, 35:79–96.

Hetherington, E. M. (1972), Effects of father-absence on personality development in adolescent daughters. *Development. Psychol.*, 7:313–326.

———Cox, M., & Cox, R. (1978), The aftermath of divorce. In: *Mother–Child, Father–Child Relationships*, eds. J. H. Stevens, Jr., & M. Matthews. Washington, DC: National Association for the Education of Young Children.

Kalter, N., & Chethik, M. (unpublished), Children of divorce: A developmental vulnerability model.

———Riemer, B., Brickman, A., & Chen, J. W. (1985), Implications of parental divorce for female development. *J. Amer. Acad. Child Psychiat.*, 24(5):538–544.

Kelly, J., & Wallerstein, J. (1976), The effects of parental divorce: Experiences of the child in early latency. *Amer. J. Orthopsychiat.*, 46:20–32.

Kulka, R. A., & Weingarten, H. (1979), The long-term effects of parental divorce in childhood on adult adjustment. *J. Social Iss.*, 35:50–78.

Lohr, R., Chethik, M., Press, S. E., & Solyom, A. (1981), Impact of divorce on children: Vicissitudes and therapeutic implications of the reconciliation fantasy. *J. Child Psychother.*, 7:123–136.

Mendell, A. E. (1983), Play therapy with children of divorced parents. In: *Handbook of Play Therapy*, eds. C. E. Schaefer & K. J. O'Connor. New York: John Wiley & Sons, pp. 320–354.

Nagera, H. (1970), Children's reaction to the death of important objects: A developmental approach. *The Psychoanalytic Study of the Child*, 25:360–400. New York: International Universities Press.

Neubauer, P. B. (1960), The one-parent-child and his oedipal development. *The Psychoanalytic Study of the Child*, 15:193–303. New York: International Universities Press.

Tessman, L. H. (1978), *Children of Parting Parents*. New York: Jason Aronson.

Tooley, K. (1976), Antisocial behavior and social alienation post divorce: The "man of the house" and his mother. *Amer. J. Orthopsychiat.*, 46:33–42.

Wallerstein, J. S. (1984), Children of divorce: Preliminary report of a ten-year follow-up of young children. *Amer. J. Orthopsychiat.*, 54:444–458.

———(1985), Children of divorce: A preliminary report of a ten-year follow-up of older children and adolescents. *J. Amer. Acad. Child Psychiat.*, 24:545–553.

———Kelly, J. B. (1974), The effects of parental divorce: The adolescent experience. In: *The Child in his Family: Children at Psychiatric Risk*, Vol. 3, eds. E. J. Anthony & C. Koupernek. New York: John Wiley & Sons.

——— ———(1975), The effects of parental divorce: Experience of the preschool child. *J. Amer. Acad. Child Psychiat.*, 14:600–616.

——— ———(1976), The effects of parental divorce: Experiences of the child in late latency. *Amer. J. Orthopsychiat.*, 46:256–269.

——— ———(1980), *Surviving the Breakup*. New York: Basic Books.

11

Complicated Mourning Over a Body Defect: The Making of a "Living Linking Object"

ROBERT ZUCKERMAN, PSY.D.
VAMIK VOLKAN, M.D.

The Representation of the Lost Object

We tend to think of uncomplicated mourning as "nature's exercise in loss and restitution" (Volkan, 1971, p. 255) and hence somehow benevolent and enriching, if painful. Furthermore, it is helpful to expand the term *loss* beyond its obvious use in connection with such catastrophic events as the death of a loved one. As we move from one phase of life to the next, from our passages through the earliest psychosexual stages and on through the rest of the life cycle, we leave behind or modify, and thus lose, what is familiar and reassuring. For example, much of the oral mother and the corresponding oral child are "lost" when the child reaches the anal phase. In the same way, when we develop secondary sex characteristics we "lose" our childhood body images. Since losses are frequent and inevitable, life is full of occasions wherein our responses to losses will be uncomplicated. What is important in the mourning process is what we do with the mental representations of the persons and things which are lost.

When mourning is not complicated, the healthy mourner ultimately develops *remembrance formation*. This term, coined by Tähkä (1984) refers to:

> [B]uilding and integrating the representation of the lost object into a remembrance of him as he was really experienced during a common period of life. Once it has been established, its later calling back to the mind, reminiscing about it and dismissing it again from the mind, are invariably experienced as activities of the self taking place exclusively on the subject's own conditions [p. 18].

Unhappily, however, not everyone is fortunate enough to develop nonpathological remembrance formation and/or to identify with the selective and enriching aspects of the lost object, as described by Hartmann, Kris, and Lowenstein (1946), Loewald (1962), and Volkan (1981). The in-depth study of complicated mourning is a study of what the mourner does, in maladaptive ways, with the representation of the lost object (Volkan, 1985). Such a representation may be "totally" (nonselectively) internalized (Ritvo and Solnit, 1958; Smith, 1975; Volkan, 1981), preserving within the mourner's self representation the ambivalent relationship which the survivor formerly enjoyed with the lost one.

Sometimes the mourner introjects but does not identify with the representation of the lost object. The representation remains within the mourner's self representation as if it were a foreign body (an introject). The mourner then maintains an internal and complicated relationship with the introject. At other times, however, the mourner keeps the representation of the lost object through linking objects. Volkan (1981) has described linking objects in detail elsewhere. They are inanimate objects made magical by the mourner to provide an external locus for the meeting of the representation of the lost one with the corresponding representation of the self. For example, an old, broken camera with a syringelike attachment became a linking object for a young man. It represented the broken dead father (he had died of multiple sclerosis) as well as the young man who had related to his sick father with ambivalence. The young man used a syringe to give his father injections while entertaining both loving and hostile thoughts about the sick man. As a linking object, the camera, which was owned by the father before his death, had to be protected at all costs and yet never be repaired. Through the utilization of the linking object, the young man *controlled* his reactions to the departed father but could not properly experience a grieving process.

For the mourner, another possibility is to inject the representation of the lost object into a living person, making the latter a kind of "living linking object" (Volkan, 1981) and then controlling the newly created reservoir/person. In our experience, most living linking objects serve parents in the complicated mourning of lost children. For example, a newborn child may become a reservoir for the representation of the dead child who was kept alive in his mother's mind. In this chapter, however, we will present the case of a woman who had a unique living linking object. Her son became a reservoir for her deformed spine. To allow her to exert absolute control over her male child/spine, along with its condensation with other symbolic meanings, the mourning over a body deformity was postponed.

Earlier, by displacement, other deformed persons came to represent her own deformed body; and as a result she avoided such persons. This phobic symptom formation, strengthened by denial, softened her experience of her anxiety. Later, when her son was born, she gave up her phobic symptoms but again relied on defense mechanisms which were familiar to her. The son became a reservoir (a displacement figure) to receive her externalization of her spine. This time, she did the opposite of avoiding the son—she controlled and protected him but she simultaneously perceived her son/spine as being in constant danger of becoming damaged. She wished to repair him, and the clinical picture she presented was of an extreme preoccupation with her son. In turn, as could be expected, he responded to his mother's pathogenic controlling behavior by developing psychological and behavioral symptomatology.

Case History

Mrs. Smith first came to one of us (R.Z.) when she presented her ten-and-one-half-year-old son, Billy, for evaluation and treatment of a long history of chronic academic difficulties consisting primarily of mediocre performance in school. Previously, this youngster had been seen by a series of education specialists and had been diagnosed as having an array of learning difficulties and emotional problems. Generally, everyone who evaluated this boy noted that he was a highly anxious child who was overshadowed by his two successful younger sisters. It was obvious that Billy spent far more time on his studies than was expected, although he generally spent more energy worrying than he did producing. His work was average at best. Likewise, his capacity to enjoy sports and friendships was compromised by his anxiety, which he experienced as a chronic and unremitting burden.

Despite his actual limitations, which were not insignificant, his mother's perception of his level of functioning far exaggerated his disabilities. If he received one failing grade on a paper, his mother would panic and become convinced that he would fail the entire year. She was vastly overinvested in her job of mediating between him and the outside world.

From his birth, Billy's mother was aware of her worries for his welfare. Early in his childhood, she found herself desperate to ensure that he would have friends. When he was three years old, she arranged an elaborate social calendar which she would tirelessly orchestrate, even though this meant, because they lived on a farm, driving miles to nearby towns to find friends to bring home for him. Her episodes of "panic" and "desperation" around this boy were numerous, and the therapist was introduced to them from his earliest acquaintance with the family.

This happened when the therapist first attempted to set up an appointment to meet the youngster for the evaluation, and offered Mrs. Smith an early afternoon hour which would require Billy to miss the last portion of the school day. Despite her experiencing, as she related much later in her treatment, a wonderful sense of hope at the scheduling of the appointment for her son, the idea that she was required to take him out of school for even a brief period caused her an episode of acute anxiety and drove her to call Dr. Zuckerman and beg him to schedule a special evening time for her son.

Mrs. Smith was the second of two daughters, first-generation American children born to Scandinavian parents. Her father was devoted to his first daughter, but wished for a son. So devastated was he that the second child was not the longed-for boy, that the patient was ignored. Frequently she would imagine that, "He would have loved me better were I a boy." When the patient was six years old, in the middle of the oedipal phase of development, as she was searching eagerly for ways to delight her father, her older sister, the father's beloved child, contracted a mild case of Scheuermann's kyphosis, a degenerative disease of the spine leading in severe cases to marked spinal curvature and pain. As a consequence of this, the father redoubled his solicitousness, and the sister was elevated to the status of "queen" in the family. Mrs. Smith recalled the thought: "I wish I had kyphosis. Then he would love me better."

Mrs. Smith did fairly well in school and social activities until she was twelve years old. At age twelve, she did indeed develop kyphosis. From the outset there was considerable delay in getting her medical attention, some of which may have been caused by the youngster's unwillingness to complain to her parents of discomfort in her back. The parents first took her to a chiropractor but subsequently medical attention was delayed even more. Ultimately, the youngster was placed for two weeks in a ward for handicapped children. In retrospect, Mrs. Smith suspects that this was simply an extended diagnostic period, although at the time she expected to undergo corrective surgery. As an adult she recalls profound rage and disappointment at being sent home without surgery: "They just gave up hope on me."

Following her return from the hospital, the patient became reclusive and increasingly isolated herself from her family. Years later, in her psychotherapy, she recalled how devastated she was: "I was just beginning to look at myself in the mirror and admire my new breasts and beautiful developing body. I was becoming a beautiful woman. If this hadn't happened I would have overcome everything—I would have been okay."

Verbalized now, these words were the expression of her thoughts from early adolescence. Having "lost" the oedipal father, as a beautiful woman she could still find a worthy man to help her repair and replace what was lost earlier.

The parents both suffered from their daughter's grotesque transformation and the mother encouraged the child to dress creatively and to wear beautiful clothing to cover up her deformity. The collusion of denial between mother and daughter was so profound that following her return from the hospital the patient managed to go through her entire life investing boundless energy in covering herself with beautiful and stylish clothing without once looking at her spine in the three-way mirrors in the dressing rooms of the fashionable stores she would frequent.

The father was convinced that the patient's illness left her barren and that she would never marry. Indeed, so hopeless was the father for his daughter's prospects that when the patient was courted by a dark-skinned Indian of a vastly different cultural, racial, and religious background, the father encouraged her to embrace the man—this despite a strong taboo against going outside the family's cultural circle as well as the girl's certainty that she could never marry someone of such an alien background.

The patient remained stable but withdrawn and isolated throughout adolescence. She had limited social interactions outside the family. While her denial of her experience of the loss of her beauty and her straight spine intensified, so did her phobic preoccupations with the deformed people she occasionally saw in her neighborhood. At age twenty-three she married a young man and, at age twenty-eight, to her father's astonishment, she gave birth to her first child—a boy. To her great surprise, she found this boy to be the apple of her father's eye and suddenly Mrs. Smith and her son were the focus of her father's intense devotion. Bewildered but delighted, the dream of the loving father, which she had abandoned years ago, was suddenly fulfilled.

Immediately following the birth of her son, Mrs. Smith found herself thrilled with her resurrected relationship with her father and miraculously freed of her preoccupation with neighborhood cripples. But now, even before she could man-ufacture rationalizations for her anxiety, Mrs. Smith found herself experiencing panic around her son. As noted above, she was soon plagued with obsessional worries about every aspect of her youngster's development, and she found him wanting in all areas of social and physical functioning. By the time he was a latency age child he had identified sufficiently with her anxiety for his academic and social functioning to be indeed impaired, and his problems continued to escalate until the family ulti-mately brought the boy for psychotherapy.

Course of Treatment

Initially, the youngster was the psychotherapy patient and the mother was available to provide information about the boy's daily life as well as for counseling to help her make changes at home which would facilitate the boy's progress. From the outset, however, Mrs. Smith and her therapist became aware that despite her best conscious intentions she was powerless to make any changes in her management of Billy.

Subsequently, exploring her paralysis, from the earliest hours she associated her son's imperfect academic performance with her own physical imperfections, and she began to describe her feelings of guilt, stating that she deserved her kyphosis for something bad she had done. This established, in part, the externalization of her bad spine onto her baby, which she then saw as vulnerable and defective, and in need of repair and protection.

From this point on, the therapeutic work with the mother was far more introspective and exploratory, and ultimately proved to be a true psychoanalytic psychotherapy. The boy and his therapist continued to meet for a short period of time, but his improvement was rapid and therapy was terminated within a year. As this chapter is concerned with the mother's psycholog-ical experiences and difficulties, we will not further address the course of events concerning Billy.

In the first dream Mrs. Smith reported, during her first session following a break for Thanksgiving, she dreamed that she met her therapist in a public place and observed that he had two broken legs. Her thought in her dream was that it was these broken legs which forced the therapist to cancel their therapy hour, which would have fallen on Thanksgiving Day, and Mrs. Smith was convinced that Dr. Zuckerman's pain because of his broken legs was less unbearable than the pain of being with her. This was her first expression in the transference of what would later appear clearly as a characteristic use of men as external representations of her vulnerable spine.

Subsequently, Mrs. Smith continued to define her dilemma with her therapist as well as with her son. In this dream, the patient found herself in the waiting room of Dr. Zuckerman's office carrying a spiral notebook. The spiral portion of this notebook, her symbolic spine, had been damaged. The therapist understood that underlying the patient's externalization of her conflicts about her spine was also her awareness that the twisted spine was a burden that she herself carried.

Very early in the course of her treatment, Billy approached his twelfth birthday, the age at which Mrs. Smith became ill. As this happened, she visualized her body as similar to her son's body at this age and she began to become preoccupied with her pathogenic identification with Billy.

She dreamed repeatedly about the therapist being injured as a result of his acquaintance with her, and through her dreams the patient and therapist both learned that as a transference figure, Dr. Zuckerman, too, became a reservoir for her spine. She reported a dream which detailed the acute anxiety associated with her deformity and the desperation which led her to the solution of externalizing the spine. In the dream the patient found herself in a car with a man in the driver's seat and a child sitting between her and the man. There was another child outside of the car (also representing the patient, but the patient stricken with kyphosis) who was screaming in agony and crying. In the dream, the patient feared any movement of the car as well as the child outside the car. As she covered her eyes and the eyes of the child in the car, she asked the man (we understood that he represented the therapist) to look at the suffering child outside. As he looked, his face disintegrated before her.

Mrs. Smith was terrified by this anxiety dream and frequently recalled it as an alien feeling throughout the next two years of her therapy, not akin to anything else in her past that she could ever remember. Yet, simultaneously, she seemed to know that the dream was a global distillation of her entire experience of the horrible illness and deformity of her adolescence. In later years, for example, she would note that she did not understand how she lived through that time and that if faced with that experience again she would surely kill herself. Indeed, in her psychotherapy, she often returned to the terror of this dream as an explanation of why she could not stand to think about the years of her illness. Later in her therapy, the dream served as a reference point for her worries about her therapist and the guilt she experienced for subjecting him to what she felt was the intolerable pain of being with her and her illness. Similarly, the dream became the standard representation of her wish that her therapist become another carrier of the damaged spine as well as the guilt derivative of such a wish.

As Mrs. Smith became more aware of her worry and fantasies about the therapist, she felt increasingly guilty. In the manifest content of another dream, the therapist became the receptacle of her deformity. She dreamed that he was alone in a shopping center which she owned. He was dressed in sloppy clothes and was impoverished. She noted that this condition was new for him and that he had been doing well in earlier days. She felt profoundly responsible for the therapist and painfully guilty.

During subsequent sessions, Mrs. Smith talked of the fragility of men and how, if she had not withdrawn from her family after becoming ill, she could have saved her father from his unhappiness which, she felt, caused the illness that eventually led to his death from cardiac disease.

As if her deformity could be passed from her body to another's, Mrs. Smith began to fear that she would pass on to the therapist all of the badness which was in her. On one occasion she even missed an hour in order to avoid contaminating him, and this event became the first foreshadowing of a temporary hiatus in her treatment which occurred when the intensity of her anxiety over such destructive fantasies became unbearable. She became aware of being plagued by the fear that she would hurt men with whom she was close, enumerating her father, her husband, her son, and her therapist. She became preoccupied with a wish to stop her psychotherapy and warned her therapist: "You would be better off without me, you don't know what you're getting yourself into."

It was in the tenth month of her treatment that Mrs. Smith revealed that her fear of deformed people in the neighborhood seemed to evaporate as soon as her son was born, and in its place she noted a heightened depression and sadness of which she was heretofore unaware. She felt unsure whether she could tolerate the therapeutic work of disentangling her illness from her preoccupation with her son, and in an effort to protect the therapist from her destructive fantasies, she made an appointment for a consultation with a psychiatrist of foreign origin. She imagined that an immigrant had been through hard times and she would not need to worry about his welfare as she worried about her therapist's. Another meaning of this consultation was to be understood later.

The patient felt a desperate need not to involve Dr. Zuckerman in her tragedy, commenting, "I hurt everyone." About fourteen months after the start of her therapy, she dreamed that she was going on a journey with the therapist and with others, including Billy. It was her job to pick out Dr. Zuckerman's clothing for the journey and this was burdensome. She tried to choose for him from an array of children's clothing, but then realized with relief that he was an adult and he probably had his own clothing. She noted: "When I think of facing my problem I feel like I'll be destroyed, like I'll disintegrate," and to the thought of disintegration she associated the face of the man in the dream reported a year earlier. It should be recalled that under her mother's influence, the two of them had attempted to cover up Mrs. Smith's deformity under beautiful clothing.

Soon her son turned twelve. She felt a wave of panic when thinking about this and was reluctant to allow him to go to overnight camp because she needed to watch over him. It was possible that he might get kyphosis during the time he was out of sight. She felt depressed when she thought about living without her preoccupation with Billy and had the conscious thought, "Now it will get me." She understood her anxiety at this time to reflect her awareness that, without an external receptacle for her deformity, she had no choice but to keep the deformed part within herself.

In the seventeenth month of her treatment, Mrs. Smith allowed herself to feel optimism about her psychotherapy, but cautioned the therapist that even if he understood her relationship with Billy, he could never understand her destiny, how unbearable was the deformity of her spine, and that these bad feelings would never go away.

She elaborated in detail worries introduced earlier—her concerns for her therapist's health and well-being. The therapist wondered with the patient if she might have a desire to damage and injure him, to break his bones and make him a cripple, too. The next hour, Mrs. Smith cut her toe on the therapist's door while crossing the threshold into his office. The talion law at work!

Following this interaction and its interpretation, Mrs. Smith began to experience increased anxiety. She worried more about losing her therapist and revealed, as if telling him a secret, that as a young teenager she dated an Indian for four years. This Indian became friends with her father and for years both the suitor and her father begged her to marry him. While she continued to date him, she never had sexual relations with him and knew she could never marry someone of a foreign background. She felt guilty, as if she were using him even though she never deceived him.

It was here that the therapist understood her wish to consult a foreign psychiatrist. Her father, for his own reasons, had felt that kyphosis would leave his daughter barren, and this meant that she would not find a suitable husband. At best she would do for a foreigner, who was perceived also as "defective." By dating the Indian, the patient was following her father's "suggestion," simultaneously living out her attempt to triumph over her rejection by her father and yet please him in order to gain his love. At this point, listening to her insistence that she would not have sex with her foreign boyfriend, the therapist wondered if the foreigner also represented an externalized image of the father, disguised under a different culture, religion, and skin color. The therapist felt that the exploration of this should await further development in the treatment.

Mrs. Smith revealed, as if all deformities must be kept secret, that she had heretofore not told her therapist that her husband's chest was disfigured in an automobile collision several years ago. As with her father's heart condition, she felt that the worries which she caused her husband were responsible for his auto accident. She believed that she hurt every man in her life and she reported feeling increasingly guilty.

At this point, two years into her treatment, Mrs. Smith's preoccupation with her need to get away from the therapist intensified, and she became increasingly convinced that he should not be a part of all this sickness. During this period, she dreamed that she stained his couch, and she detailed a simultaneous desperation to be with him and a feeling that she must escape, the meaning of which became clearer later on. She dreamed of mourning for a badly treated child, and wondered how she could possibly survive the course of this psychotherapy.

In the following session, the patient reported dreaming of a girl with an injured and disfigured face. The therapist thought that after an intense reliving in the transference of her finding a reservoir in others for her damaged spine and after the interpretation of this process, Mrs. Smith was once more beginning to take responsibility for her feelings about her deformity. It was then that Mrs. Smith revealed that when she was a young girl of about six years of age, her older sister contracted a mild case of kyphosis. Her sister was demanding and exhausting in her burdening of the family with her illness. Mrs. Smith recalled wishing that she, too, would get kyphosis so that she could demonstrate to her father how she would not be demanding and how she would not burden him in the same way. Again, the patient worried about the therapist and needed to remind herself that he was delicate. She worried about staining his couch and considered saving him from disappointment by consulting another therapist—a dark skinned foreigner!

By the twenty-sixth month of treatment the patient gained a greater understanding of the role of her kyphosis in her

oedipal conflict. She now understood that her spine represented, in part, a wished-for penis. Her sister's kyphosis had
turned Mrs. Smith's attention to her own spine in the midst of
her oedipal phase. She would be willing to have kyphosis, to
have her spine ruined, to give up her fantasied penis, in order
to have her father love her. Furthermore, the patient detailed
a profound oedipal–incestuous guilt that she felt deserved
punishment. For both reasons, she was unable to mourn the
"loss" of her spine when it finally occurred. In an association,
she recalled that she began her menstrual period just before
she was sent to the hospital for her kyphosis and linked this
recollection to worries about staining her therapist's couch. She
felt she must flee the therapist in order not to repeat the history
with her father. During her hours she caressed the couch with
her hand and described feeling closer to the therapist through
touching the couch. This led her to feeling guilty for being "too
attached . . . I'm bad for you."

As noted earlier, when her son was born her father showered
her with attention. At her son's christening her father gave her
an extravagant gift. She underscored that this gift was from the
father alone and not from both parents. Her wish to have her
oedipal wishes fulfilled was fantasied as being possible if her
penis/spine was given to her son whom her father also adored.
However, Mrs. Smith never totally wished to give up the hope
for a fantasied penis. She once remarked that when she was
buried, her spine would be straightened in her casket!

Two weeks later, Mrs. Smith exhibited increased anxiety. The
manifest content of her dreams suggested that if she were to
remain in treatment the therapist would die. His attempts to
explore these feelings did not ease Mrs. Smith's anxiety and,
indeed, she interrupted her treatment against her therapist's
recommendation.

Now, without the benefit of her treatment, her old symptoms
returned. She became preoccupied with Billy. Realizing this,
two months after interrupting her treatment, she returned to
resume her therapeutic work. She seemed now more committed than ever to understanding other issues that were unconsciously connected with the deformity of her spine.

This time she could not lie on the couch lest she be flooded with anxiety. Instead, she sat up on the couch and the therapist encouraged her to relate her fantasies. She stated that if she were to lie down, she would "lose" her therapist because he would be unable to see her as a beautiful woman (her breasts); he would only see her spine. Further exploration of her thoughts revealed the intensity of her unresolved oedipal strivings.

As noted earlier, we formulated that, for Mrs. Smith, "losing" her erect spine was perceived as a feminizing, albeit, masochistic, process. Before she developed kyphosis—when the oedipal phase was in the ascendancy—she had wished this illness upon herself in order to win her father's attention. When she actually developed kyphosis, at puberty, she paradoxically felt that she could not attract men. Her father joined in this thinking and made her believe that she could only attract foreigners, men representing the devalued father/persons.

She reported a series of events heretofore unrevealed. It seems that after she returned from the hospital where her kyphosis was diagnosed, the events had caused regressive reactivation of early conflicts. The "loss" of her spine became condensed with other psychosexual issues and conflicts. She wished to be sure that she would not lose her oedipal father.

At the time that she returned from the hospital, her parents slept in separate bedrooms. Now Mrs. Smith was able to tell her therapist that she would crawl into bed with her father and wish that he make love to her. At the same time she was terrified of such a possibility. In reality, she never told her father about her thoughts and he indeed never approached her sexually.

When she could no longer tolerate this conflict, she withdrew from her father as well as from the other members of her family, but her incestuous wishes remained. When, much later, the father developed heart disease, she had a fantasy that something "bad" within her (her incestuous wishes) caused his illness and his death. Later still, she felt that she caused her husband's auto accident. The patient referred to herself as "ruthless" and "heartless." Now the therapist understood why, when the intense oedipal longings were coming into focus in the transference, the patient had to interrupt her treatment.

She was, in part, saving his life! With this understanding, the therapy now took a new turn.

Since our aim in this chapter is to illustrate how Mrs. Smith could not successfully mourn the "loss" of her spine, and instead kept it alive in a "living linking object," the many other aspects of her treatment (which is currently in the third year and progressing well—Mrs. Smith has returned to lying on the couch) are outside the scope of our presentation and will not be dealt with here. We are, of course, fully aware that this is a highly selective presentation, and we are in no way diminishing the importance of other aspects of the treatment not discussed here.

Discussion

Clinical work, as well as observations of the early relationship between children and their mothers, have shown that a mother's anxiety is conveyed to her child. In a general sense, under stressful conditions a young child reflects the anxiety of an anxious mother. If the mother is chronically anxious, her condition produces a lasting effect on her developing child.

There exists, however, a different, although associated phenomenon in which something is also conveyed to the child from the early mother. Volkan (1981) described this phenomenon and stated:

> Unassimilated object and self-representations that are located, so to speak, within the mother, can be deposited within the child during the early mother–child interaction. If we compare the conveying of anxiety from the early mother to her child with the conveying of an infection by the transmission of germs, we may compare the passage of unassimilated self and object representations, with their related affect dispositions, from mother to child with the inheritance by the child of the mother's genes [p. 318].

Volkan uses the term *generational continuity* in describing the passage of unassimilated self and object representations from the mothering persons to their children. Such unassimilated representations of others become depersonalized and absorbed into the child's self system as identifications. If the unassimilated self and object representations were originally idealized by the mother, such identifications enrich the child's self representation.

However, if the unassimilated representations which are conveyed to the child remain unintegrated and continue to have a "life" of their own, a pathological inner adaptation may develop. For example, Volkan (1981) showed that when a mother, under traumatic conditions, has lost someone close to her and cannot complete her mourning, she may use her newborn child as the recipient of her representation of the deceased. The newborn then becomes a replacement child (Cain and Cain, 1964; Green and Solnit, 1964; Poznanski, 1972) and a living link to the lost object, whose representation she keeps alive in her mind. Deposited, as it were, within her child, it may not meld into his or her self representations, but may instead stay to some extent encapsulated, leading to the existence of two confusing and incompatible identities in the same person. Poznanski (1972) states:

> Replacing a child with another allows the parents partially to deny the first child's death. The replacement child then acts as a barrier to the parental acknowledgement of death, since a real child exists who is a substitute [p. 1193].

In other words, the establishment of a reservoir to receive the representation of the lost object, the formation of a living linking object, prevents the parents from progressing through a proper mourning process.

What is interesting in the case study described in this chapter is that Billy became a reservoir not for the representation of a previously lost sibling, but his mother's "lost" spine, with its repressed unconscious, symbolic meanings. Mrs. Smith fantasied that she could straighten her spine in Billy if she continually protected it/him. At the same time, however, she behaved as if the spine/son were in perpetual jeopardy. Mrs. Smith kept herself in limbo by "twisting" the development of the boy/spine while simultaneously keeping a ceaseless vigil to protect him/it from all possible adversity. Thus, her mourning for her damaged spine, which in the long run would end with her acceptance of her deformity, was arrested.

Billy was the living reservoir for a lost object. Our clinical case study would be complete if we were able to understand and examine, in depth, the representation of his mother's spine in his mind. However, Billy's treatment was a form of supportive therapy. In treatment, we learned of the general effects his mother's controlling attitude had upon him. Once his mother underwent a psychoanalytic psychotherapy, Billy improved. We hope, however, in spite of this very selective report, that our understanding of Mrs. Smith's intrapsychic experience as her treatment progressed provides sufficient clinical evidence to illustrate that externalization of "lost" body parts into another living being does occur.

The utilization of a child as a living linking object is one way to attempt to resolve a mother's complicated mourning. As already stated, on occasions this leads to the enrichment of the child's developing psyche. For example, the child as an adult may exhibit a sense of mission to repair others (Volkan and Itzkowitz, 1984). But it may also lead to psychopathology, as in Billy's case.

In our diagnostic interviews and treatment with patients, we have become more sensitive to issues pertaining to generational continuity and have been impressed with the frequency of our encounters with living linking objects. Mrs. Smith's case shows us how living linking objects are established. Furthermore it reminds us that, when mourning is complicated, it is not only the dead person's representations that are passed to new generations, but also the representations of "lost" body parts with their accompanying symbolic meanings.

Finally, it seems useful to note that, as Volkan (1981) observed in his case of the "Night of the Living Dead," there are many examples in clinical literature as well as in life of people becoming living linking objects. This chapter, to our knowledge, is the first presentation of both sides of this phenomenon—how the mourner (in this case Mrs. Smith) experiences the other (her son) as a representation of the lost object (her spine) and how the "receptacle" of this representation assumes the expected characteristics.

References

Cain, A. C., & Cain, B. S. (1964), On replacing a child. *J. Amer. Acad. Child Psychiat.*, 3:443–456.

Green, N., & Solnit, A. J. (1964), Reactions to the threatened loss of a child: A vulnerable child syndrome. *Pediatrics*, 34:58–66.

Hartmann, H., Kris, E., & Loewenstein, R. (1946), Comments on the formation of psychic structure. *The Psychoanalytic Study of the Child*, 2:11–38. New York: International Universities Press.

Loewald, H. (1962), On the therapeutic action of psychoanalysis. *Internat. J. Psycho-Anal.*, 41:16–33.

Poznanski, E. O. (1972), The "replacement child." A saga of unresolved parental grief. *Behav. Pediat.*, 81:1190–1193.

Ritvo, S., & Solnit, A. J. (1958), Influences of early mother–child interaction on the identification process. *The Psychoanalytic Study of the Child*, 13:64–85. New York: International Universities Press.

Smith, J. H. (1975), On the work of mourning. In: *Bereavement: Its Psychological Aspects*, eds. B. Schoenberg, I. Gerber, A. Wiener, A. H. Kutscher, D. Peretz, & A. C. Carr. New York: Columbia University Press, pp. 18–25.

Tähkä, V. (1984), Dealing with object loss. *Scand. Psychoanal. Rev.*, 7:13–33.

Volkan, V. D. (1971), A study of a patient's "re-grief work" through dreams, psychological tests, and psychoanalysis. *Psychiat. Quart.*, 45:255–273.

———(1981), *Linking Objects and Linking Phenomena: A Study of the Forms, Symptoms, Metapsychology, and Therapy of Complicated Mourning*. New York: International Universities Press.

———(1985), The scope of depressive states. In: *Depressive States and Their Treatment*, ed. V. D. Volkan. New York: Jason Aronson, pp. 1–17.

———Itzkowitz, N. (1984), *The Immortal Atatürk*. Chicago: University of Chicago Press.

Part IV

Empirical Studies
on Loss and
Their Implications:
Research Perspectives

12

Early Childhood Parent Death, Psychic Trauma and Organization, and Object Relations

DAVID R. DIETRICH, PH.D.

Painful and enduring effects of object loss and trauma were noted though poorly understood long before psychoanalysis existed. From its very beginnings, psychoanalysis has evidenced a deep and abiding clinical and theoretical interest in loss and trauma and their pervasive impact upon psychic organization and functioning. The clinical, theoretical, and research problems arising from the spectrum of complex effects that early childhood parent loss has upon intrapsychic and personality functioning are vast indeed. This is especially so when a young child's parent dies. Psychoanalytic researchers have devoted substantial clinical and theoretical efforts toward the clarification of the various problems relating to object loss (Freud, 1917; Deutsch, 1937; Rochlin, 1959, 1965; Pollock, 1961, 1962, 1972; Fleming and Altschul, 1963; R. Furman, 1964; Wolfenstein, 1966, 1969; E. Furman, 1974; Dietrich, 1986a), and object relations (Freud, 1905, 1915; Hartmann, 1939; Mahler, 1960; Jacobson, 1964; Mahler, Pine, and Bergman, 1975; Panel, 1978; Boesky, 1983; Greenberg and Mitchell, 1983).

Trauma has also been the focus of considerable psychoanalytic study (Freud, 1920, 1939; Greenacre, 1952; Furst, 1963; Krystal, 1968, 1978). However, while a substantial clinical literature exists, almost no empirical psychoanalytic research has been available which directly addresses the effects of the early death of a parent, specifically upon object relations and object representations.

For the past several years, the author has been actively involved in psychoanalytic research on various facets of object loss, and in particular early parent loss by death (Dietrich, 1979, 1981, 1983, 1984b, 1986a,b), and in developing scales for assessing aspects of object relations and object representations (Dietrich, Bell, Lycaki, and Sitaram, 1984; Dietrich, 1986a).

I shall limit the present chapter to a discussion of one type of psychic trauma, early childhood death of a parent, and some of its specific, and apparently enduring, effects upon aspects of object relations, object representations, and intrapsychic organization. I will also briefly include some findings regarding certain problems which often arise in the psychoanalytic psychotherapy of these patients.

A further aim is to describe a clinically relevant psychoanalytic research instrument and strategy which the writer and associates have found to be useful in acquiring relevant data in this area.

Moreover, the clinical and research evidence which I review and present in this chapter has led me to posit a developmental line of mourning and what I have referred to as the lost-immortal parent complex.

Within the context of this chapter I will always be referring to loss brought on by death of a parent, unless otherwise indicated.

Drive Organization, Fixation, and the Trauma of Early Childhood Parent Death

Some degree of decline, dissolution, and resolution of the Oedipus complex is a necessary and in fact crucial condition for the eventual adequate development of drive control. Children who grow up with a single parent and whose sexual drives remain, so to speak, unrestricted to a significant degree, often have inadequate ability to sublimate (Buxbaum, 1980). The observation that individuals who have experienced early childhood death of a parent typically reveal problems in superego structuralization has been reported by Pollock (1961), Fleming and Altschul (1963), E. Furman (1974), and Dietrich (1984b).

Depending upon the phase-dominance of the psychosexual and ego levels of development the child has thus far achieved, and the specific conflicts which were in the ascendancy at the time of the parent's death, drives may not become adequately fused and drive development may not proceed normally. There are, in addition, relevant pre- and postloss factors and influences (the degree of the child's ambivalence toward the deceased parent [E. Furman, 1974] as well as the deceased and surviving parent's ambivalence toward the child). Libidinal cathexis of varying degrees of intensity then remains attached to the representation of the lost, dead object. In his 1962 paper "Internalization, Separation, Mourning and the Superego," Hans Loewald writes, "Figuratively speaking, in the process of internalization, the drives take aspects of the object with them into the ego" (p. 492). Hartmann (1952) noted "One may well say that in man the human objects are by far the most important sector of reality" (p. 255).

I agree with E. Furman (1974) when she states that "The mental representation of the lost love object retains some cathexis. The amount varies and depends on many factors" (p. 52). What should be added, however, is that one would anticipate drive organization *always* carries the stamp of this type of early object loss, which is reflected in the persistence of the dominant phase of drive development which is present at the time of the loss. Yet, evidence suggests not all such children become neurotic, or develop some other type of more malignant psychopathology. In "Aspects of Internalization," Schafer (1968) suggests that Rapaport's (1951) conceptual organization of memories is contradicted by what Schafer calls the immortality of the object. The immortality of the object "stems from the drive organization of memories, that is, from memories— usually unconscious memories—having remained subject to the primary process. *In the drive organization, memories are not memories but realities:* they follow Freud's hypothetical model of the hallucinated wish-fulfilling object of infancy; they represent all those objects that exist in psychic reality simply because they are remembered (or imagined) objects of drives" (p. 222).

For Schafer, in what he terms the *drive organization of anticipations,* the lost loved object is not an individual who will return in the future at some point in time, but rather someone who exists. Freud's "indestructible unconscious" (1900) and "immortal id" (1932) are emphasized by Schafer in his discussion in support of his views. I concur with Schafer when he comments that objects which are of importance later in development are inexorably based upon those of importance earlier in development.

With the experience of early parent loss, drive organization becomes altered and affected in major respects. Since the object which was the aim of drive derivatives is in reality suddenly and traumatically gone, the object becomes contaminated by qualities of the drives which have now become immortal, so that drive development and organization is fundamentally fixated. This has, in a majority of cases, significant implications for a number of developmental areas. These include resolution of the oedipus complex, structuralization of the superego, further ego development including the synthetic function (Nunberg, 1931) and integrative functions of the ego, development of object relations, including self and object representation development, the developmental course of narcissism, development of characterologic traits and defensive styles, and the developmental course and specific organization of conflicts and compromise formations.

With the type of loss I am discussing in the present chapter, libidinal cathexis remains, to a significant extent, tied to the object, which as mentioned, has been transformed into a particular type of immortal object; that is, one which is experienced subjectively as not really lost yet lost, not really dead yet dead, not actually gone but gone, not irretrievably lost, not inexorably dead. Drive fusion cannot develop adequately or optimally, nor can drive development otherwise proceed as it normally does.

What I am suggesting here is that the young child, to a large degree, does not withdraw libido from the lost-dead parent, in terms of their drive organization and in the primary process realm. Erna Furman (1974) has written: "The development of self-esteem, the investment of ego functions and activities, depend to a considerable degree on the libidinization by the most important love object" (p. 53). And: "The loss of the vital love object endangers both the building up of the personality and the varied narcissistic satisfactions derived from its functioning" (p. 53).

I would add to this that early childhood parent death also very often alters and endangers the building up of developmentally phase-appropriate object relations and representations and their corresponding respective anlage and precursors. However, it is important to keep in mind this can be profoundly influenced by availability of a libidinal replacement. As Erna Furman (1974) goes on to point out: "For the young child, decathexis of the mental representation of the love object can diminish or even abolish these satisfactions and prevent their further development. In the prelatency child particularly, the 'sum of narcissistic gratifications' may therefore not exercise a demand for withdrawing his attachments but rather for clinging to the representation of the dead love object" (p. 53).

As Schafer (1968) has noted, it is on the higher levels of psychic functioning and ego (and cognitive) organization, conceptualization, and comprehension that the individual conceptualizes and "understands" object loss. What I am attempting to show is that the child can only intellectually understand and synthesize in terms of secondary process operations the reality-based aspects of parent death as a direct function of his or her level of psychological and ego development. This would indicate the need for a developmental line of mourning, which I posit later.

In other words, complete oedipal resolution is very often impaired with a lost parent, one who is dead and at the same time psychically lost yet immortal: one who is frozen in time, on the one hand, yet simultaneously undergoing transformational change primarily as a function of the child's developing and increasingly more complex ego and unconscious fantasy life. At first glance there is an apparent paradox in these cases. There is an immutable core that remains fixed, despite transformational and developmental changes. When the death of a parent occurs early enough, such as in the prephallic oedipal child, whatever oedipal resolution eventually takes place occurs largely within the context of typical triangular oedipal resolution with the new replacement parent (or with a parent substitute), if one is available. Yet, instead of a triangular situation, what psychically exists for the child is a triangular situation plus one. Two oedipally longed-for parents exist: the one, a memory, a longed-for ghost, lost but not forgotten, cathected (to varying degrees), and idealized. Very often the other (the replacement parent or parent substitute) is experienced as an imposter, a real individual who is a pale imitation, a poor substitute for the original, loved parent.

The type of psychic trauma I am here discussing has elements of ongoing strain trauma, as well as searching, pining, and longing for the lost parent, which is more intensely reexperienced at each new developmental step the child, adolescent, or adult takes.

Also, this type of trauma has some features of psychic shock trauma. Early parental death exerts effects upon many facets of self and object representations, and the child's representational world (Sandler and Rosenblatt, 1962). A great many areas of development, as noted earlier, are to varying degrees affected by this type of trauma because of the typically comprehensive nature of its traumatic effects upon virtually all aspects of intrapsychic functioning.

These individuals often exhibit important distortions in their experience of time. The experience of the parent death is not limited to a discrete, time-focused, time-limited, singular event but may reverberate in different ways at different times throughout the individual's life. Rather, various aspects of the object loss and trauma may be experienced almost continuously, intermittently but throughout and in time—the loss is lived and reexperienced in time—and are always present. The loss and lost object do not simply recede into the past, for the past is always temporally a part of the present; that is, the present is always partially experienced as missing, lost, dead, gone away, removed in the representation of the lost, though paradoxically present parent. Terr (1984) has discussed in some detail some effects of trauma on the experience of time.

Due to the relatively indelible imprinting upon the unconscious fantasy system of the child of this type of trauma, it creates a lifelong, nuclear, central unconscious fantasy system. Again, typically the degree of the impact (quantitatively) of the loss is greater than in certain other types of psychic traumata because of the enduring deleterious and pathogenic effects early childhood parent death has on developing psychic organization and structures. These effects occur by virtue of the fact that an actual, available parent is immensely necessary for optimal development of most psychic structures. Again, such effects can be altered to some extent by the nature of the replacement parent (if available), and the quality of the replacement object. The body ego is also altered in early childhood parent loss cases, although this will not be further dealt with here. Therefore, (1) as a result of the effect early parent death has on identification and how the identification process is interfered with; and (2) due to the effect it exerts on the aggressive drives (and the common unconscious experience of having killed one's own parent); (3) and, related to this, the unique manner in which competitive and murderous impulses are experienced as having come true—the death as being caused by the child (and therefore becoming in fantasy, and in a certain sense *in reality,* the oedipal victor *or* loser); and (4) of the great and profound ongoing experience of rejection (experienced as the parent leaving, abandoning them, departing, preferring someone or something else to them; once more, depending upon the age and psychosexual level at which the loss occurred and the meaning it had and has for the child), I am suggesting that early childhood death of a parent is a type of psychic trauma with its own special, specific, and organized constellation of structural and developmental sequelae, psychic consequences, layering of unconscious fantasies, clinical or less often subclinical constellations, and compromise formations. In short, it has its own enduring, specifiable, largely unconscious configuration which I have referred to as the lost-immortal parent complex (Dietrich, 1986a).

With early childhood loss by death of a parent, the exquisite, reciprocal, ongoing interaction between child and parent is not present. The sense of intergenerational continuity and immortality is broken and lost. The knowledge the child who has suffered parent loss early has or will have at a later date is of being parented by another adult, not their own mother or father. The loss is lifelong. It can impair self-esteem regulation, as noted. The loss can affect the child's sense of self and, if it takes place early enough, aspects of gender identity and later sexual identity. Naturally, the stage at which the child finds out they lost a parent will affect what it comes to mean to the child. Virtually every line of development is typically affected in some manner, with certain exceptions.

Therefore, it should not be surprising that there are typically profound, lifelong, and far-reaching effects upon the individual's psychic life and personality stemming from this type of early trauma. Clinically, in many of these individuals, I have found facets of object relations suffused with deep, unconscious wishes, longings, and expectations for and feelings of entitlement, restitution, reparation, and restoration. There is a common fantasy of undoing the tragedy of the loss (trauma of the death) and the experience of suffering repeated deprivations and loss of gratifications, and reexperiencing the loss at each developmental step and milestone achieved.

At this point, I should make explicit that I am concerned with some of the enduring, long-term consequences of childhood parent loss by death in this chapter. This is not to imply that the less enduring, more immediate psychologic and intrapsychic effects of the parent's death have less importance or assume less significance for the child. Of course, they are also of great importance. However, I will not discuss these here.

The Immortal Mother, the Immortal Father

The mother's great, profound, continual, and mutually interdependent influence upon the infant, toddler, and young child is well known. Mahler (1968) and Mahler, Pine, and Bergman (1975) have mapped out, in impressive detail and with methodologic sophistication, the profound importance of the mother in the evolution and unfolding of the separation–individuation process.

Accordingly, we may say, in a general sense, the mother (or father) will be immortalized following the experience of the parent's death, in part as a function of the developmental level and age of the child. More specifically, the mother (or father) will be immortalized in the lost-immortal parent complex as a function of the entire psychic apparatus, including the unique internal interplay of the developing drives, ego and intrapsychic conflicts, superego precursors, and the fantasies and unconscious meanings the loss has to the child.

My findings, which I shall report in the present chapter, do not support Schafer's view (1968) that all objects are immortalized in a similar manner. The evidence I will present strongly indicates that there are profound and specifiable effects of actual early object loss, specifically, parent death, upon the individual's internal object world and object relations.

But this being so does not mean all objects—all mothers or fathers—are in actuality enshrined as immortal objects, or immortal mothers or fathers to the same degree and under the same conditions, and with the same psychic effects. Simply put, they are not. The lost immortal mother, the immortalized object of the two-and-one-half-year-old-child who is mother-bereaved is not and will not be the same immortalized object as for the two-and-one-half-year-old-child with a mother who does not die during childhood. That this is so becomes clear when we consider that the young child who loses a parent by death has no available interactional mode whereby he or she can compare, revise, assimilate, reevaluate, and progressively alter in an ongoing relationship with the parent via developing secondary process thought, the cathected representations, wishes and drive aims, and memories of the lost-immortal object, the dead parent. In other words, the child with living and libidinally available parents has the ongoing opportunity to constantly check, compare, and revise aspects of unconscious and conscious mental representations of the immortal mother with unconscious, preconscious, and conscious representations, experiences, and perceptions of the actual living mother. The ego of the parent-bereaved child does not have this important opportunity.

Therefore, an essential difference is, whereas for the early childhood parent-bereaved child, the immortal (lost, dead) parent remains more deeply embedded in the primary process and drive organization, for the child with living, available parents it does not (or not to the same degree). Nonetheless, it can appear puzzling that not all instances of childhood parent death result in neurosis, or other conditions of psychopathologic proportions.

The lost-immortal parent for the early parentally bereaved child is, to a greater extent, a product of primary process presences (as Schafer [1968] refers to it). In the child who has not suffered the loss of a parent, the parent is typically partially a primary process presence, but to a relatively greater extent also a final product of secondary process, conscious thought organization as well. For the child with living, available parents (and here I exclude the psychotic parent), more of the representations of the parents are closer to secondary process thinking, as compared to the parent-bereaved child. What I am trying to demonstrate is how this heretofore unexamined phenomenon makes for an important distinction, one that Wolfenstein (1966, 1969) and Schafer (1968), as well as others, do not make. In other words, these individuals who experienced early childhood loss of a parent by death do exhibit the ego split described so well by Wolfenstein (1969), and the immortal object, as eloquently delineated by Schafer (1968). They display, as do all individuals, not only parent-bereaved ones, enduring internalized object relations with the immortal object. However, in addition to the ego split that Wolfenstein describes, these early parent-bereaved individuals manifest a greater degree of self and object representations vis-à-vis the lost parent that is more deeply embedded within the drive organization, and less accessible to higher level, secondary process thought organization. The fate of the immortal (lost) object here is different from the fate of the immortal object of the nonbereaved individual. This is a point I shall return to in the next section.

The anal phase child who loses a mother will have a different lost-immortal mother than will the phallic–narcissistic phase child, or the phase-dominant phallic–oedipal child. The same holds true for the lost-immortal father. The father of the child in the passionate throes of the phallic–oedipal phase is a very different father indeed—as he is experienced, feared, hated, and loved, interacted with, and fantasized about—than the father of the prelibidinal object constancy child, of, let us say, ten months. It is not my purpose in the present contribution to describe clinically how these differences show up.

Following from this, the child of the lost-immortal father, the passionate, competitive, and frightened boy in the phallic–oedipal phase, who loses his father by death at this time, will have a very different immortal father than the boy whose father does not in reality die at this time. The child who loses his or her father or mother during prelibidinal object constancy when self and object representations are still amorphous, partially fused, and only vaguely differentiated, will inherit a lost-immortal parent who is less distinct to them and who will subsequently be recurrently and repeatedly resurrected in the unconscious (and to a lesser degree preconscious and conscious). The lost-immortal parent of the prelibidinal object constancy child will be very different, more a "primary process presence," than the lost-immortal parent of the early latency phase.

The Lost-Immortal Parent Complex

With the early childhood experience of death of a parent the lost-immortal parent complex is born (Dietrich, 1986a). Through a large number of individuals seen in psychoanalytically informed studies and patients seen in treatment (all of whom experienced childhood and adolescent parent loss by death)—and the relevant psychoanalytic literature, as well as cases seen by colleagues—I became very interested in the psychological richness, the intricacy, and analytic implications of this complex. I shall not describe this complex in clinical detail here.

The lost-immortal parent complex has been in certain of its aspects partially implicit in some psychoanalytic writing, including Freud's (1927) two cases of childhood parent death where he described a "denial of some part of reality" in both cases with regard to accepting their parent's death. Helene Deutsch (1937) observed an "absence of grief" in patients who had experienced the death of a parent during childhood. Anna Freud and Dorothy Burlingham (1943), in their study of wartime children without fathers, found intense and persistent attachments to a "fantasized father."

In spite of his incorrect assumption of infantile and very early childhood "mourning" (Dietrich, 1983), Bowlby (1980) emphasizes in his writing the continuing search for the lost object. Rochlin's (1959, 1965) "loss complex"—a very useful concept, particularly with regard to the etiology of depressive states—is similar to the author's lost-immortal parent complex in some respects, but differs in important and fundamental ways. Rochlin, for example, uses his term to apply to any loss experience and circumstance and does not restrict its definition by linking it directly to the trauma of childhood parent death. Rochlin does not fully address the pervasive, ongoing, enduring fantasized relationship with the dead parent, nor does he discuss the specific, organized constellation of particular unconscious fantasies pertaining to the "immortal parent."

Wolfenstein (1973) evocatively described some clinical features of the repetitive search for what she termed "the image of the lost parent," although she understands the denial of these individuals to stem from an ego split which comprises only a part of the picture of these individuals. Jacobson (1965), in a similar vein, spoke of the "illusory parent" in such cases.

In describing the lost-immortal parent complex I am referring to a different phenomenon from Schafer's (1968) discussion of immortal objects, and am using it for a different category than does he. In other words, if the object, the parent, was not lost there would not result a lost-immortal parent complex, where the object is both lost and simultaneously immortal.

Typically, the child gives up and restructures the image—object representations, as well as corresponding self representations—and, to some extent, the primary process organization of the mother and father in a progressive fashion. In each subsequent developmental phase new representations are reconstituted and reintegrated. The process occurs differently for the parent-bereaved child. Here the lost parent is centrally immortalized internally within the child's ego, superego, and id organization, and within the child's specific constellation of compromise formations and inner object world. Here the lost, dead parent is immortalized in a core: an organized constellation of unconscious fantasies, and is reflected in various facets of object relations, self and object representations, in identifications, introjects, incorporated objects,[1] as well as in preconscious and conscious longings, wishes, and fantasies.

Thus, the lost-immortal parent complex is ushered in as a result of the early parent death. In my clinical experience, patients who are parent-bereaved comprise a special category of Freud's (1916) exceptions. They often exhibit intense and deep-seated feelings of entitlement, reflected in the wish to be treated at a reduced fee, or for no fee at all, at times insistently conveying the message that the analyst or therapist ought to feel privileged or obligated to simply be treating them! Problems related to entitlement in such individuals in part stem from unconscious, intensely cathected longings for restitution, reparation, and restoration.

As I have tried to demonstrate, the multiple images and representations and primary process organization of the lost, dead mother or father remains immortalized and lost simultaneously, frozen in time yet timeless, frozen in space yet not spatially bound; a beloved (ambivalently loved) parent which the individual seeks and hopes will return.

The lost-immortal parent complex is comprised of a *relatively* specific, enduring, organized constellation of compromise formations and unconscious fantasies, which intermingle with aspects of many developmental lines. Moreover, it should be kept in mind that the lost-immortal parent complex must be viewed from multiple points of view, not only from the perspective of the drives or of unconscious fantasy activity alone, but from each metapsychological point of view.

One common fantasy of the lost-immortal parent complex is

---

[1]*Incorporated object* is the term Schafer (1976) prefers over *introject* in *A New Language for Psychoanalysis.*

that the child was the parental destroyer: that, out of aggressive impulses and hostile wishes the parent was killed by the child. This guilt then becomes a part of the lost-immortal parent complex. Another common fantasy of the lost-immortal parent complex derives from oedipal guilt if the parent who is lost (by death) is the same sex as the child, so that the child is a kind of oedipal victor in reality. Moreover, if the parent of the opposite sex dies, the child will often unconsciously both idealize the parent (Fenichel, 1953) while at the same time experience the dead parent to be, in a sense, their "very own." This may, as noted, represent a different sort of eternal, fantasized oedipal union. And yet, whether the lost parent is of the opposite or same sex, this powerful and central unconscious fantasy, that the lost parent is and has become the bereaved's "very own," in part makes possible an ongoing, fantasized relationship with the dead parent. This is an important hallmark of the lost-immortal parent complex. It is as if the cruel vicissitudes of fate that tore the parent away from the child have now been transformed, with the result that now the child "owns" the parent in their wishful and fantasy life, and can call him or her up to visit, be comforted, or chat. This is so regardless of however much of a poor substitute, and imperfect, this ghostly lost-immortal parent may be.

Inner dialogues with the dead parent, similar in certain respects to those characterizing the imaginary companion (Nagera, 1981) of some children, are typically present as part of the lost-immortal parent complex. An important difference is, however, that the inner dialogues of the lost-immortal parent complex do not typically end but continue on, through adolescent and adult development, in the inner life of the individual. And here, of course, we are not speaking of an imaginary parent who never existed—as is the case with an imaginary companion—but rather a lost-immortal parent, who in reality once lived.

Colorful, evocative, and moving external, creative manifestations of the lost-immortal parent complex can be vividly experienced in the creative productions and lives of certain individuals, especially writers, artists, sculptors, composers, poets, playwrights, and others. Creations reflective of the lost-immortal parent complex can be seen in the architectural achievements of Buckminster Fuller—the re-created, enclosed, "perfect world," controlled (as opposed to what was experienced passively as a child with the death of his parent), and self-contained. Also illustrative of the lost-immortal parent complex is the fascinating, lifelong journey and philosophic, mystical, and theological world of Thomas Merton. The enduring impact of early parent death on their subsequent creative work and life has been beautifully portrayed in the work of Magritte by Wolfenstein (1973) and Viederman (1985), and in the writing of A. E. Housman by Wolfenstein (1973), among others.

The lost-immortal parent complex is heir to the experience of early parent death: the psychic trauma, and its enduring, multiple impact upon the majority of developmental lines.

A Developmental Line of Mourning: From Separation Reactions to Grieving and Adult Mourning

I am positing here a specific developmental line of mourning (A. Freud, 1965). Certain elements of this viewpoint are partially approached, to varying degrees, in the contributions of Rochlin (1959), Pollock (1961), Wolfenstein (1966, 1973), and E. Furman (1974). I have felt for some time that a developmental line of mourning is needed.

A. Freud (1965) wrote: "What we are looking for are the basic interactions between id and ego and their various developmental levels, and also age-related sequences of them which, in importance, frequency, and regularity, are comparable to the maturational sequence of libidinal stages or the gradual unfolding of the ego functions" (p. 63). Anna Freud (1965) goes on to emphasize how developmental lines are inexorably "contributed to from the side of both id and ego development" (p. 63). An integral and important component of the developmental line of mourning I am here positing which has been noticeably absent from most psychoanalytic discussions of mourning and reactions to death, loss, and the ability of the child to mourn, is from the side of ego development; namely, the role of cognitive understanding and level of comprehension of death, as a developmentally changing concept in the child's capacities to engage in mourning processes.

Development of the capacity for mourning has been related far more often and successfully to the development of object relations (Mahler, 1961; R. Furman, 1964; E. Furman, 1974) by psychoanalytic writers than it has to those relevant aspects of ego and cognitive development associated with the developmental steps in the comprehension and understanding of death (and loss). The psychoanalytic literature on mourning has essentially neglected the considerable and important literature concerning the development of the concept of death, and the complex and varying manner in which death is understood and comprehended, as well as the multiple meanings it holds for the child, at increasing and progressive developmental steps or stages.

Death is understood and viewed by children roughly up to the age of seven as reversible, changeable, able to be avoided and evaded. The vast majority of analytic investigators of mourning, whether they are discussing childhood, infancy, adolescence, or adulthood fail to adequately integrate these relevant findings in their work. To my mind, it will be beneficial to attempt to integrate, in appropriate and carefully considered ways—to whatever degree is optimal and possible—these useful psychological findings of our nonanalytic colleagues.

The outline of a developmental line of mourning which I shall now describe is a contribution toward this end and borne of this effort.

My purpose here, in introducing this outline of a developmental line of mourning, is to suggest how such a developmental line can contribute to a clarification in our understanding of (1) how the anlage, precursors, and selective reactions of mourning proper progressively unfold; and (2) some of the controversies which have characterized some of the psychoanalytic literature on mourning in infancy and childhood.

The first stages of the developmental line relate primarily and predominantly to the prestages of mourning and mourning reactions. I shall trace this developmental line only in terms of its earliest stages, extending and elaborating upon its stages elsewhere, so that it is not yet complete. The following devel-

opmental line is representative of all children, and not restricted to those who have suffered object loss.

Stage 1

The first stage begins at birth. The first weeks of life are what
Mahler et al. (1975) refer to as the normal autistic phase of the
separation–individuation process. They write: "the function of
this period is best seen in physiological terms" (p. 41). Ferenczi
(1913) referred to the autistic orbit of the infant during this
period. Hoffer (1952) noted the object has no existence of its
own initially for the infant; it is part of the internal narcissistic
milieu.

The beginning of the first subphase of separation–
individuation occurs at around four to five months (Mahler et
al., 1975), and includes "checking back to the mother." The
initial, beginning precursors of grief appear during this first
stage. Nagera (1981) views object loss which occurs during this
period as a "developmental arrest" and places the development
of a mental representation, "even if only a part object," after the
second or third month (p. 372). He goes on to emphasize that
if the object (maternal object) is lost at this point the baby will
react with distress.

Klein (1935), however, felt that resolution of the infantile
depressive position is the initial experience of mourning. Spitz
(1965), however, described the objectless stage of development.
No evidence indicates any concept of death is present during
this stage. During Stage 1 only the most rudimentary grief
anlage, primarily of a behavioral–physiological nature, are
present. Mourning of whatever type, appears to not be present.

Stage 2

The various essentials of Stage 2 are the differentiation and
unfolding of ego apparatuses, as exemplified by the practicing
subphase; the child's growing awareness of separateness from
the mother occurring during the rapprochement phase
(Mahler et al., 1975). Stranger anxiety, which occurs from
roughly six to eight months, indicates "the infant is beginning

to develop a hierarchy of first-level object relatedness" with its mother or primary care giver (Parens, 1980, p. 469). Burlingham and Freud (1942) observed intense affective reactions in toddlers even to short-lived separations from their mothers.

During Stage 2 there appear more organized, progressively more complex intrapsychic precursors of mourning. We begin to see, during this stage, isolated, lower level, fragmentary, and highly selective features of mourning equivalents (certain mourning affects) and mourning responses. Loss during this period (without adequate replacement) leads to what Spitz (1965) termed anaclitic depression.

Maurer (1964) places the earliest precursors of the concept of death in the peek-a-boo game of infancy, and Kastenbaum and Costa (1977) found awareness of concepts of cessation of bodily functions and finitude in sixteen-month-olds. Self–object differentiation is facilitated by attachments to transitional phenomena (Galenson, 1980). During this time the child has likely experienced repeated separations and has developed the capacity to trust the parent (to go away and return) (Erikson, 1959).

According to Anna Freud (1965), object constancy is achieved at roughly twelve months. Interestingly, E. Furman (1974) holds that in loss of the mother during early object constancy, "something must happen to the object representation of the mother that resembles the hypercathexis and decathexis in mourning" (p. 42). She also places the capacity for maintaining the cathexis of the lost object as early as sixteen months (E. Furman, 1974).

During Stage 2, the infant or child reacts to the mother's (or caretaker's) separations with certain manifest grief reactions; however, this does not constitute mourning. A number of anal stage issues associated with loss of stool, breast, power, and autonomy come to the fore during this period (Settlage, 1980).

Stage 3

This stage signifies the actual beginning of a potential for more organized and complex selective aspects of early childhood mourning. Stage 3 spans roughly twenty-four to forty-eight months (although children may enter or leave the stage at earlier or later ages), partially overlapping, with regard to psychosexual theory, the anal, genital, and oedipal stages (Settlage, 1980).

Anna Freud (1960) believed that by the age of two or three a child that had reached her definition of object constancy—a very different definition from the one Mahler et al. (1975) utilize for their concept of libidinal object constancy—is able to comprehend the external fact of loss. Piaget's (1958) distinction between the sensorimotor period (roughly to the age of two) and the preoperational stage (roughly from two to seven years) clarifies how a number of ego and cognitive features and skills, essential for an understanding of death, are still not available to the child during this period. Research has confirmed that comprehension of death develops progressively in stages linked with age and ego and cognitive development initially identified by Piaget (Berlinsky and Biller, 1982).

Stage 3 begins approximately when Mahler's third subphase, rapprochement, comes to a close (22–24 months). This stage of the developmental line I am postulating, partially overlaps with Mahler et al.'s (1975) subphase of libidinal object constancy. The increasing development of language and its progressive complexity are of great importance "in enabling the child to accept and tolerate both the inevitable libidinal separations, whether voluntary or involuntary on the part of the parent, and the lengthening but time-limited physical separations" (p. 536). Mahler's libidinal object constancy is achieved during Stage 3 of the present developmental line of mourning.

Although, as noted earlier, certain selective, temporary or episodic, isolated, and partial beginning aspects of a mourning process can be observed it is not until Stage 4 that *childhood mourning* (a term preferred by Sekaer and Katz [1986]) proper occurs. Toleration of painful affects, the capacity for decathexis, and ego development necessary for adequate reality testing with regard to the meaning of death required for mourning, presage the attainment of what appear, minimally, to be necessary and sufficient *developmental* capacities *for mourning* which may be present in the next stage (Stage 5).

James and Joyce Robertson (1971), in an important study of

thirteen young children separated from the mother (seventeen months to two years five months in age), nine of whom remained in their own homes and were cared for by a relative, and four of whom were cared for by the Robertsons, did not find evidence of mourning in the children. They write, "our findings do not support Bowlby's generalizations about the responses of young children to loss of the mother per se; nor do they support his theory on grief and mourning in infancy and early childhood" (p. 313).

Stage 4

This stage roughly spans the ages from four through six. Several investigators report mourning is possible, *under certain given circumstances,* by the age of four years (R. Furman, 1964, 1968; Laufer, 1966; E. Furman, 1974; Kliman, Feinberg, Buchsbaum, Kliman, Lubin, Ronald, and Stein, 1969; Raphael, 1983). Although here we are talking about mourning of a kind different from that characterizing adult mourning and the model of adult mourning, as we certainly would be led to expect due to the many crucial developmental differences. Wolfenstein (1966, 1969) and Nagera (1981) emphasize, however, how very difficult it is for the young child within his developmental capacities to continue to sustain the painful and arduous prolongation of mourning.

I saw a boy in child therapy, aged four, whose father had been killed in an automobile accident when the child was two. I observed in his play with toy cars repetitive reenactments of car crashes along with fears that a monster would come out of the school sandbox. Only selective elements and affects of mourning were experienced.

The child during this stage manifests mourning, when it is present, on a more intermittent, time-limited basis than does the older child or adolescent. Children at Stage 4 do not yet have a capacity for a complete or comprehensive understanding of death. During this stage children continue to believe death is temporary; that it is possible to reverse and evade it (Nagy, 1948; Rochlin, 1967; Melear, 1973).

Important advances in the ability of the child to bear, in

developmentally increasing doses, sad and painful affects, and the thoughts associated with such affects (and their counterpart), take place during this stage.

Robert Furman (1973) has written:

> To withdraw a feeling investment from a mental image of a lost loved one, to decathect the internal representation of the lost object, the child must first have a stable internal representation that can survive and endure after the vast majority of loving investment has been removed. Our theoretical knowledge and clinical experience would indicate to us that this is possible after the achievement of object constancy dominance and a mastery of the ambivalence conflicts of the anal sadistic phase of development. In an otherwise emotionally healthy child it is reasonable to anticipate this level of development sometimes around age four. [p. 227].

A. Freud and Burlingham (1943) observed phallic–oedipal phase children (who lost their fathers by death) who talked of their fathers as if they were alive. These children referred to visits from their dead fathers more frequently than to visits from living fathers. They emphasize, "In some cases this happens under the direct influence of mothers who hide the truth from the child to spare it from pain; in other cases phantasies of an identical nature are the child's spontaneous production" (p. 641).

Stage 5

In a useful contribution on children's concepts of death, Speece (1986) examines widely researched components of children's understanding of death. Irreversibility refers to the permanency of death, its irrevocability, finality. Nonfunctionality refers to cessation, namely, that life-defining functions stop at death. Universality refers to "the understanding that all living things die" (p. 72).

Prior to understanding irreversibility, children view death as reversible, like sleep, as something that is temporary. Prior to attainment of understanding nonfunctionality, children attribute certain abilities to the dead, such as they can feel, or move, or hear, or see (although not as well as the living). And, finally, before children understand that death is inevitable and universal, they believe certain individuals can avoid death, such as their parents, themselves, or teachers, and that, by certain actions, they can avoid death. Speece (1986) points out that the evidence, overall, suggests that these components are "understood by a majority of children by age 7" (p. 75).

This being the case, it becomes more understandable why Stage 4 (I would refer to Stage 4 as "early childhood mourning"; qualifying somewhat the term *childhood mourning* used by Sekaer and Katz [1986]), in the majority of children, is the first stage in the developmental line of mourning when mourning proper under the appropriate conditions and typically with analytic or therapeutic treatment (or exceptionally empathic and facilitative ongoing responses on the part of the surviving parent) *may* actually occur.

This stage (Stage 5) typically spans approximately the ages from seven through eleven. Mourning for the loss of a loved one (typically the death of a love object) is possible during this stage, and while the mourning processes which do occur in some respects resemble the mourning of older adolescents and adults, mourning during this stage is not identical with these developmentally higher and later forms of mourning. The capacity to tolerate the multiple painful affects associated with mourning over an extended period of time remains limited, as does the ability to successfully decathect the multiple representations of the mourned for love object. Stage 5 overlaps almost entirely with the latency phase in psychosexual development.

Wolfenstein (1966), however, reported observing rage as opposed to grief or mourning in her child patients who had lost a parent by death. She writes, "for immature individuals the loss of a parent is also an intolerable injury to their fantasied omnipotence" (p. 459). And, further: "Feelings of protracted grief are avoided, and the finality of the loss is denied. The representation of the lost parent remains intensely cathected . . ." (p. 432).

Robert Furman (1973) has noted one difficulty in adequately assessing a child's capacity to mourn is the "utilization of certain manifestly grieving adults as the model for mourning" (p. 226).

In light of my own clinical experience with children in this age range (as well as latency age children) who have lost an important love object, as well as my reading of the literature, I believe Wolfenstein somewhat overemphasizes the reaction of rage in children who have lost a parent by death to the exclusion of mourning processes commensurate with their own developmental capabilities, requirements, and level.

To assert that one can observe in children object relations different from object relations observed in adults is not to say object relations do not exist in children. The same, to my mind, holds true for mourning and mourning processes; because we can observe differences between the mourning of children and the mourning of adults does not mean mourning is absent in all children. Wolfenstein's observations of hypercathexis of the lost object (as compared with slow and protracted decathexis over time) can be understood as constituting a part of the lost-immortal parent complex but do not necessarily suggest, as Wolfenstein argues, that a *certain type* of mourning (again, different from that of adult mourning) does not occur. The available data (analytic, psychotherapeutic, and observational) seem to show that the hypercathexis Wolfenstein observed is present in children who lose a parent by death, as well as, in some children, the mourning reactions observed by the Furmans and others.

To this writer, some of the reasons, among others, for the discrepancy in clinical data and its inferences between Wolfenstein and the Furmans stem from: (1) the adult model of mourning Wolfenstein uses, to which she compares children's external and internal responses; (2) the Furmans' use of analytic data as compared with psychotherapeutic data, the former offering a richer and more finely detailed base from which to trace and study mourning reactions; and (3) the fact that Wolfenstein (as well as Nagera) seems to apply adult criteria with regard to the length of time the child can tolerate, and is engaged in, painful remembering, and painful affects associated with memories of the deceased, as compared to what might be more appropriate, developmentally, for a given child.

Stage 6

Attainment of Piaget's stage of formal operations (at roughly the age of twelve) is associated with gains in abstract reasoning and the cognitive ability to simultaneously consider multiple facets of a situation. Death, at this stage, is completely understood in both its reality and abstract terms (Koocher, 1974; Kane, 1979; Berlinsky and Biller, 1982).

Wolfenstein (1966) views adolescence as a type of trial mourning. The adolescent is forced to radically decathect his first loves, the parents, in seeking a nonincestual love object. Other writers have also emphasized how this process resembles mourning (Root, 1957; A. Freud, 1958; Blos, 1962; Jacobson, 1964). Blos (1962) observes, "This adolescent loss is more final and irrevocable than the one which occurs at the end of the oedipal phase" (p. 187). He goes on to point out, "This work of mourning involves the ego in well-known reactions. It accounts in part for the depressive states of adolescents, as well as for their grief reaction as a postponement of affect. To complete the work of mourning requires repetition and time" (p. 187).

The question of whether even the adolescent mourns identically to the adult, or instead mourns in a manner with internal features commensurate with their developmental and maturational level, is one which awaits further research. My own view is that the developmental line of mourning I have here postulated continues throughout the life span. Although I have only outlined six stages of the developmental line here, I shall elaborate in greater detail and extend this line in another contribution.

The Importance and Relevance of Empirical Psychoanalytic Research on Early Object Loss

Noteworthy here is Martha Wolfenstein's suggestion, made at a panel at the 1972 meeting of the American Psychoanalytic Association chaired by Jonathan Call, which correctly emphasized the need for study of groups of nonpatients if we are to extend our understanding of effects of early object loss, including parent loss by death. Similarly, Daniel Offer (1980) has eloquently and convincingly delineated some of the important and necessary reasons for detailed, in-depth investigation of the so-called normal adolescent for an adequate, complete psychoanalytic understanding and account of adolescence. Michaels (1980) also argues more study of normal adult development is needed in psychoanalysis. Interestingly, Bowlby (1980) observed: "Unfortunately, despite enormously increased attention to the subject during recent years, empirical data regarding how individuals of different ages respond to losses of different kinds and in differing circumstances are still scarce" (p. 8). I would add that empirical psychoanalytic and psychoanalytically informed studies of various types of object loss are far fewer yet.

It was for these reasons, as well as the fact that a relatively large and rich clinical psychoanalytic literature exists which addresses patients who lost a parent early in life, that a nonpatient group was selected for the study to be described later in this chapter.

Most of the research on psychologic effects of childhood parent death, done by nonanalytic colleagues over the past fifteen to twenty years, has focused upon manifest behaviors and overt symptom pictures, and typically does not go beyond establishing the existence of the link between early childhood object loss and the specific diagnostic or psychological variable under study.

Psychoanalytic interpretation of projective data from certain clinical diagnostic psychological tests and instruments, its contributions to psychoanalysis, including psychoanalytic psychology and psychiatry, and the many research, clinical, and conceptual ways such data can appropriately and constructively be utilized to contribute to psychoanalytic knowledge, has a long and fruitful tradition (Rorschach, 1921; Murray, 1943; Rapaport, Gill, and Schafer, 1944–1946; Rosenzweig, 1945; Schafer, 1954; Mayman, 1968; Blatt, 1975; Fisher and Greenberg, 1977).

One of my purposes in the present chapter is to share with the reader a new method, a scale, which my colleagues, students, and I have found useful in clinical research and clinical work for organizing and assessing detailed aspects of object relations and object representations.

Psychoanalytically Informed Research Method and Strategies

Later in this chapter, I shall further discuss some of the aforementioned theoretical and clinical implications of early childhood parent death, and will end with a recent, empirical study of mine from the Parent Loss Project, a study which is, to my knowledge, the first empirical psychoanalytic investigation demonstrating conclusively that certain, specific aspects of the quality and level of object relations are very often powerfully affected by early childhood parent death.

I should make clear, however, that I have found projective data, specifically data gleaned from the Thematic Appercep-tion Test (TAT), richly useful and quite relevant—at a certain level of conceptualization[2]—for empirically validating some aspects of psychoanalytic concepts, theory, and clinical hypo-theses, and have utilized such data in various studies with various types of patients and nonpatients. The TAT has not enjoyed the same degree of enthusiastic, widespread interest and use in empirical and clinical research as has the Rorschach technique. Yet, perhaps its potential value for validating psy-choanalytic hypotheses may prove to be greater. The TAT can be utilized in empirical psychoanalytic research so that each TAT card which is selected involves a human being or people as a projective template for the patient's (or subject's) uncon-scious, preconscious, and conscious object representations and a rich representative sampling of aspects of internalized object relations. In other words, the TAT may be a more object centered or "object sensitive" diagnostic tool for assessment of object relations than the Rorschach.

---

[2]I shall not here go into the unresolved issues, important as they are, pertaining to differing levels of conceptualization of analytic data. I do not exclude, as some authors do, data from outside the analytic situation, but on the contrary find this data very useful and of relevance for validating certain psychoanalytic concepts and constructs (for example, from investigators such as Mahler, Greenspan, and Mayman). We must, however, be very careful when attempting to compare data from differing contexts, levels of concep-tualization, and from differing contents.

To the best of my knowledge, virtually no psychoanalytic studies of object relations or other psychoanalytically relevant consequences of early object loss, specifically early parent death, have been undertaken or reported using nonpatients, apart from Anna Freud and associates' classic observational work with children orphaned by the war at the Hampstead nurseries. Martha Wolfenstein (1966, 1969), Robert Furman (1964), Erna Furman (1974), and their associates, all report clinical material from therapy patients. Rochlin (1965) included selective, brief play interview material, which was transcribed, of children who had not presented for clinical reasons, although all of the children Rochlin included in his report had not experienced childhood loss of a parent by death. The study to be described is the first psychoanalytically informed empirical research studying the effects of early parent death utilizing a so-called normal population of nonpatients.

The Study: Effects of Early Parent Death on Object Relations and Object Representations

Method

The study was carried out as part of the author's Parent Loss Project, an ongoing clinical research project at the Detroit Psychiatric Institute, Wayne State University School of Medicine, Department of Psychiatry. The TAT protocols of a group of forty-two individuals, thirty-one of whom had lost a parent by death during early childhood (up to and including the age of six), and eleven of whom had not lost a parent (controls) were scored for aspects of the individual's level and quality of object relations and object representations using the Dietrich Object Relations and Object Representations Scale (Dietrich, 1985).

Eight individuals who had experienced the death of a parent prior to the age of three (thirty-six months) comprised the first group. This group was made up of those who had lost a parent prior to complete attainment of libidinal object constancy (Mahler et al., 1975). Ten individuals who had experienced the death of a parent between the ages of three years and five years comprised the second group. This group was composed of individuals who were parentally bereaved during phallic–oedipal phase development. Thirteen individuals who experienced the death of a parent between the ages of five and seven years comprised the third group. This group was made up of persons who lost a parent by death during early latency (Sarnoff, 1976).

The majority of the subjects were university and college students, and ranged in age from eighteen to twenty-eight years of age. All of the subjects volunteered to participate in the study, and were interviewed by the author. The majority of the subjects were white. Socioeconomic status, and other types of loss or death experiences such as parental divorce or sibling death, were controlled for by matching, and statistically, by analysis of covariance. All TAT data were scored independently by two investigators, both of whom were blind as to the individual's age, sex, the time of the parent death, diagnosis, and treatment history (if any), whether the individual had experienced parent death or not, and all other identifying characteristics. The investigators met at periodic intervals (after assigning forty to eighty scale scores) to go over agreements and disagreements in scores, and where differences occurred, agreement was reached in conference, and that score was used in the final data analysis.[3] Interrater reliability was found to be quite acceptable. Out of a total of 710 separate scale scores, percent agreement was 76 percent, which represents exact agreement or a difference in scoring of only 1 scale point. The hypotheses were, on the basis of the relevant clinical psychoanalytic literature and my own prior research and clinical work, that there would be greater degrees of impairment and distortions in object relations and object representations in those who lost a parent by death during early childhood as compared with those who had not been parentally bereaved. Moreover, I also expected differential degrees of impairments in object relations

[3]The author was one of the scorers of the TAT data in this study. However, since the author had scored these TAT protocols in previous research he cannot be considered an altogether unprejudiced scorer. I wish to thank Patrick Pope, Ph.D., who served as a research assistant, for his help in scoring the protocols, and Brian Donovan, M.A., for his statistical consultation and data analysis.

and object representations as a function of when the individual's parent died in the child's psychosexual, ego, and object relational development. Therefore, I expected the greatest degree of impairment in object relations and representations in those parentally bereaved prior to complete attainment of libidinal object constancy (Mahler et al., 1975). Next, I expected somewhat less impairment in those who were parentally bereaved during the phallic–oedipal phase. I expected less impairment yet in those parentally bereaved during the early latency period, though greater impairment than in the nonloss group. Finally, I expected greater impairment in object relations and representations in childhood parent-bereaved individuals (all groups combined) compared to the nonloss group.

Results and Discussion

Results of the study indicated there were statistically significant differences between those who lost a parent by death, regardless of the age at the time of the death, and those who had not lost a parent by death for all of the ten categories of the object relations scale, in the anticipated directions ($p<.01$ univariate F-ratios). For those who experienced childhood parent death, the following was found (all differences are significant): object investment was lower; sadistic versus neutralized aggression was lower (more sadistic aggression); object warmth was lower; quality/level of object relatedness was lower; empathy was lower; object love was lower; superego harshness versus superego benevolence (more superego harshness); degree of depression was higher; psychological mindedness was lower; helplessness versus internal sense of control (more helplessness). An overall discriminant function analysis revealed the following categories to be significant at the same level ($p<.01$): superego harshness; psychological mindedness; object warmth; quality/level of object relations; and depression. The individuals who lost a parent by death in childhood were significantly lower on quality/level of object relations, object warmth, psychological mindedness, and significantly higher on superego harshness and depression than were those who had not lost a parent by death. No significant differences were found between any of the groups as a function of age at the time of loss. (I shall not discuss here the issue of loss of the mother as compared to loss of the father, or loss of the opposite-sex versus loss of the same-sex parent. Certain aspects of these considerations I have discussed elsewhere [Dietrich, 1984b].)

The present study is, to the best of my knowledge, the first psychoanalytic empirical research demonstrating conclusively that various specific aspects of object relations are powerfully affected by early childhood parent death. What appears to override the fact of when, developmentally, the parent death occurs, is the fact that there *was* a traumatic parent loss by death at all. In other words, from this study's data, what appears to be of primary significance in addition to other multiple influences is not whether the parent death took place when the child was twenty months old or four-and-a-half years old, *but rather whether or not there was a parent (death) loss,* a trauma of this particular type and magnitude. One reason which may account for the present study findings, namely, that it is not so much when the parental death occurs (including the first six years of childhood) but whether a parental death occurs, is that since all of the loss groups consisted of individuals who lost a parent prior to complete superego structuralization, the results obtained—with respect to aspects of object relations and object representations—appear highly similar. Another possible reason for these results is the fact that for the infant (roughly a third of the preobject constancy group), replacement of the lost parent is typically more readily and easily accepted because of the infant's less differentiated ego organization, and therefore less pathogenic than it is for the older child. At the same time, the older (latency age) child has a more adaptive and resilient ego and greater personality resources (and can more effectively obtain gratifications from the environment) available, so that certain pathogenic effects would tend to be somewhat offset.[4] Also, because of the regression in ego functions and object relations which usually results from the trauma of early parent

_____

[4] I wish to thank R. M. Gonzalez, M.D., for this view of understanding the results. His comments followed a presentation of this research to the Department of Child Psychiatry, Mt. Carmel Hospital.

death, group differences might be expected to appear more similar than dissimilar.

The prevalence of malevolent and sadistic object representations including increased superego harshness, combined with internalized object relations characterized by significantly lowered object warmth, quality/level of object relatedness, psychological mindedness, and an increased experience of depression, indicate the presence of important, internalized differences in object relations and representations between those traumatized by early childhood parent death and those not. Bowlby, in *Attachment and Loss* (1980), has rightly emphasized: "Whether an author is discussing the effects of loss on an adult or a child, there is a tendency to underestimate how intensely distressing and disabling loss usually is and for how long the distress, and often the disablement, commonly lasts" (p. 8). And he states in the same volume: "Again and again emphasis will be laid on the long duration of grief, on the difficulties of recovering from its effects, and on the adverse consequences for personality functioning that loss so often brings" (p. 8). My empirical findings support the clinical findings of various authors (Pollock, 1961; Rochlin, 1965; E. Furman, 1974) that relate this type of early object loss experience with degrees of internalization and superego structuralization, and levels of object relational and ego development achieved.

The findings of this investigation also suggest a heretofore unmentioned explanation for the function and meaning of some of the clinical symptoms of these individuals and patients. The strikingly heightened sense of helplessness and depression, the increased coloring of sadistic as opposed to more neutralized aggression in their various object representations, the relative lack of object warmth, lowered object cathexis, and diminished quality/level of object relatedness closely approximate the clinical descriptions, the manner in which many of these individuals present for treatment, and the inner experience of these patients as revealed in the course of their analysis or psychotherapy. To talk of the patient who has experienced the trauma of early childhood parent death without appreciation for these finer distinctions—as is too often generally done, whether in the literature or clinic—is unsupported by these data. Therefore, a global or general view of severe psychopathology (Bowlby) or developmental arrest (Fleming and Altschul) resulting from this type of object loss must therefore be questioned.

The present study findings confirm some of the clinical findings of Fleming and Altschul (1963) and diverge from other aspects of their results. Fleming and Altschul (1963) found an arrest in object relations at the level reached at the time of the parental loss experience. My results suggest there are impairments in some selective areas of object relations and object representations, though the impairments do not appear to affect *all* areas of object relations and representations in the same manner, or to the same degree. In addition, my empirical data indicate that impairments in object relations are not directly linked with the level of object relations achieved at the time of the parent death, but suggest that any parent death experience occurring during the first six years of a child's life produces effects upon object relations and representations which, in many respects, appear highly similar.

Problems in the Psychoanalytic Psychotherapy of Early Parent-Bereaved Patients: Additional Findings from the Parent Loss Project

I shall now examine some of the issues and problems which often arise in the psychoanalytic psychotherapy of early parent-bereaved patients. I shall only adumbrate some of my observations and thoughts on certain of these problems and issues. I am very much aware of the inherent complexity and limitations of selectively commenting upon various therapeutic problems and issues which *often* arise during the treatment of such patients. For a richer and more comprehensive account, considerable, detailed clinical material would be useful, I shall nevertheless present certain selected observations, as space permits, to augment the literature addressing this area.

Psychoanalytic clinicians and researchers have paid relatively little attention to the specific problems and issues often associated with the psychoanalytic treatment of early parent-loss cases (i.e., to loss by death). The evidence for these observations derive from nine clinical cases which I have treated or seen for consultation, and from case material submitted to me by colleagues. For purposes of exposition, problems will be subsumed under the following headings: the opening phase of treatment, the transference, acting out, ego development, and superego development.

The Opening Phase of Treatment and the "Therapeutic Alliance"

An initial problem that I have found which frequently surfaces in such cases is linked with the very beginning of treatment. Many of these patients seem to have considerably greater than usual difficulty in beginning treatment. For many of these patients, therapeutic help means, unconsciously, a continuation of the inhibitions, conflicts, defenses, and resistances against the painful activation of mourning, and a continuation of the relationship, as well as a fantasied reunion, with the lost parent, as well as restitution and separation from the original loss. A pattern which has become evident in some cases is a partial reenactment of an unconscious fantasy which sometimes takes the following form. The patient calls to make the first appointment and is hesitant and tentative. Following the first appointment, which is often filled with ill-defined and vague complaints, a second appointment is made, and then not kept for one manifest reason or another. This is frequently followed by the patient making another appointment, which is often kept. For the subsequent hour, the patient will either fail to show or call to cancel, with various explanations such as they have little confidence in treatment or the therapist.

In adults and adolescents who have lost a parent by death during early childhood, I have observed (Dietrich, 1984a) that there is a recurrent unconscious fantasy that the (dead) parent somehow exists in some way. This is part of the lost-immortal parent complex. The step taken to begin treatment and the initial appointment itself threatens and precipitates the breakdown of this delicately fashioned fantasy. The first step the patient has taken (initiating treatment) toward beginning to understand this central fantasy and much of their day-to-day psychic life connected with both the parent and the loss itself activates anxiety, character defenses, and compromise formations against the dreaded revival of affects connected with the original trauma (the experience of being overwhelmed) and the painfulness of mourning work.

In an attempt to avoid reexperiencing this traumatic experience, with its attendant affects, and various sequelae, a partial reenactment occurs, with the accompanying unconscious fantasy that this time things will turn out differently. The patient is, in part, attempting to turn what was a passive, traumatic, and overwhelmingly painful experience into a current active one, to rewrite that sector of sad history, thereby attempting to simultaneously locate and reunite with the lost parent and reject and punish the parent (for dying), thus providing a sense of mastery for the patient. At the same time, the patient communicates, often nonverbally, to the therapist split-off and unwanted aspects of their self representations and particular fantasies pertaining to aspects of the experience of the loss itself by evoking specific countertransference fantasies and reactions.

Fleming (1972) reported on two cases in control analysis, as well as other cases that demonstrated similar resistances to the expectable evolution of a therapeutic alliance. My own clinical data seem to support this finding. Though he does not approach it from the point of view of an early object loss case, Brenner's (1959) clinical material illustrates some of the difficulties described here.

The Transference

Potential for acting out. Acting out is essential for all patients (Boesky, 1982). In many of these patients, however, I have found an increased frequency and special intensity of acting out. Particularly for such patients, acting out appears as a special form of remembering, as Fenichel (1945) has shown. One example is the pattern of unconscious enactment I referred to earlier. Often, in such cases the memories of the lost parent and the affects associated with those memories are repressed and unavailable to the patient. I have observed in several such patients, as mentioned earlier, a greater tendency toward action, along with a greater than usual tendency to act out by suddenly fleeing or quitting treatment, an observation which Fleming also made about the cases she treated.

Following a two-week vacation of mine, one of my patients, a twenty-two-year-old legal clerk, announced she was going to Spain for several months. Her father had died there when she was two. In addition, she told me that she was stopping treatment for a while because she felt she could not afford to pay the bill each month. While in Spain, she wrote letters to me, sent a postcard, and telephoned me while I was in session with another patient. In one letter, she wrote: "I've also started to go to church, which, by the way, I haven't gone to in such a long time. It's a great feeling, going to church. At least there are two people still in *this* world who care and can help me, God and you." By leaving treatment, the patient was in part acting out the loss of me (the father) while simultaneously attempting to undo the loss (turning what was passively experienced into an active experience), and enacting her enduring libidinal tie to me (the father) via the letters, phone call, and church experience, to recapitulate and recover aspects of the preloss relationship with the father.

Ego Development and Organization. With regard to the ego, I have noticed in certain cases, and let me state clearly, this is a matter of degree (I am not, of course, placing such patients in diagnostic categories), certain deficiencies in ego integration, synthesis, and further differentiation, similar to the "immature ego organization" that Fleming described. Loewald has commented, "The more intact the ego of the patient, the more of this integration taking place in the analytic process occurs without being noticed" (1960, p. 21). I have noticed, as well, certain inadequacies in basic ego functions; namely, various types of magical thinking and distortions in reality testing and reality sense. Also, ego flexibility is often affected, in that the capacity to tolerate internal conflict and anxiety appears to be diminished. Sterba's "therapeutic ego split" and the functions of the self observing ego are often less available to the patient, making treatment more difficult.

Superego Development. Concerning the structuralization of the superego, frequently I have found the superego to be relatively immature, more incomplete and lacking in regulation, and not allowing for a reasonable amount of drive gratification and self-esteem. Schafer (1960) has written: "There is a loving and beloved aspect of the superego; it represents the loved and admired oedipal and pre-oedipal parents who provide love, protection, comfort and guidance" (p. 186). It is important to note that this optimally takes place if the parents are present and available to the child. In the cases I have studied, one of the pathways of ego and superego identification was not available to the individual as a result of the parent death, with the consequent outcome of an impaired, often immature, and at times, overly harsh superego.

These patients are struggling unconsciously with pervasive denial that the parent is dead, which, as I have noted, often interferes with aspects of ego organization and functioning, along with fantasies of the parent's current existence, or return. After four years of analysis, one patient, who lost her mother as a child, said to her analyst, following a silence: "I sometimes talk with my mother inside my head; it's much better than talking out loud because I don't have to actually say anything." With this denial, there are longings and expectations for restitution and reparations—which are often suffused with phallic–oedipal and preoedipal conflicts and fantasies. In addition, quite often, there is unconscious guilt over the childhood death wishes toward the parent apparently being realized, especially if it is the same-sex parent who is lost, and guilt over the oedipal victory if the opposite-sex parent survived. Once more, various aspects of the lost-immortal parent complex are found, and can be understood in these patients as analysis or psychotherapy proceeds.

As I have tried to show, these patients appear braced for sudden and abrupt traumatic abandonment, a reexperiencing and recapitulation of the original trauma within the transference. Often certain sequelae and reactions to the loss may not show up until many years later, and may, at first glance, appear to be unconnected with the loss. With some adolescent patients, especially those who lost a parent early in adolescence, I have seen a reactivation or resumption of mourning occur later in adolescence, when the patient is faced with certain crises, such as graduation from high school, going off to college, or ending an important relationship.

Some of what I have already discussed bears directly or indirectly upon termination. I shall not here discuss termination with these patients except to say that termination is an issue throughout the treatment. There is a double risk or danger for the patient, who now stands to lose both the therapist and the parent representation which has been resuscitated in the transference. The patient is often overwhelmed by the fear of reexperiencing the original trauma. Also, ideas of growing up, learning or becoming a parent can represent a destruction of the parent for the patient.

It is my hope that by becoming more aware of the real and potential effects such loss so often exerts on our patients' lives and treatment, we can become better informed and prepared for what lies ahead, and better assist them in their resolution of the difficult and painful journey.

Appendix: Dietrich Object Relations and Object Representations Scale

The Dietrich Object Relations and Object Representations Scale (Dietrich, 1985) which I devised and which we have been using since 1985 in investigations in the Parent Loss Project is a method and tool for assessing, organizing, and extracting specific aspects of the individual's internalized object relations and object representations from projective data, such as the TAT. The scale, however, is not limited to use with the TAT, and has been applied as well to clinical interview data and other types of projective data. The Dietrich Object Relations and Object Representations Scale (DORRS) is the outgrowth of several years of clinical research employing and developing other types of TAT scales—applied to understanding problems arising from traumatic experiences such as loss of a parent through death, and unconscious fantasies relating to the loss (Dietrich, 1981, 1986b); deficient or traumatic mothering in depressed borderlines (Dietrich et al., 1984); parent loss and death fear (Dietrich, 1979); and loss of a parent through psychosis (Shabad, Worland, Lander, and Dietrich, 1979). The scale itself is comprised of ten categories, some interrelated and partially overlapping, which allow for the clinical and quantitative assessment of specific aspects of object relations and object representations. In other words, the scale provides a tool and method for assessing nonglobal aspects of object relations, as opposed to the all-too-often global description or rating of poor versus good object relations. The scale, as noted earlier, has been found to have good reliability (interrater reliability of 76 percent), its face validity is also good,[5] being derived from clinically measurable, meaningful, psychoanalytically relevant constructs.[6] Much of the prior clinical research on object relations, by the way, has suffered from this problematic use of a global measure of object relations.[7]

For its proper use this scale requires that the clinical researcher have some clinical experience and at least moderate familiarity with psychoanalytic theory.

Definitions of Categories, Scoring Criteria, and Rules

1. *Object investment.* This category represents the degree or extent to which objects (people, characters in the TAT story), as well as the object world, are libidinally invested or cathected. *Scoring criteria.* Score a 1 if there is the least amount of evidence, a virtual absence of investment in objects (people, characters, including activities), and the object world. The lower the score the greater the bleakness, bareness, lack of feeling in terms of interactions and interest in people. Score a 3 if there is some evidence of object investment and libidinal cathexis (though it should be less than at the midpoint of the scale category). Score

---

[5]A large-scale validity dissertation study with this scale is currently under way.

[6]In further, ongoing research we have obtained results (using the MMPI) suggesting the Dietrich Object Relations and Object Representations Scale has discriminate validity which we intend to publish shortly.

[7]This point was made by S. Blatt, Ph.D., in discussion of a research-in-progress presentation at the 1985 Fall meeting of the American Psychoanalytic Association, New York.

a 4 if there is some significant investment in objects (people, characters in the story); this is a midrange score. Score a 5 if there is slightly more evidence of object investment. Score a 7 for the highest possible level of libidinal and object investment.

Examples of TATs scored using the Dietrich Object Relations and Object Representations Scale on the Object investment category are as follows: TAT story no. 1 is scored 2; TAT story no. 2 is scored 4; TAT story no. 24 is scored 6.

2. *Sadistic versus neutralized aggression.* This category represents the degree or extent to which objects (people, characters) show evidence of varying amounts of aggression representing varying degrees of neutralization of aggression. This category reflects the relative amount of aggressive derivatives that are characterized by sadistic, hostile, or hurtful aspects. Extent of coloring of type (sadistic or more neutralized) of aggression in relating with others. *Scoring criteria.* Score a 1 when objects (characters) are experienced and perceived as most hostile, attacking, hurtful, sadistic; or when they are attacked, killed, mutilated, and so on. A 1 is scored when the greatest amount of sadistic aggression is present. Score a 3 when sadistic aggression predominates somewhat over neutralized aggression. Score a 4 when evidence of neutralized, nonsadistic aggression equals sadistic aggression. Score a 5 when neutralized, nonhostile, nonhurtful aggression predominates slightly over sadistic aggressive interactions, behaviors, or intentions. Score a 7 for the highest possible amount of neutralized, nonsadistic aggression. For this category, the greater the intention or desire on the part of an individual to hurt, kill, or harm another individual, the lower the score.

Examples of TATs scored using the Dietrich Object Relations and Object Representations Scale on the Sadistic versus neutralized aggression category are as follows: TAT story no. 4 is scored 1; TAT story no. 5 is scored 4; TAT story no. 6 is scored 6.

3. *Object warmth.* This category represents the degree or extent of warmth experienced toward objects (people, characters); the amount of warm, close feelings an individual has toward another, or of another object toward the subject. *Scoring criteria.* Score a 1 if there is the lowest possible amount of

warmth or warm feelings expressed, or experienced, felt, or perceived, between objects (people), or simply on the part of one person. Score a 1 if there is a virtual absence of warmth. Score a 3 if there is evidence of warmth in the story, but slightly less warmth than a midpoint score. Score 4 if there is a moderate amount of warmth in the story. Score a 5 if there is evidence of warm feelings, thoughts, warmth expressed, perceived, experienced; slightly more than a midrange score. Score a 7 if the highest possible amount of warmth is conveyed within the TAT story.

Examples of TATs scored using the Dietrich Object Relations and Object Representations Scale on the Object warmth category are as follows: TAT story no. 7 is scored 1; TAT story no. 8 is scored 5; TAT story no. 9 is scored 6.

4. *Quality/level of object relatedness*. This category reflects the degree or extent of capacity for mature, developmentally higher levels of object relations; degree of richness, complexity, and rewarding capacity of object relations. *Scoring criteria*. Score a 1 for the lowest possible amount of evidence of quality of object relations; for the lowest possible level of object relations; for a virtual absence of object relatedness as experienced, expressed, felt, enacted, or perceived by objects (people, characters). Score a 3 if there is some evidence of somewhat higher level object relations. Score a 4 if there is a moderate degree of quality, richness, and complexity of object relatedness; a moderate level. Score a 5 if there is somewhat of a higher level of—and quality of—object relations than a midpoint score. Score a 7 for the highest possible quality/level of object relations vis-à-vis other objects (characters) in the story. The higher the score the more reciprocally rewarding, in general, interactions with others seem to be.

Examples of TATs scored using the Dietrich Object Relations and Object Representations Scale on the Quality/level of object relatedness category are as follows: TAT story no. 10 is scored 1; TAT story no. 11 is scored 4; TAT story no. 12 is scored 7.

5. *Empathy*. This category reflects the degree or extent to which an object or objects (people) shows evidence of being able to empathize, or "put themselves in the other's place"; "extent to which one experiences, behaves, or thinks—revealing the

capacity to 'feel with' another"; degree to which one interacts with others empathically. *Scoring criteria.* Score a 1 if there is no evidence of empathy, or virtually no evidence of empathy, between objects (people) or within an individual. Score a 4 if there is a moderate amount of capacity for and evidence of empathic relating or experiencing between objects (characters) in the story. Score a 7 for the highest possible amount of evidence for empathy within the story, between the individuals; where it is clear, strong, and present in a major way. If empathy is evident, but it is not expressed in the story between objects (people), it is scored one point lower than when it is explicitly present in interactions between characters. In other words, where empathy is communicated from the patient's or subject's point of view, it is scored one point lower than it otherwise would be.

Examples of TATs scored using the Dietrich Object Relations and Object Representations Scale on the Empathy category are as follows: TAT story no. 13 is scored 1; TAT story no. 14 is scored 4; TAT story no. 15 is scored 6.

6. *Object love.* This category represents the degree of that type of love (and caring) relation with another person when that individual is libidinally invested; and the capacity for this type of attachment. Object love, as used in this category, is assumed to be at a higher, more integrated level than narcissistic love. The lower the score the less object love characterizes interactions with others and object relationships. *Scoring criteria.* Score 1 when there is a virtual absence of object love in interactions with objects (characters) and how they are experienced. Score a 3 when there is some evidence of object love, though slightly less than that at the midrange. Score a 5 if there is evidence of greater (4 = midrange score) object-related love in the thoughts and feelings toward others, and in interactions with them. Score a 7 for the greatest amount of object love vis-à-vis other objects (characters) in the story.

Examples of TATs scored using the Dietrich Object Relations and Object Representations Scale on the Object love category are as follows: TAT story no. 16 is scored 1; TAT story no. 17 is scored 4; TAT story no. 18 is scored 7.

7. *Superego harshness versus superego benevolence.* This category

represents the degree or extent of punitiveness, harshness, of the object's (character's) superego, as compared with the degree of benevolence, or of a loving superego. *Scoring criteria.* Score a 1 when the object (character)—the primary or main protaganist—experiences or shows the greatest amount of harshness and punitiveness, and guilt, in thoughts and feelings. Score a 3 when superego harshness predominates slightly over the degree of benevolent and loving aspects of the superego. Score a 5 when superego benevolence (and loving) predominate slightly over harsh, punitive, and guilty aspects of the superego in terms of thoughts and feelings (and how the main character experiences his actions, behaviors, and himself). Score a 7 when there is a virtual lack of superego harshness in the TAT story; and when the degree of superego benevolence is highest.

Examples of TATs scored using the Dietrich Object Relations and Object Representations Scale on the Superego harshness versus superego benevolence category are as follows: TAT story no. 19 is scored 1; TAT story no. 20 is scored 4; TAT story no. 24 is scored 6.

8. *Helplessness versus internal sense of control.* This category reflects the degree to which objects (characters) experience themselves (and others) as helpless, passive, hopeless, as not in control of choices in their life. In scoring the category, extent of helplessness and hopelessness, the focus is more on the character who will be lowest (if there are multiple characters in the story), but not to the exclusion of other characters. *Scoring criteria.* Score a 1 for the virtual absence (lowest degree) of an inner experience or sense of control, and for the highest degree of experiencing oneself, the situation, as well as others, as helpless. Score a 3 if a sense of helplessness predominates slightly in the story over a sense of internal control. Score a 5 if an internal sense and experience of control (experiencing oneself as an origin of actions, choices, behaviors, etc.) predominates slightly over an inner sense of helplessness. Score a 7 if there is the greatest sense of control, and for a virtual absence of an experience of helplessness.

Examples of TATs scored using the Dietrich Object Relations and Object Representations Scale on the Helplessness versus internal sense of control category are as follows: TAT story no.

22 is scored 2; TAT story no. 23 is scored 3; TAT story no. 24 is scored 6.

9. *Psychological mindedness.* This category reflects the degree or extent to which the object (character and subject) thinks of the causes, meanings, and significance of behavior and thoughts and the degree to which motives and meanings of self and others are considered and valued. This category is scored on the basis of the extent of psychological mindedness within, or between, characters in the TAT story. If, however, there is evidence of psychological mindedness in the wording of the story itself (apart from the characters), this should be scored, but weighted somewhat less (scored 1 point lower than it would otherwise be scored). *Scoring criteria.* Score a 1 for no evidence or sign of interest or awareness of motives, meanings, or reasons why individuals behave the way they do. Score a 3 if there is some evidence of psychological mindedness (though a score of 3 is slightly below the midway point). Score a 5 if there is more than a moderate degree of evidence of meanings, motives, and reasons for individual interactions in the story. Score a 7 for the highest degree of evidence of psychological mindedness possible.

Examples of TATs scored using the Dietrich Object Relations and Object Representations Scale on the psychological mindedness category are as follows: TAT story no. 25 is scored 1; TAT story no. 26 is scored 4; TAT story no. 27 is scored 7.

10. *Degree of depression.* This category represents the extent to which depressive, sad, melancholic affects, feelings, and thoughts are experienced and are in evidence. Degree of bleakness, of depressive "coloring" in TAT story. Extent to which objects (characters) and the world are experienced in a depleted, sad, joyless, pleasureless, depressed manner. *Scoring criteria.* Score a 1 for the greatest degree of depression; depressive affect, feelings and outlook; bleakness. Score a 3 for somewhat less depressive coloring and affect in the story and character or characters (a score of 3 is slightly less than the midpoint). Score a 5 when there is considerably less depression. Score a 7 when there is an absence of sad, melancholic, depressive feelings, thoughts, affects, in the story.

Examples of TATs scored using the Dietrich Object Relations

and Object Representations Scale on the Degree of depression category are as follows: TAT story no. 28 is scored 1; TAT story no. 29 is scored 4; TAT story no. 9 is scored 6.

TAT Story 1 & 19

C. 8BM 5" Hum 25". It looks like those two guys in the back are performing some kind of surgery—and that it might be the boy in the front's father. He feels scared about it. He doesn't feel like he has any control over it. Uhm, he feels like he might be left alone. Uhm, my feeling is that the outcome of the surgery is not positive. Cause it's almost like the boy is just remembering it—like he didn't really see it. And he's dealing with the aftereffects now. The way he's all dressed up it looks like he might be being sent off to live with a relative. And that's about it. (A. else?) He's scared about being sent off to a relative and he feels sad. (A. else?) No.

TAT Story 2

C. 2 12". Let's see, this is a girl, she's coming home from school, she's been at school all day. Oh I know, she's just coming home from school, and she looks kind of sad 'cause she's just seen her mother, this lady leaning against the tree. And her mother's looking kind of sad too, 'cause they both like this guy, whoever this guy is tilling the soil. And uhm, well like the mother's worried that the daughter's worried that the mother likes him, and they're like competing for this guy, and I think the outcome of the story will be that he won't want either one of them. (A. else?) That's all.

TAT Story 3

C. 8BM 5". Uhm—the kid's about fifteen, and he's remembering when he was bitten by a snake, uhm, on an African safari, and the doctors that were staying in the village, taking care of the villagers, had to cut the wound open, to get the venom out. And, that's the thing, the point where his memory starts to think back to his whole memory, do you understand? Or, that's what he remembers most about the trip. But he's puzzled as to why he can't feel the same intensity about remembering the situation as he did while it was happening. Uhm, he'd kind of naive, and insensitive—(Outcome?) He'll grow up to be a naive and insensitive businessman and he'll have, what are those plaques of animal heads, you know—trophies on his walls. (A. else?)—And he'll pretend to be happy, uhm, materialistically (A. else?) but he'll feel empty inside.

TAT Story 4

C. 8BM (5″ laughs) 20″. I'm not sure whether it's a murder or a doctor. I'd say from the look on the child's face it's a doctor, he's mortified. That picture's out of my frame of reference, it really is, I even watch "Emergency," the TV program. It looks like it was a long time ago, before medicine was as it is today, and this man's had an appendicitis attack. Ahm, a town doctor is performing his emergency operation on the spot, and the boy had either blocked out the experience as it's going on, or he's remembering it this way. Either way he seems to be rather stoic about the situation. Actually, I can identify with it better if I can think about it as a memory. Ah, well, the man dies, and the kid just walks away. (Th./feeling?) Ah, well, the, everybody? The doctor's, there's a man in the background who looks like he cares, he seems to be handling the situation, and the man whose performing—he almost looks like he could maybe be a brother. And the doctor, he's trying, he looks like he's trying—I got away from the murder. (Phone rings) God there's a gun. It's a bullet wound. I didn't see the gun before. Oh, maybe the kid shot the father, boy, we're getting to ink blots, the whole story can change. Now the kid looks self-satisfied. He changes his expression when you look at it from that point of view. I'm changing my story, he hated the person, he shot him and he's glad. He's feeling very intense, very intense, and he's glad he did it. (A. else?) The thing is though, I get crazy though, if it's the new story the man doesn't die, but the boy has made whatever point it was he wanted to make. It doesn't serve any purpose if he dies, it does if he lives. And he never has to be part of this man's life again. (Later, after putting down card)

Boy, I could get really angry about that one if you want to get real personal, it's my mother and myself.

TAT Story 5

C. 2. 10″. I'm supposed to make up a story? Okay. Uhm. 40″ Okay. Uhm, I'm trying to think. These are the parents. And the girl's gone off to read and you can tell that she just wants to be alone. She just found out that her parents are separating and she's definitely upset by this. Hum, she's just gone off to read and think. And the mother, looks like it's really okay with the mother; the separation. And the father looks like he's going to go to work, he looks like it's not as okay with him. The outcome—is that it's going to be okay. The girl's going to accept it but it'll be okay. She looks so cold.

TAT Story 6

C. 10 5″. Well, we have two lovers, ah, I don't think they're married, they're probably coming to the end of the relationship, and contemplating the parting. They're both very sad, and ah, oh dear, in the future they're going to part and have no regrets about having the relationship, and since it was intense they'll both remember it very dearly. Ah, well, ah, I guess in the future they'll go their separate ways and probably remember their fond remembrances, but with a deep feeling of loss. (A. else?) Ah, no.

TAT Story 7

C. 15 3″ Yuk. Hum 20″. Well, this person is in a graveyard—they look like they're trying to be penitent about somebody's death, but they're not. He looks kind of angry. He feels like really crowded in by all the gravestones and crosses around. I think he feels angry that this person died, and it's like that feeling's going to be holding him in the way he's holding his hands. It's almost as if there's some kind of shackles around his hands. That's it. (A. else?) This picture makes me feel angry looking at it. (Is that all?) I feel like I was that person in the picture. I'd want to push the gravestones away—kind of knock them down.

TAT Story 8 & 26

C. *10 12"*. An affectionate embrace—that looks, with the eyes closed, it gives the impression that it's just after a great deal of tension, or grief, or conflict or something or other. Seems as if the woman is trying to cling to the man, yet the man appears a little bit inanimate, and after having been through the previous questioning, he almost has a kind of gloomy, morbid air. And the fact that none of his body, or that only his head is visible—almost gives him a type of, almost spiritual aura. Ah, I'm at a loss at what else to say. (*Th.*/feeling?) Well, I'd mentioned that the man seems to be, seems to be pictured as cold, or impassive, or I don't know, he doesn't project a lot of animation to me, whereas the woman seems to be looking for a lot of comfort, attachment. Or perhaps the man just looks very weary, and the woman looks maybe warm and affectionate. (Outcome?) (laughs) —Well, I guess, uhm, assuming it's some sort of friendly embrace that's ending past tensions, the outcome could be the reestablishment of past ties, or making amends of some sort. (A. else?) I'd say that about does it.

TAT Story 9 & 12 & 15 & 18

C. *10 15"*. Well, it's a man and a lady and they were very relieved to be together, 'cause they hadn't seen each other in such a long time, because the man went away to war and had been gone for about four years. It was World War II. (*Th.*/feeling?) They're happy and relieved and glad to be with each other and they want to go home and start living together again, and they hope that things can be the way they were after awhile. (A. else?) Nope.

TAT Story 10

C. *8BM 20"*. This one looks a little bit grizzly. Uhm—it looks as if either the man who's lying down is either being operated on or autopsied, or—the position of the gun in front makes me think, I don't know whether he's dead or alive. Well, I guess he's dead with the pensive young man in the front. Well, with the guy in front it almost has a dreamlike magic quality, it almost looks like he's dead, and the streaks that are emanating from the back almost, I was just going to say, I don't know, the gun seems to break things apart instead of tie things together— (Led up to it?) Well, I guess the gun, the gun has something to do with that—presumably, I should say a hunting accident. (What's happening now?) Oh, assuming that we have a hunting accident or a person being operated on, and by the look on the young man's face, let's assume that he died. (*Th.*/feeling?) Well, assuming that the lying man is dead, he doesn't have any feelings, thoughts. The doctor seems to be engrossed in his labors, and his assistant seems to be looking on professionally, and the person in the front, assuming there is some kind of relationship, seems to be in shock or a daze, and the disjointed background seems to suggest a disjointed maze of thoughts that aren't particularly put together in a coherent manner. (Outcome?) — Uhm, well I had already kind of presumed that the lying man had died. I don't know what more outcome there is, the doctors went back to be doctors and the boy continued to live. (A. else?) Uhm, not that I perceive.

TAT Story 11

C. 10 20″. Okay. This looks like an embrace, and the woman with the man had her arms around his shoulder, and the man, I would imagine he had his arms around her. He looks somewhat at ease—and she a little more uneasy than he is. He looks as though he may be comforting, or consoling her; your ideas of death are sticking in. He's in black, she's in white. It could mean he's a priest or some sort of clergyman, but it doesn't look like a funeral or she would be dressed in black. She looks emotionally upset—but the circumstances that caused it— it doesn't look like they're very severe. That's about it.

TAT Story 12 (see TAT Story 9)

TAT Story 13 & 25

C. 15 15" .I think this person—in a graveyard looking like he was lonely or lost—I assume he lost a wife, or the last one he had left so to speak. Assuming that it was his wife, it looks like he has the air about him—not concern about her but concern about him, like why me? Okay. It looks like it was depicting night, adding more to the gloominess of it. He just looks like he's in for bewilderment or (?) why death has occurred. Or why death has occurred and uhm, this one. That's it.

TAT Story 14

C. 10 21". I guess that's a man and a lady, I guess, and it looks like he's comforting her, like there's something wrong. And she just wants to lean on him I guess. (*Th*./feeling?) Well, she's upset or say he's just, I don't know, it doesn't look like he's upset about whatever it is, it just looks like he's upset about what she's upset about. But, I don't know what they're upset about. Obviously, it's not over losing a friend, a lover. (Outcome?) Well, hopefully she'll feel a little better.

TAT Story 15 (see TAT Story 9)

TAT Story 16

C. 8BM 15". Okay. This looks like the thoughts of the person in the suit, the bottom right-hand side. The man on the table looks like he's very much in pain, looks like the doctor's trying to rectify this through surgery. A picture of a rifle barrel makes everything look pretty uneasy. The person on the table could have been shot. And from his clothes, and from the bookcases on the bottom right, makes the person look like he's pretty well-to-do. This person could be the one on the table or he could be the one who inflicted the wound, but from the clarity of the picture I would say that he's the one who inflicted the wound. Or, he's thinking about doing it. If he is thinking about doing something like this or if he's done it he looks like he's having second thoughts. Beams of light look like they're coming in from the window giving the whole picture a religious point of view. That's it.

TAT Story 17

C. *8BM Uhm, Okay. 10″.* Somebody's getting operated on. And the person in front is upset about, is worried about it. You know, he's upset about somebody having an operation and it's a relative, he just wants to know what's going on. (*Th./*feeling?) Well, the guy who's getting operated on is not real thrilled about it, he's in pain, but the doctors are just being doctors, I don't think they think about it. Ah, the guy in the front is worried, scared that something is going to go wrong. But hopefully everything will work out. (A. else?) No.

TAT Story 18 (see TAT Story 9)

TAT Story 19 (see TAT Story 1)

TAT Story 20

C. *2 Oh Jesus. 35″.* Okay. The first thing that comes to mind with this is that each of the people in the picture aren't connecting with each other in terms of eye contact or anything. And it's like each of them is doing their own thing. It looks like each of them is getting involved at their own level almost as a way of avoiding something. The two women look sad—the one woman who looks like she's pregnant. She looks like she's waiting out her time period just before she has her baby. The young girl looks like she's gone off to school but she's distracted, she's not really interested in doing it—she looks sad too. And the man is getting into working. It looks like he's not really, really anything. Uhm, it does seem like they've experienced some kind of loss and that they're not sharing what they feel about it. And I think that as a result of not sharing—their cohesion—but that as a family unit their cohesion isn't really gonna last—if it's there at all.

TAT Story 21

C. *8BM 12″*. An intern. And a, it reminds me of a war. The soldier was severely hurt. And uhm, the doctors will perform an operation. Well, okay, try to save his life. Am I going too fast? (No) And ah, the intern was supposed to watch the operation but uhm, the way he was hurt reminds him of the brutality of the war and he didn't want to watch it. That's all. That's about it.

TAT Story 22

C. *15. Can I ask you who drew that? (Don't know) Strange. 120″*. This, ah, to me it feels like this picture expresses the person in the center—who's a girl—really feels like in her own mind, as opposed to, as opposed to the way she functions out in the world. Ah, this is not a real scene, this is a mental expression of a person who's alone, and ah, unloved by, what the, by someone who's important to love her (?). We could say her mother for personal sake, and that the graveyard represents having locked her into this feeling, it sort of took away her freedom to open up, she's sort of in this closed position, and there's—it also feels like time has sort of stood still. Her world on the outside continues to change but on the inside it's still at the same place. But she also looks like she's making a decision whether to stay in this place or to make the effort to break out of this mental and physical captivity. And the outcome is, ah, she walks out and she doesn't look back, she's going to make it. (A. else?) Nope.

TAT Story 23 & 29

C. *2. God, I don't know what to say. 45″*. This girl's on the way home from school and she uhm, I guess this is where she lives. I don't know what's going on. (You're doing okay.) This is hard. Well, the other two people know each other, I don't know how they're related but they know each other somehow. And the woman looks like she's mad about something. And, oh, maybe she was having a fight with the guy 'cause it looks like he's getting all frustrated and going back to work. And uhm, I don't know. (Outcome?) She'll go home, and the guy will go on working, the lady will get angry and go on home, and she'll finish up some other time I guess. (A. else?) No.

TAT Story 24

C. 10 17″. In this I got two different ideas about—either like husband and wife in a love embrace, or they're in an embrace because of sorrow. (Led up to it?) Ah, the sorrow would be if someone close to them passed away, and the love embrace, I would say, just because they loved each other. (*Th./feeling?*) Excuse me. (repeat) I would say it's a deep feeling of love for one another, and that would be for both, the love and the sorrow. And it looks like they need each other. The outcome, let's see, I would say that they would stay together for a long time. (A. else?) I can't see a mouth on the man, but maybe he's whispering something to her. That's about all.

TAT Story 25 (see TAT Story 13)

TAT Story 26 (see TAT Story 8)

TAT Story 27

C. 15 3″. Well, this definitely represents death. I don't see how you could see anything different—all the tombstones, black; the old man. His hands are pointing downward, maybe to hell. He maybe represents the devil. His hands are boney, sort of a sinister face. None of the tombstones have names on them, which suggests anonimity. His hands look like they might be bound which might represent he's there against his will. The fact that he doesn't have eyes could represent again the devil or death, or both. They're sort of intertwined. (Led up to it?) Hum, what might have led up to it? Well, well it could be, which is highly improbable—that this man came to the cemetery to pay respects to someone who died, 'cause his hands are folded—that's not too likely. Or he could be a caretaker, again that's not too probable, or he could be death. A guardian or gatekeeper of the cemetery. And the way the tombstones are situated it, it sort of gives the message that death comes to everyone—the grim reaper sort of thing. (*Th.?*) Well, if he is a death figure or devil figure, I really can't speak. If he is a mourner he's probably feeling grief. He does look very melancholy. You can't see his eyes, which generally express someone's feelings. But his general features are cold. He's sort of a doomed figure. Maybe he's feeling this is a place where I might eventually end. (A. else?) No.

TAT Story 28

C. 8BM 20". Well, it looks like someone was shot and the person who did the shooting is here in the front—with some kind of a gun, it looks like a gun, and it looks like it's taking place in a barn someplace and either a doctor was called in or a friend was called in to take out the bullet—and the friend or a doctor is looking over his shoulder. Okay, uhm, it looks like the man with the bullet is in a lot of pain—'cause his face is turned away and his eyes are opened, and the man who did the shooting, he looks like a boy. But he looks like he doesn't regret anything and I see him getting away with it—the way he's dressed and everything—it seems like he has money and he never really gets caught. (A. else?) Uhm, I see the, the shot, the man who was shot as living through it all and as not really seeking revenge. (A. else?) Uhm, not really.

TAT Story 29 (see TAT Story 23)

TAT Story 30

C. 15 9". It looks like a guy standing in a graveyard with all these headstones. He's not a ghost or anything, he's a person who's alive. Maybe he's looking at his wife's tombstone. It's dark out. It's late at night. Maybe he's just come to look at a tombstone, and he'll just stand there till the morning till the grass cutter comes and finds him standing there, that's all. (*Th. ?*) He's sad and afraid too of being there in the dark, but he's sad too 'cause it's his wife's grave. (A. else?) No.

References

Berlinsky, E., & Biller, H. (1982), *Parental Death and Psychological Development*. Lexington, MA: Lexington Books.

Blatt, S. (1975), The validity of projective techniques and their research and clinical contribution. *J. Pers. Assess.*, 39:327–343.

Blos, P. (1962), *On Adolescence: A Psychoanalytic Interpretation*. New York: Free Press.

Boesky, D. (1982), Acting out: A reconsideration of the concept. *Internat. J. Psycho-Anal.*, 63:39–55.

———(1983), The problem of mental representation in self and object theory. *Psychoanal. Quart.*, 52:564–583.

Bowlby, J. (1980), *Attachment and Loss*, Vol. 3. New York: Basic Books.

Brenner, C. (1959), The masochistic character. *J. Amer. Psychoanal. Assn.*, 7:197–226.

Burlingham, D., & Freud, A. (1942), *Young Children in War-Time*. London: Allen & Unwin.

Buxbaum, E. (1980), Between the oedipus complex and adolescence: The "quiet" time. In: *The Course of Life: Psychoanalytic Contributions Toward Understanding Personality Development*, Vol. 2, ed. S. Greenspan & G. Pollock. Washington DC: U.S. Department of Health & Human Services, pp. 121–136.

Deutsch, H. (1937), Absence of grief. *Psychoanal. Quart.*, 6:12–22.

Dietrich, D. (1979), *Psychopathology and Death Fear: A Quasi-Experimental Investigation of the Relationships Between Psychopathology and Death Fear and Fantasies as Psychological Sequelae in Young Adults Who Experienced the Death of a Parent During Childhood or Adolescence*. Unpublished doctoral dissertation. Washington University, St. Louis, MO.

———(1981), Psychopathologic and medical effects of early parent death in adults. Paper presented to the Annual Meeting of the American Psychological Association, Division of Clinical Psychology, Los Angeles, August.

———(1983), Bowlby and childhood mourning: A critical evaluation twenty years later. Paper presented to the Annual Meeting of the American Psychological Association, Division of Psychoanalysis, Los Angeles, August.

———(1984a), Problems in the psychoanalytic psychotherapy of early parent bereaved patients. Paper presented to the Annual Meeting of the American Psychological Association, Division of Psychoanalysis, as part of the panel "Loss and Mourning: Current Psychoanalytic Perspectives," D. Dietrich, chair. Toronto, August.

———(1984b), Psychological health of young adults who experienced early parent death: MMPI trends. *J. Clin. Psychol.*, 40:901–908.

———(1985), Dietrich Object Relations and Object Representations Scale. Unpublished scale. Wayne State University School of Medicine, Detroit.

———(1986a), Object relations, traumatization and object relations: Psychoanalytic research approaches. Paper presented to the Annual Meeting of the American Psychological Association, Division of Psychoanalysis, as part of the panel "New Studies on Object Loss: Implications for Psychoanalytic Theory," D. Dietrich, chair. Washington DC, August.

———(1986b), The bereaved child's psychological health several years later. In: *Children and Death*, ed. G. Paterson. London, Ontario: King's College, pp. 91–100.

———Bell, J., Lycaki, H., & Sitaram, N. (1984), Ego functions, object representations, and object relations and biological correlates in depressed borderline patients and the affective disorders. Paper presented to the American Psychoanalytic Association Annual Meeting, December, New York.

Erikson, E. (1959), Identity and the Life Cycle. Monograph, *Psychological Issues*. Vol. 1. New York: International Universities Press.

Fenichel, O. (1945), *The Psychoanalytic Theory of Neurosis*. New York: W. W. Norton.

———(1953), Specific forms of the Oedipus complex. In: *The Collected Papers of Otto Fenichel*, ed. H. Fenichel & D. Rapaport. New York: W. W. Norton, pp. 203–220.

Ferenczi, S. (1913), Stages in the development of the sense of reality. In: *Sex in Psychoanalysis: The Selected Papers of Sandor Ferenczi*, Vol. 1. New York: Basic Books, 1950, pp. 213–239.

Fisher, S., & Greenberg, R. (1977), *The Scientific Credibility of Freud's Theories and Therapy*. New York: Basic Books.

Fleming, J. (1972), Early object deprivation and transference phenomena: The working alliance. *Psychoanal. Quart.*, 41:23–49.

———Altschul, S. (1963), Activation of mourning and growth by psychoanalysis. *Internat. J. Psycho-Anal.*, 44:419–431.

Freud, A. (1958), Adolescence. The Psychoanalytic Study of the Child, 13:255–278. New York: International Universities Press.

———(1960), Discussion of Dr. John Bowlby's paper. The Psychoanalytic Study of the Child, 15:53–62. New York: International Universities Press.

———(1965), *Normality and Pathology in Childhood: The Writings of Anna Freud*, Vol. 6. New York: International Universities Press.

———Burlingham, D. (1943), *War and Children*. New York: International Universities Press.

——— ———(1944), *Infants Without Families*. New York: International Universities Press.

Freud, S. (1900), The Interpretation of Dreams. *Standard Edition*, 4 & 5. London: Hogarth Press, 1953.

———(1905), Three essays on the theory of sexuality. *Standard Edition*, 7:125–243. London: Hogarth Press, 1961.

———(1915), Instincts and their vicissitudes. *Standard Edition*, 14:117–140. London: Hogarth Press, 1961.

———(1916), Some character-types met with in psychoanalytic work. *Standard Edition*, 14:309–333. London: Hogarth Press, 1957.

———(1917), Mourning and melancholia. *Standard Edition*, 14:237–258. London: Hogarth Press, 1961.

———(1920), Beyond the Pleasure Principle. *Standard Edition*, 18. London: Hogarth Press, 1957.

———(1927), Fetishism. *Standard Edition*, 21:147–157, London: Hogarth Press, 1957.

————(1932), New Introductory Lectures on Psychoanalysis. *Standard Edition*, 22:5–182. London: Hogarth Press, 1957.

————(1939), Moses and Monotheism. *Standard Edition*, 23. London: Hogarth Press, 1957.

Furman, E. (1974), *A Child's Parent Dies*. New Haven, CT: Yale University Press.

Furman, R. (1964), Death and the young child: Some preliminary considerations. *The Psychoanalytic Study of the Child*, 19:377–397. New York: International Universities Press.

————(1968), Additional remarks on mourning and the young child. *Bull. Philadelphia Assn. Psychoanal.*, 18:51–64.

————(1973), A child's capacity for mourning. In: *The Child in His Family: The Impact of Disease & Death*, Vol. 2, ed. E. J. Anthony & C. Koupernik. (Yearbook of the International Association for Child Psychiatry & Allied Professions). New York: John Wiley, pp. 225–231.

Furst, S., ed. (1963), *Psychic Trauma*. New York: Basic Books.

Galenson, E. (1980), Characteristics of psychological development during the second and third years of life. In: *The Course of Life: Psychoanalytic Contribution Towards Understanding Personality Development*, Vol. 1, eds. S. Greenspan & G. Pollock. Washington DC: U.S. Department of Health & Human Services, pp. 459–500.

Greenacre, P. (1952), *Trauma, Growth and Personality*. New York: International Universities Press.

Greenberg, J., & Mitchell, S. (1983), *Object Relations in Psychoanalytic Theory*. Cambridge, MA: Harvard University Press.

Hartmann, H. (1939), *Ego Psychology and the Problem of Adaptation*. New York: International Universities Press, 1965.

————(1952), The mutual influences in the development of ego and id. In: *Essays on Ego Psychology*. New York: International Universities Press, 1964.

Hoffer, W. (1952), The mutual influences in the development of ego and id: Earliest stages. *The Psychoanalytic Study of the Child*, 7:31–41. New York: International Universities Press.

Jacobson, E. (1964), *The Self and the Object World*. New York: International Universities Press.

————(1965), The return of the lost parent. In: *Drives, Affects and Behavior*, Vol. 2, ed. M. Schur. New York: International Universities Press, pp. 193–211.

Kane, B. (1979), Children's concepts of death. *J. Genet. Psychol.*, 130:141–153.

Kastenbaum, R., & Costa, P. (1977), Psychological perspectives on death. *Ann. Rev. Psychol.*, 28:225–249.

Klein, M, (1935), A contribution to the psychogenesis of manic-depressive states. In: *Contributions to Psychoanalysis, 1921–1945*. New York: McGraw-Hill, 1964.

Kliman, G., Feinberg, D., Buchsbaum, B., Kliman, A., Lubin, H., Ronald, D., & Stein, M. (1969), Facilitation of mourning during childhood. Paper presented to the American Orthopsychiatric Association, New York, April.

Koocher, G. (1974), Talking with children about death. *Amer. J. Orthopsychiat.*, 44:45–52.

Krystal, H., ed. (1968), *Massive Psychic Trauma*. New York: International Universities Press.

———(1978), Trauma and affect. *The Psychoanalytic Study of the Child*, 33:81–116. New York: International Universities Press.

Laufer, M. (1966), Object loss and mourning during adolescence. *The Psychoanalytic Study of the Child*, 21:269–293. New York: International Universities Press.

Loewald, H. (1960), On the therapeutic action of psychoanalysis. *Internat. J. Psycho-Anal.*, 41:16–33.

———(1962), Internalization, separation, mourning, and the superego. *Psychoanal. Quart.*, 31:483–504.

Mahler, M. (1960), Symposium of psychotic object-relationships: III. Perceptual de-differentiation and psychotic "object relationship." *Internat. J. Psycho-Anal.*, 41:548–553.

———(1961), On sadness and grief in infancy and childhood: Loss and restoration of the symbiotic love object. *The Psychoanalytic Study of the Child*, 16:332–351. New York: International Universities Press.

———(1968), *On Human Symbiosis and the Vicissitudes of Individuation*, Vol. 1. New York: International Universities Press.

———Pine, F., & Bergman, A. (1975), *The Psychological Birth of the Human Infant*. New York: Basic Books.

Maurer, A. (1964), Adolescent attitudes towards death. *J. Genet. Psychol.*, 105:75–90.

Mayman, M. (1968), Early memories and character structure. *J. Projective Tech. & Pers. Assess.*, 32:303–316.

Melear, J. (1973), Children's conceptions of death. *J. Genet. Psychol.*, 123:359–360.

Michaels, R. (1980), Adulthood. In: *The Course of Life: Psychoanalytic Contributions Toward Understanding Personality Development*, Vol. 3, eds. S. Greenspan & G. Pollock. Washington DC: U.S. Department of Health & Human Services, pp. 25–34.

Murray, H. (1943), *Thematic Apperception Test*. Cambridge, MA: Harvard University Press.

Nagera, H. (1981), *The Developmental Approach to Childhood Psychopathology*. New York: Jason Aronson.

Nagy, M. (1948), The child's theories concerning death. *J. Genet. Psychol.*, 73:3–27.

Nunberg, H. (1931), The synthetic function of the ego. *Internat. J. Psycho-Anal.*, 12:123–140.

Offer, D. (1980), Adolescent development: A normative perspective. In: *The Course of Life: Psychoanalytic Contributions Toward Understanding Personality Development*, Vol. 2, eds. S. Greenspan & G. Pollock. Washington DC: U.S. Department of Health & Human Services, pp. 357–372.

Panel (1976), Effect on adults of object loss in the first five years, M. Wolfenstein, reporter. *J. Amer. Psychoanal. Assn.*, 24:659–668.

———(1978), Current concepts of object relations theory. V. Spruiell, reporter. *J. Amer. Psychoanal. Assn.*, 26:599–613.

Parens, H. (1980), Psychic development during the second and third years of life. In: *The Course of Life: Psychoanalytic Contributions Toward Understanding Personality Development*, Vol. 1, ed. S. Greenspan & G. Pollock.

Washington DC: U.S. Department of Health & Human Services, pp. 459–500.

Piaget, J. (1958), *The Growth of Logical Thinking from Childhood to Adolescence*, trans. A. Parsons & S. Seagrin. New York: Basic Books.

Pollock, G. (1961), Mourning and adaptation. *Internat. J. Psycho-Anal.*, 42:341–361.

———(1962), Childhood parent and sibling loss in adult patients: A comparative study. *Arch. Gen. Psychiat.*, 7:295–305.

———(1972), Bertha Pappenheim's pathological mourning: Possible effects of childhood sibling loss. *J. Amer. Psychoanal. Assn.*, 21:328–332.

Rapaport, D., ed. (1951), *Organization and Pathology of Thought*. New York: Columbia University Press.

———Gill, M., & Schafer, R. (1944–1946), *Diagnostic Psychological Testing*, Vols. 1 & 2. Chicago: Yearbook Publishers.

Raphael, B. (1983), *The Anatomy of Bereavement*. New York: Basic Books.

Robertson, J., & Robertson, J. (1971), Young children in brief separation: A fresh look. *The Psychoanalytic Study of the Child*, 26:264–315. New York: Quadrangle Books.

Rochlin, G. (1959), Loss and restitution. *The Psychoanalytic Study of the Child*, 8:288–309. New York: International Universities Press.

———(1965), *Griefs and Discontents*. Boston: Little, Brown.

———(1967), How younger children view death and themselves. In: *Explaining Death to Children*, ed. E. Grollman. Boston: Beacon Press.

Root, N. (1957), A neurosis in adolescence. *The Psychoanalytic Study of the Child*, 12:320–334. New York: International Universities Press.

Rorschach, H. (1921), *Psychodiagnostics*. New York: Grune & Stratton, 1949.

Rosenzweig, S. (1945), The picture-association method and its application in a study of reactions of frustration. *J. Personal.*, 14:3–23.

Sandler, J., & Rosenblatt, B. (1962), The concept of the representational world. *The Psychoanalytic Study of the Child*, 17:128–145. New York: International Universities Press.

Sarnoff, C. (1976), *Latency*. New York: Jason Aronson.

Schafer, R. (1954), *Psychoanalytic Interpretation in Rorschach Testing*. New York: Grune & Stratton.

———(1960), The loving and beloved superego in Freud's structural theory. *The Psychoanalytic Study of the Child*, 15:163–188. New York: International Universities Press.

———(1968), *Aspects of Internalization*. New York: International Universities Press.

———(1976), *A New Language for Psychoanalysis*. New Haven, CT: Yale University Press.

Sekaer, C., & Katz, S. (1986), On the concept of mourning in childhood: Reactions of a 2½-year-old girl to the death of her father. *The Psychoanalytic Study of the Child*, 41:287–314. New York: International Universities Press.

Settlage, C. (1980), The psychoanalytic theory and understanding of psychic development during the second and third years of life. In: *The Course of Life: Psychoanalytic Contributions Toward Understanding Personality Development*, Vol. 1, eds. S. Greenspan & G. Pollock. Washington DC: U.S. Department of Health & Human Services, pp. 523–539.

Shabad, P., Worland, J., Lander, H., & Dietrich, D. (1979), TAT indicators of psychotic breakdown in children at risk. *Child Psychiat. & Hum. Develop.*, 10:49–59.

Speece, M. (1986), Children's understanding of death: Three components. In: *Children and Death: Proceedings of the 1985 King's College Conference*, ed. G.Paterson. London, Ontario: King's College, pp. 71–79.

Spitz, R. (1965), *The First Year of Life*. New York: International Universities Press.

Terr, L. (1984), Time and trauma. *The Psychoanalytic Study of the Child*, 39:633–665. New Haven, CT: Yale University Press.

Viederman, M. (1985), Loss, mourning and creativity in the life of Magritte. Paper presented at the Eighth Annual Richard & Editha Sterba Lecture, Bloomfield Hills, MI, April.

Wolfenstein, M. (1966), How is mourning possible? *The Psychoanalytic Study of the Child*, 21:93–123. New York: International Universities Press.

———(1969), Loss, rage and repetition. *The Psychoanalytic Study of the Child*, 24:432–462. New York: International Universities Press.

———(1973), The image of the lost parent. *The Psychoanalytic of the Child*, 28:433–456. New Haven, CT: Yale University Press.

13

Father Loss, Cognitive and Personality Functioning

Henry B. Biller, Ph.D.
Margery Salter, Ph.D.

In its broadest sense, father loss can be conceptualized within the context of paternal deprivation. Any child who has not received adequate fathering can be viewed as having lost a significant positive influence, as having suffered from not experiencing a caring, involved, and competent male parent. Some of the more dramatic types of paternal loss involve the death of the father or, in other cases, the father's extreme unavailability associated with desertion or a bitter divorce. However, children may also experience a profound sense of paternal loss because of a father's neglect, rejection, physical abuse, or betrayal, as in the case of incest. Father loss can be associated with continua relating to the quality of fathering as well as to continua describing physical availability–absence. The father-absent child is not necessarily at a disadvantage when compared to all father-present children, especially those who may have maltreating fathers. The child who has an emotionally detached, physically abusive father may fare far worse than the child who is reared by a competent single mother (Biller, 1974c; Biller and Solomon, 1986).

Father loss is a much more pervasive problem with respect to the number of children who are affected than is mother loss. Far more children lose fathers than mothers through death, divorce, and other forms of physical and psychological separation. Furthermore, if a child is parent deprived, in most subcultures, there are likely to be many more "mother surrogates" available than there are "father surrogates." Children who do not receive consistent emotional support from their biological father, particularly if they are young, are relatively unlikely to receive compensatory male influence whereas most children, even if the mother is somewhat inadequate, are exposed to a variety of caring females, including other female relatives and teachers (Biller, 1974c; Biller and Solomon, 1986).

During the past decade, there has been a tremendous increase in research data relating to the importance of the father's behavior in child development. In fact, some of the most impressive data underscore the significant and positive impact that involved fathers contribute during the infancy period, even in the first few months of the child's life. In addition to the father's biological contribution, there are also other potential prebirth sources of paternal influence. For example, the degree to which the expectant father is emotionally supportive of the expectant mother, and responsive to her needs, can be a major factor in the relative adequacy of prenatal care. On the other hand, the loss, or lack of physical and/or emotional availability of the father during the prenatal period or during early infancy is often associated with later difficulties for the developing child (Berlinsky and Biller, 1982; Biller and Solomon, 1986).

Psychoanalytic Perspectives

Any serious student of early parent–child relationships is deeply indebted to the groundbreaking work of Freud (1905, 1933, 1939). We have found that Freud's work is the starting point for an understanding of the complex processes involved in the child's identification with the mother and father and that most theories of parent–child interactions and attachment are to some extent derivatives or extensions of psychoanalytic conceptions (Biller, 1971, 1974c). Despite the fact that Freud did give some consideration to the preoedipal role of the father, he for the most part emphasized paternal influence beginning with the oedipal phase (Biller and Borstelmann, 1967; Machtlinger, 1976, 1981; Ross, 1977, 1979).

No other group of clinicians or scientists has stimulated more research concerning parent–infant relationships than have psychoanalysts. Yet, many psychoanalysts have been somewhat less than forthcoming in giving attention to the remarkable explosion in data linking variations in paternal behavior with infant and family functioning (Cath, Gurwitt, and Ross, 1982). With few exceptions, it was not until the mid-1970s that analysts began to acknowledge the preoedipal role of the father, or that father loss could have a direct impact on the infant's development.

We believe that the degree to which fathers have a potential impact upon early infant development is still somewhat underappreciated in the psychoanalytic literature. Unquestionably, in the vast majority of families, mothers are the primary parents for infants and toddlers; but in increasing numbers, fathers play an equally significant role, and in some families are indeed the primary parent. It is perhaps important to emphasize that for a father to have a crucial role in the child's development from birth on does not necessarily mean that the mother has to be absent, severely depressed, or otherwise handicapped. There are many families in which infants seem to be more attached to the father, but who also display a very strong and healthy attachment to the mother (Biller, 1974c; Biller and Solomon, 1986).

Throughout much of the important book *Father and Child* (Cath et al., 1982) there are many references to the universality of an initial and primary "feminine" identification with the mother which must be shifted and/or modified in the separation–individuation process. Our point is not to deny or deemphasize the general prevalence of initial maternal identifications, but to suggest that this is neither biologically imperative or necessary for healthy infant and child development. No doubt, as some of the provocative clinical examples presented in the Cath et al. (1982) volume so clearly demonstrate, many fathers become highly involved early in the infant's life as a function of some type of maternal inadequacy or abdication of parenting, but it is also clear from much of the parent–infant research of the 1970s and 1980s that the father may play a primary role from birth onwards within the context of healthy marital and family functioning. The view of an involved male parent as generally a "mothering individual" for the infant seems to exclude the fact that a man's parenting style may be basically masculine (e.g., active, playful, stimulating) and that it can be based as much on a primary identification with his own father as with his mother (Biller 1974c; Biller and Solomon, 1986).

The preceding comments are not intended to minimize the value of psychoanalytic contributions to our understanding of the father's role in development as presented in *Father and Child* (Cath et al., 1982). We are merely suggesting that there seems to be some distance to transverse before there is a more complete integration of psychoanalytic theory and research and other existing data on the father and family development.

Father Absence and Masculine Development

Many researchers have speculated that the primary effects of father absence are manifested in terms of deficits and/or abnormalities in the boy's sex-role development (Biller, 1970, 1971, 1981b). In this section, research findings concerning the relationship between father absence and the boy's sex-role development are discussed. A comparison of the sex-role development of father-absent and father-present boys suggests some of the ways in which fathering and paternal deprivation influence personality development. Masculinity is a complex and multidimensional concept. The relative degree of overt masculinity, as expressed in interests, activities, and interpersonal style, in and of itself, does not necessarily reflect level of psychological health. For example, adolescent or adult males who are labeled as highly masculine may actually be quite aloof and insensitive, have unconscious conflicts in terms of passive feminine longings, and an insecure sexual identity. However, the young boy's happy embrace of what he perceives as masculine endeavors is often an expression of a healthy identity and a strong feeling of identification with his father (Biller 1974c; Biller and Solomon, 1986).

There are many studies which suggest that early father absence retards the young boy's development of independence and other masculine behaviors (Leichty, 1960; Green, 1974). There is also cross-cultural evidence which indicates that early father absence is often associated with sex-role conflicts among males in other societies (Whiting, Kluckhohn, and Anthony, 1958; Burton and Whiting, 1961; Stephens, 1962; Rogers and Long, 1968; Burton, 1972).

In a study that included a longitudinal format and an impressive array of sex-role measures, Hetherington, Cox, and Cox (1982) found relatively clear-cut differences in sex-role functioning between young boys (five- and six-year-olds) from intact families and those who were father absent for two years because of divorce. The father-absent boys had lower masculine sex-role preference scores but higher feminine sex-role preference scores than did the father-present boys. On the Draw-A-Person Test, the father-absent boys more often drew a female first and also demonstrated less differentiation between their drawings of males and females than did the father-present boys. In addition, father-absent boys spent more time playing with females, younger peers, and in activities generally regarded as feminine.

A study of lower-class fifth-grade boys by Santrock (1970b) revealed that boys who became father absent before the age of two were more handicapped in terms of several dimensions of personality development than were boys who became father absent at a later age. For example, boys who became father absent before age two were found to be less trusting, less industrious, and to have more feelings of inferiority than boys who became father absent between the ages of three to five. Other evidence is consistent with the supposition that early father absence is associated with a heightened susceptibility to a variety of psychological problems (Biller, 1971, 1974c; Hetherington, Cox, and Cox, 1978, 1982). Research by Wallerstein and Kelly (1974, 1975, 1976, 1980b) has clearly shown that developmental stage is a crucial factor in determining the type of reaction that children have to divorce and separation from the father. Studies relating the effects of the timing of father absence upon various dimensions of personality development are reviewed in later sections of this chapter.

Different Aspects of Sex-Role Development

As the findings on developmental stages have suggested, different aspects of sex-role development may be affected in differential ways by father absence. Because of such deprivation effects, it is common, for example, for young father-absent children to intensely seek the attention of older males. Furthermore, father-absent children often have a strong motivation to imitate and please potential father figures (which makes them particularly susceptible to maltreatment by nonfamily members). In this way, father-absent boys may strive to act in a masculine fashion in some facets of their behavior while continuing to feel unmasculine or feminine at an unconscious level. Demands for masculine behavior may not become apparent to the boy until he reaches school age, or even adolescence, but in any case under such conditions his sex-role preference and/or sex-role adoption may differ from his basic feelings of sexual identity (Biller and Borstelmann, 1967).

In a study with lower-class, six-year-old children, Biller (1968b) found that father-absent boys were significantly less masculine than father-present boys on a projective measure of sex-role behavior which was used to assess sex-role orientation. However, the two groups were not consistently different in terms of their direct sex-role preferences (the toys and the games that they said they liked) or teachers' ratings of sex-role adoption.

An examination of data from several other studies suggests the hypothesis that, particularly by the time of adolescence, there is relatively little difference among lower-class father-present and father-absent boys with respect to many facets of sex-role awareness, preference, and adoption (Tiller, 1961; McCord, McCord, and Thurber, 1962; Greenstein, 1966; Mitchell and Wilson, 1967; Biller 1974c, 1981a).

Surrogate Models

Paternal absence or paternal inadequacy does not, of course, rule out the possible preference for other male models. An older brother, uncle, grandfather, or male boarder may provide the child with much competent adult male contact. An important compensatory and identificatory role can be played by peers, neighbors, and teachers. Male teachers seem to have much potential for positively influencing father-deprived boys in terms of their sense of personal adequacy and social functioning (Biller, 1974a,b,c; Lee and Wolinsky, 1973).

The child may even learn some masculine behaviors by patterning himself after and identifying with a movie or television star, an athlete, or a fictional hero. Anna Freud and Dorothy Burlingham (1944) described how a fatherless, two-year-old boy developed a fantasy role model. Bob's mother had told him about a nine-year-old boy, whom he referred to as "Big Bobby," and thereafter Bob actively used Big Bobby as a masculine model, attempting physical feats that he thought Big Bobby could perform. Bob perceived Big Bobby as physically superior to everyone else.

Some investigations have found that masculinity is related to the general amount of contact boys have with adult males. Nash (1965) studied a group of Scottish orphans who went to live in cottages run by married couples, the husbands thus offering them a masculine model. Even though less masculine (in terms of a variety of sex-role measures) than boys who were raised in a typical family setting, they were more masculine than a group of orphans brought up entirely by women.

Stepfathers can have a facilitating effect on the father-absent child's development, particularly if the stepfather–child relationship begins before the age of four or five. The very young child who feels paternally deprived may find it much easier to accept a stepfather than the latency aged boy or adolescent who may have already established a stronger sense of independence. The stepfather may also react more favorably to the young affectionate child than to the older child who refuses to accept his presence and authority. The quality of the mother–child relationship and the mother's attitude toward the stepfather are also very important factors influencing the stepfather–child relationship (Biller and Meredith, 1974; Biller and Solomon, 1986).

Siblings. Older brothers can be very important masculine models for children. For example, paternal deprivation may have a much different effect on a five-year-old boy who is an only child than on a five-year-old boy who has two older brothers who themselves were not paternally deprived in early childhood. Obviously, many other variables have to be considered including the frequency and quality of interactions and degree of ambivalence among siblings. A problem with many of the sibling studies is that they consider only the presence or absence of a particular type of sibling. This is somewhat analogous to studies which take into account only whether a child is father present or father absent (Biller, 1974c; Biller and Solomon, 1986).

Interestingly, in two-child, father-absent families, there is some evidence that boys with brothers suffer less of a deficit in academic aptitude than do boys with sisters (Sutton-Smith, Rosenberg, and Landy, 1968). In Santrock's (1970a) study, father-absent boys with only older male siblings scored as more masculine (on a maternal interview measure of sex-role behavior) than father-absent boys with only female siblings. In an extension of Santrock's investigation, Wohlford, Santrock, Berger, and Liberman (1971) found that father-absent children with older brothers were less dependent than those with older sisters in data derived from both doll play and maternal interview measures. However, the presence or absence of older female siblings was not related to the sex-role measures and did not affect the older brothers' influence. Although the presence of male siblings may lessen the effects of father absence, data from one of Biller's (1968a) investigations were consistent with the conclusion that the presence of a father is generally a much more important factor in masculine development than is the presence of an older brother.

Peers. The masculine role models and objects for identification provided by the peer group can be particularly influential for the paternally deprived boy. In a subculture in which instrumental aggression and physical prowess are very important as a means of achieving peer acceptance, many father-absent boys are likely to strive to emulate their masculine peers. Peer models seem especially important in lower-class neighborhoods. Miller (1958) emphasized the centrality of such traits as toughness and independence in the value system of lower-class adolescents. Lower-class boys honor aggressiveness more than do middle-class boys, and one of the types of boys that they most admire is the aggressive, belligerent youngster who earns their respect because of his toughness and strength. Because of his identification with the aggressor and passive feminine longings, the paternally deprived boy is especially susceptible to being overly influenced and abused by dominant peers (Biller and Solomon, 1986).

The boy who is physically well equipped may find it relatively easy to gain acceptance from his peers. Many paternally deprived boys behave in a generally effective and masculine manner. For example, an additional case study analysis of some of the five-year-old boys in Biller's (1968a, 1969b) studies indicated that father-absent boys who are relatively mesomorphic are less likely to be retarded in their sex-role development than are father-absent boys with unmasculine physiques. A boy's physique has important stimulus value in terms of the expectations and reinforcements it elicits from others as well as important dynamic meaning for him and it may, along with correlated constitutional factors, predispose him toward success or failure in particular types of activities. The influence of the child's anatomical, temperamental, and cognitive predispositions on parental and peer behavior must be taken into account (Biller, 1974c; Martel and Biller, 1987).

Methodological Issues

In addition to its obvious theoretical and practical relevance a possible methodological justification for studying the effects of father absence is the fact that father absence is a "naturalistic manipulation," a naturally occurring variation in family structure. It can be argued that father absence is typically an antecedent rather than a consequence of unconscious processes, fantasies, and behaviors in children.

A particular problem with studies comparing father-absent and father-present children is that investigators have usually treated both types of children as if they represented homogeneous groups. There has been a lack of concern for the meaning of father absence and father presence. For example, there have been few attempts to ensure that there is a group of children who have a high level and quality of father availability to compare with children who are father absent.

Most researchers have treated father absence in an overly simplistic fashion. In many studies, there has been no specification of such variables as type, length, and age of onset of father absence. Potentially important variables such as the child's sex, intelligence, constitutional characteristics, birth order, relationship with his mother, and sociocultural background as well as availability of father surrogates are not taken into account, either in subject matching or in data analysis. When careful matching procedures are followed, more clear-cut findings seem to emerge (Biller, 1969b, 1971; Blanchard and Biller, 1971; Hetherington, 1966, 1972; Hetherington, Cox, and Cox, 1978, 1982).

Even though children living with their mothers subsequent to a divorce may technically be considered father absent, there is a tremendous variability in the amount of contact they have with their fathers (Biller and Meredith, 1974; Keshet and Rosenthal, 1978). Some children of divorced parents may never again see their fathers; whereas other children may have contact with their fathers on a daily basis and may even spend more time with them than they did prior to the divorce. Many children whose fathers do not live with them spend more time with their fathers than do children in so-called "father-present" families. Research has clearly supported the advantages that a high level of father–child interaction has for children, even when the parents are divorced (Biller and Meredith, 1974; Hetherington, Cox, and Cox, 1978; Grief, 1979; Wallerstein and Kelly, 1980a; and Biller and Solomon, 1986).

The Father and Cognitive Functioning

There is a great deal of data indicating that strong father–child relationships, even in infancy, can facilitate the child's intellectual competence (Biller, 1974c; Radin, 1976, 1981; Biller and Solomon, 1986). Much of the evidence concerning the father's importance to the child's cognitive development has come indirectly from studies in which father-absent and father-present children have been compared. However, many investigators have reported evidence consistent with the supposition that not only father-absent children, but also father-neglected children are less likely to function well on intelligence, aptitude, and achievement tests than are father-present children (Deutsch and Brown, 1964; Sutton-Smith, et al., 1968; Lessing, Zagorin, and Nelson, 1970; Blanchard and Biller, 1971; Santrock, 1972).

Early Paternal Deprivation

Blanchard and Biller (1971) attempted to specify different levels of father availability and to ascertain their relationship to the academic functioning of third-grade boys. They examined both the timing of father absence and the degree of father–son interaction in the father-present home. The boys were of average intelligence and were from working-class and lower middle-class backgrounds. Four groups of boys were studied: early father absent (beginning before age three); late father absent (beginning after age five); low father present (less than six hours per week); and high father present (more than two hours per day). In order to control for variables (other than father availability) which might affect academic performance, there was individual subject matching in terms of the characteristics of the early father-absent group. The subjects were matched so that each boy from the early father-absent group was essentially identical with a boy from each of the other three groups in terms of age, IQ, socioeconomic status, and presence or absence of male siblings.

Academic performance was assessed by means of Stanford Achievement Test scores and classroom grades. (The teachers did not have the children's achievement test scores available to them until after final classroom grades had been assigned.) The scores and grades of the high father-present group were far superior to the other three groups. With respect to both grades and achievement test scores, the early father-absent boys were generally underachievers, the late father-absent and lower father-present boys usually functioned somewhat below grade level, and the high father-present group performed above grade level.

The early father-absent boys were consistently handicapped in their academic performance. They scored significantly lower on every achievement test index as well as in their grades. The early father-absent group functioned below grade level in both language and mathematical skills. When compared to the high father-present group, the early father-absent group were inferior in skills relating to reading comprehension. In a study of elementary school boys, Dyl and Biller (1973) also found early father absence to be associated with deficits in reading comprehension.

Santrock (1972) reported additional evidence indicating that early father absence can have a very significant debilitating effect on cognitive functioning. Among lower-class junior high and high school students, those children who became father-absent before the age of five and particularly before the age of two, had scored significantly lower on measures of IQ (Otis Quick Test) and achievement (Stanford Achievement Test) that had been administered when they were in the third and sixth grades, than did those from intact families. The most detrimental cognitive and intellectual effects occurred when father absence was due to divorce, desertion, or separation rather than to death. The data of this study also provided some support for the finding that there are positive remedial effects of a stepfather for boys, especially when the stepfather joined the family before the child was five years of age.

Pedersen, Rubinstein, and Yarrow (1979) found that among five- to six-month-old black male infants, measures of cognitive functioning were correlated with the degree to which they were involved with their fathers. Frequent interaction with fathers (maternal report) was associated with high Bayley scores of mental and psychomotor functioning for sons. Although girls did not seem to be influenced by family structure, Pedersen et al. (1979) also presented evidence that father-absent infant boys were less cognitively competent than boys with both fathers and mothers. Father-present boys demonstrated more social responsiveness, sensorimotor precociousness, and novelty-seeking behavior than did father-absent boys.

Having found no discernible differences in the behavior of married and husbandless mothers, Pedersen et al. attributed variations in the infant boys' behavior to the degree of interaction with fathers who tend to behave in a qualitatively different way toward infants than do mothers. In families where both parents are involved with the infant, fathers are much more likely than are mothers to engage in physically arousing social play and to stimulate the male infant's basic independence, curiosity, and exploratory competence (Biller, 1974c; Parke, 1979; Yogman, 1982; Biller and Solomon, 1986).

Cognitive Style

Carlsmith (1964) made an interesting discovery concerning the relationship between father absence and differential intellectual abilities. She examined the College Board Aptitude Test scores of middle-class and upper middle-class high school males who had experienced early father absence because of their father's military service during World War II. Boys who had lost their fathers in early childhood were more likely to have a feminine pattern of aptitude test scores. In contrast to the typical male pattern of math scores being higher than verbal scores, males who had experienced early separation from their fathers more frequently had higher verbal scores than math scores. She found that the earlier the onset of father absence and the longer the father absence, the more likely was the male to have a higher verbal than math score. The effect was strongest for students whose fathers were absent at birth and/or were away for over thirty months. Higher verbal than math functioning is the usual pattern among females, and Carlsmith speculated that it reflects a feminine global style of cognitive functioning. Results from other studies have also indicated a relationship between father absence and a feminine pattern of aptitude test scores among males (Biller, 1974c).

A study with adolescent boys by Barclay and Cusumano (1967) supports the supposition that difficulties in cognitive–analytical functioning are often related to father absence. Using Witkin's rod and frame procedure, Barclay and Cusumano found that father-absent males were more field-dependent than those who were father present. Wohlford and Liberman (1970) reported that father separation (after the age of six) was related to field dependency among elementary school children from an urban section of Miami. In complementing those data, some investigators have reported findings which suggest that warm, close father–child relationships stimulate sons to be field independent (Bieri, 1960; Dyk and Witkin, 1965). It is also relevant to note that paternal behavior seems to be an important factor in facilitating or inhibiting creative ability in children (Biller, 1974b; Lynn, 1974).

Sex Differences

Most of the research concerning paternal influence and the child's personality development and cognitive functioning has focused on the father–son relationship. Current evidence suggests that various types of paternal deprivation have a more negative effect on the cognitive abilities of boys than girls (Lessing et al., 1970; Santrock, 1972; Shinn, 1978; Hetherington et al., 1978, 1982; Radin, 1981). However, the quantity and quality of fathering can, of course, also affect the daughter's development (Biller, 1971, 1974c,d; Biller and Weiss, 1970).

There is data suggesting that fathers have much to do with the development of their daughters' cognitive functioning and intellectual attainment. Plank and Plank (1954) discovered that outstanding female mathematicians were particularly attached to and identified with their fathers. Bieri (1960) reported that high analytical ability in college women was associated with a strong positive father identification. Crandall, Dewey, Katkovsky, and Preston (1964) found that elementary school girls who did well in both reading and mathematics had fathers who consistently praised and rewarded their intellectual efforts.

Data from a number of studies when taken together indicate that high paternal expectations derived from a context of a warm father–daughter relationship are conducive to the development of autonomy, independence, achievement, and creativity among females (Biller, 1974c; Lozoff, 1974; Radin, 1976, 1981).

On the other hand, emotional maltreatment and abuse by the father can inhibit the daughter's intellectual development. Lack of paternal interest seems related to deficits in female functioning in certain types of cognitive tasks (Heilbrun, Harrell, and Gillard, 1967). Findings from a study by Hurley (1967) suggest that paternal hostility toward the daughter can be particularly detrimental to a girl's scholastic achievement.

Social Class

Lack of father availability and interest seems to be associated with much more serious consequences among lower-class children than among middle-class children (Biller, 1971, 1974c; Shinn, 1978). Some research has suggested that among father-absent children, those who are from working-class backgrounds are more consistently handicapped in their cognitive functioning than are those from middle-class backgrounds (Lessing et al., 1970). A general depression in academic achievement associated with father absence has usually been found with working-class or lower-class children (Blanchard and Biller, 1971; Santrock, 1972). Middle-class, father-absent children often do well in situations requiring verbal skills. Members of Carlsmith's (1964) middle- and upper middle-class father-absent group apparently were equal or superior to her father-present group in verbal aptitude, although inferior in mathematical aptitude. Lessing et al. (1970) found that middle-class father-absent children had higher verbal scores, although lower performance (e.g., perceptual–manipulative) scores than did father-present children. Dyl and Biller (1973) found that although lower-class father-absent boys were particularly handicapped in their reading skills, middle-class father-absent boys functioned quite adequately in reading. Because academic achievement is so heavily dependent on verbal and reading ability, father-absent middle-class children do not seem to be very handicapped.

Since there is ample documentation of the association between socioeconomic status and various aspects of children's cognitive and social functioning, many investigators have argued that the impact of father absence and divorce on children's development may actually be secondary to that of socioeconomic status. However, some research suggests that single-parent status may actually be a more powerful predictor of the academic and social functioning of young children upon entering school than is socioeconomic status or other family background, developmental history, and health variables. Guidubaldi and Perry (1984) reported striking evidence that single-parent status is highly predictive of performance on various indices of academic and social competence, even when controlling for socioeconomic status. Although family structure was not associated specifically with intellectual ability measures, children from single-parent homes were much more at risk for poor academic performance and psychological and behavior difficulties upon entering school than were children from two-parent families (Guidubaldi, 1983; Guidubaldi and Perry, 1984).

Personal and Social Adjustment

Reuter and Biller (1973) studied the relationship between various combinations of perceived paternal nurturance and availability and college males' personal adjustment. A family background questionnaire was designed to assess perceptions of father–child relationships and the amount of time the father spent at home when the subjects were children. The personal adjustment scale of Gough and Heilbrun's Adjective Checklist and the socialization scale of the California Psychological Inventory were employed as measures of personal and social adjustment. High paternal nurturance, combined with at least moderate paternal availability, and high paternal availability combined with at least moderate paternal nurturance, were related to high scores on the personal adjustment measures.

In contrast, high paternal nurturance combined with low

paternal availability, and high paternal availability combined with low paternal nurturance were associated with relatively poor scores on the personal adjustment measures. Males who reported that their fathers had been home much of the time but gave them little attention seemed to be especially handicapped in their psychological functioning. A boy with an ungiving father may actually be better off if his father is not very available. This is consistent with evidence that suggests that father-absent boys often have better personality adaptation than boys with passive, ineffectual fathers (Biller, 1974c, 1982).

There are some very extensive longitudinal data which underscore the importance of both the father and the father–mother relationship to the child's adaptation. In general, Block (1971) found that males who achieved a successful emotional and interpersonal adjustment in adulthood had fathers and mothers who were highly involved and responsible in their upbringing. In contrast, poorly adjusted adult males had fathers who were typically neglectful and uninvolved in child rearing, and mothers who tended to exhibit neurotic problems.

In a related investigation, Block, von der Lippe, and Block (1973) reported that well-socialized and successful adult males were likely to have had highly involved fathers and come from homes where their parents had compatible relationships. In contrast, adult males who scored relatively low in certain socialization skills and personal adjustment were likely to have grown up in homes in which the parents were incompatible, and in which the fathers were either uninvolved, or weak and neurotic.

Moral Development and Impulse Control

A number of clinicians, including Aichhorn (1925) and Lederer (1964), have written about inadequacies in the development of impulse control and the superego in the father-absent boy. From his experience as a psychotherapist, Meerloo (1956) observed that a lack of accuracy in time perception, often associated with difficulties in impulse control, was common among father-absent individuals. In a study of elementary school children, Wohlford and Liberman (1970) reported that father-absent children had less well-developed future time perspectives than did father-present children.

Meerloo (1956) hypothesized that the father represents social order and that his adherence to time schedules gives the child an important lesson in social functioning. The paternally deprived child may find it very difficult to follow the rules of society. Antisocial acts are often impulsive as well as aggressive, and there is evidence that the inability to delay gratification is associated with inaccurate time perception, lack of social responsibility, low achievement motivation, and juvenile delinquency (Mischel, 1961a,b).

Paternal involvement in discipline, combined with a high level of paternal affection, is strongly associated with male children's sensitivity to their transgressions (Moulton, Burnstein, Liberty, and Altucher, 1966). Holstein (1972) found that morally "mature" adolescents were likely to have warm, nurturant, and highly moral fathers.

Hoffman (1971a) reported data concerning the conscience development of seventh-grade children. Father-absent boys consistently scored lower than father-present boys on a variety of moral indices. The scores of father-absent boys were lower on measures of internalized moral standards, guilt following transgressions, acceptance of blame, and rule conformity. In addition, they were rated as higher in aggression by their teachers which may also reflect difficulties in impulse control. Although there were generally no clear-cut differences in terms of the measures that Hoffman had used, Santrock (1975) found that among elementary school boys, father-absent boys were consistently rated by their teachers as having a lower level of moral maturity than those who were father present. The implications of such research data for certain deficiencies in superego formation are striking.

Hoffman (1971a,b) also found that a weak identification with one's father among father-present boys was related to less adequate conscience development than was strong father identification. Identification with the father was determined by responses to questions involving the person whom the boy felt most similar to, most admired, and most wanted to resemble when he grew up. Among the seventh graders that Hoffman studied, boys with strong father identifications scored higher on the measures of internalized moral standards and conformity to rules than did boys with low father identifications.

The quality of the father–child relationship seems to have particular influence on whether the child takes responsibility for his own actions or projects responsibility upon external forces. Having a father who is actively committed to the child facilitates the development of responsible behavior. When children have a warm relationship with a competent father who can constructively set limits for them they are much more likely to develop an internal focus of control (Biller, 1974c; Biller and Solomon, 1986).

Delinquency

Early father absence has a particularly strong association with delinquency among males. Anderson (1968) found that a history of early father absence was much more frequent among boys sent to reform school. He also discovered that father-absent nondelinquents had a much higher rate of father substitution (stepfather, father surrogate, etc.) between the ages of four to seven then did father-absent delinquents. In studying the recidivism rate among male delinquents, Kelly and Baer (1969) found a 12 percent rate among father-present male as compared to a 39 percent rate among males who had lost their fathers before the age of six. However, boys who became father absent after the age of six had only a 10 percent recidivism rate.

Herzog and Sudia (1973) cited much evidence indicating that lack of general family cohesiveness and supervision rather than father absence is the most significant factor associated with juvenile delinquency. Many familial, personality, and intrapsychic factors have to be considered, and in only some cases is father absence directly linked to delinquent behavior. For example, boys in father-absent families who have an effective and close relationship with their mothers seem to be less likely to become delinquent than are boys in father-present families who have inadequate mothers (Biller, 1971, 1974c; McCord et al., 1962).

Father-present juvenile delinquents generally appear to have had very unsatisfactory relationships with their fathers. For example, Andry (1962) found that delinquents characterized their fathers as glum, uncommunicative, and as employing unreasonable punishment and little praise. Father–son communication was particularly poor. Andry's findings are consistent with those of Bandura and Walters (1959), who reported that in intact families, the relationship between delinquent sons and fathers is marked by rejection, hostility, and antagonism. McCord et al. (1963) found that within the context of general parental neglect and punitiveness, a deviant, aggressive father was strongly related to juvenile delinquency among boys.

As with other types of developmental outcomes, it is again important to caution against a simple "poor (or absent) father-troubled child" hypothesis. Many males who commit aggressive criminal acts may have some biological deficit contributing to their personalities, along with intrapsychic and other contributions.

Retrospective data suggest that a great many of these males even as young children, had undiagnosed, untreated learning disabilities, including attention deficit problems (Berman and Siegel, 1976a,b). The extent to which the father is positively involved very much influences the learning disabled child's development. In some cases, fathers express their disappointment in the child's level of intellectual functioning by means of rejection. There are also situations in which a child's disabilities can be a contributing factor to marital conflict and subsequent divorce and father absence. One could also speculate about a cross-generation link: the impulsive father leaving the family and subjecting the impulsive child to paternal loss. In sum, it may be said that if the father perceives his learning disabled child as stubborn or lazy or incompetent and mistreats him, the child is more likely to act out in a delinquent manner than if the father is supporting and accepting of the child's individuality (Biller and Solomon, 1986).

Interpersonal Relationships

The father–child relationship can have much impact on the child's subsequent relationship with others. Infants who have little contact with their fathers are more likely to experience greater separation anxiety regarding their mothers and more negative reactions to strangers (Biller, 1974c; Spelke, Zelazo, Kagan, and Kotelchuck, 1973).

The availability of an interested and supportive father can greatly facilitate the boy's ability in interacting with females. There is considerable evidence indicating that the male's adaptation to marriage is related to his relationship with his father and his parents' marital relationship (Biller, 1974c; Biller and Solomon, 1986).

Jacobson and Ryder (1969) conducted an exploratory interview study with young married couples who suffered the death of a parent prior to marriage. The death of the husband's father prior to the age of twelve was associated with a high rate of marital conflict and dissatisfaction. Husbands who had lost their fathers early in life were described as immature and as lacking interpersonal competence. In general, their marriages were relatively devoid of closeness and intimacy. In contrast, when the husbands had lost their fathers after the age of twelve, they were more likely to be involved in positive marital relationships; such research may imply that husbands who lost their fathers after twelve had much more opportunity to internalize and identify with their fathers than did those who lost their fathers at a younger age. Other evidence indicates that individuals who have lost a father because of a broken home situation in childhood are more likely to have their own marriages end in divorce or separation (Biller, 1974c; Biller and Solomon, 1986).

Although the etiology of homosexuality is certainly multiply determined some investigators have suggested that as a group, father-absent males are more prone than father-present males to become homosexual (West, 1967). An intense sexualized mother–son relationship seems more common in father-absent homes than in father-present homes, and along with other related factors lessens the probability of the boy entering into meaningful heterosexual relationships.

Both Bieber (1962) and Evans (1969) found that more fathers of homosexuals than fathers of heterosexuals were described as detached and hostile. Mothers of homosexuals were seen as especially close to their sons and relatively uninvolved with their husbands. Bené (1965) reported that more male homosexuals than heterosexuals perceived their fathers as weak and were hostile toward them. Similarly, studies by Apperson and McAdoo (1968) and Saghir and Robbins (1973) suggested a pattern of very poor father–child relations during the childhoods of male homosexuals. A picture of an emotionally abusing father is encountered quite frequently in the background of homosexuals (Biller and Solomon, 1986).

A particularly extensive study of the family backgrounds of homosexuals was conducted by Thompson, Schwartz, McCandless, and Edwards (1973). College-aged homosexuals were recruited through their friends, and their family backgrounds and childhood activities were compared with those of a control group. Homosexual men recounted very little interaction with their fathers and a relative lack of acceptance by their fathers during their childhoods. The homosexuals generally viewed their fathers as weak, hostile, and rejecting. In general, Thompson et al. found the classic male homosexual pattern of paternal deprivation coupled with an overly intense, mother–child relationship, and the early avoidance of masculine activities.

Those heterosexuals who also avoided masculine activities in childhood reported feeling distant from both their fathers and men in general. It should also be noted that more homosexuals than heterosexuals described themselves as frail or clumsy during childhood; there may be other mediating constitutional factors in the development of some cases of homosexuality. The data fit well with the hypothesis suggesting that paternally deprived males are quite vulnerable to the need for contact with older males, a need that may culminate in masochistic and/or homosexual relationships (Biller and Solomon, 1986).

Psychopathology

Berlinsky and Biller (1982) found much research linking death of a parent during childhood to severe psychopathology in adulthood. They did an extensive review and analysis of available data pertaining to the impact of death of a parent on psychological development. They emphasized the importance of looking at the total context of parental death, including the child's individual characteristics (age, cognitive level, temperament); the reason for parental death; the relationship with the parent prior to the loss; the quality of subsequent family interaction (reaction of the remaining parent to the loss, siblings and extended family support network, etc.); and sociocultural and socioeconomic factors.

In general, they found that father loss was at least as predictive of later developmental problems as was mother loss, that death of the father before the child was seven years old was strongly associated with self-concept and social adjustment difficulties and that daughters seem to be affected as much as sons by father loss. (It should be noted that there is much more research specifically concerning father loss than there is relating to mother loss, and that male children are more often included in such research than are female children.) Paternal loss as a function of the father's death was related to an inhibited, dependent, conforming personality style for both males and females, as well as to risk for depression in later life. Paternal deprivation as a result of divorce was more likely to be associated with acting out, impulse control problems, and cognitive deficits than was father loss due to death. Although at risk to suffer from self-doubt, insecurity, withdrawal, anxiety, depressive tendencies, and passivity, father-bereaved individuals were more often viewed as having made a socially appropriate adaptation than were those who suffered from father loss due to divorce.

Eisenstadt (1978) presented some provocative data suggesting that death of a parent, particularly a father, during childhood could actually be a stimulating factor in the achievement of occupational eminence and genius. He compared the family histories of individuals who were preeminent in their professions with family histories of individuals from various other populations. He consistently found that a greater proportion of those with unusual accomplishment had experienced the death of their fathers during childhood. He also cited other research which supported the notion that death of a father may, in some cases, spur an individual on to great creative accomplishment. Constitutional factors are particularly important in determining whether the bereavement process can lead a particular individual toward the pathway to eminence and genius (Berlinsky and Biller, 1982).

Types of Paternal Deprivation

There are some data which suggest that boys from father-absent homes are in many cases less damaged in their personality development than are boys from intact matriarchal families (Biller, 1968a; Reuter and Biller, 1973). In Nye's (1957) study, children from broken homes were found to have better family adjustments, and to have lower rates of antisocial behavior and psychosomatic illness than were children from unhappy, intact homes. Other research has also indicated that a child may function more adequately in a father-absent home than in one in which there is a severely dysfunctional husband–wife relationship (Hetherington et al., 1978, 1982; Biller and Solomon, 1986).

Father-absent children may be more influenced, in some respects, by factors outside the home than are children from intact, but unhappy and/or mother-dominated families. Some children may be particularly affected by attention from an adult male because of their intense feelings of paternal deprivation. Children with inadequate fathers often become overly resigned to their situation (Biller, 1974c; Biller and Solomon, 1986).

Research which is described in this section and in other sections indicates that mistreatment by the father and/or father absence predisposes children toward certain developmental problems. However, there are many paternally deprived children who appear to be generally well adapted in terms of psychological health. Such children should be more carefully studied in order to determine how, in what particular ways, and why they differ from less well-adjusted paternally deprived children.

The Father and Female Personality Development

Mistreatment by a father can have a profound impact on the way in which a daughter views herself as a female and experiences her femininity. The results of an investigation by Fish and Biller (1973) suggest that the father plays a particularly important role in the girl's personality adjustment. College females' perceptions of their relationships with their fathers during childhood were assessed by means of an extensive family background questionnaire. Subjects who perceived their fathers as having been very nurturant and accepting of them scored high on the Adjective Checklist personal adjustment scale. In contrast, subjects who perceived their fathers as having been rejecting scored very low on the personal adjustment measure.

Block's (1971) analysis of data collected from the Berkeley Longitudinal Study highlights the importance of both the father–daughter and father–mother relationships in the later quality of the daughter's personality functioning. For example, the females who were the most well adjusted as adults grew up in homes with two centrally involved parents. Their mothers were described as affectionate, personable, and resourceful, and their fathers as warm, competent and firm. A second group of relatively well-adjusted females came from homes with extremely bright, capable, and ambitious mothers but rather passive yet warm fathers. In contrast, poorly adjusted females were likely to have been reared in homes where either one or both parents were very inadequate. Even though they represented a wide range of personality adaptations, the poorly adjusted women were likely to have come from homes where there was little opportunity to have observed a positive mother–father relationship.

The most well-adjusted females in Block et al.'s (1972) longitudinal study also tended to come from homes where both parents had been positively involved with them. Their fathers were described as warm and accepting, and their mothers appeared to be oriented toward rationality, achievement, and intellectual attainment. A variety of complex family patterns emerged among the less well-adjusted females, but it was clear that few, if any, had backgrounds marked by a combination of a compatible father–mother relationship and an accepting father.

Other data reveal the significant influences that the father–daughter relationship can have on marriage. Fisher (1973) presented evidence indicating that paternal deprivation in early childhood is associated with infrequent orgasms among married women. A woman's ability to have a successful marriage relationship is increased when she has experienced a warm, affectionate relationship with a father (Biller, 1974c, 1981a). It is also relevant to note that inappropriate and/or inadequate fathering is a major factor in the development of homosexuality in females as well as in males (Biller, 1974c; Biller and Solomon, 1986).

Father Absence

Results from some studies suggest that father-absent girls are not usually inhibited in terms of their development of sex-typed interests (Lynn and Sawrey, 1959; Santrock, 1970; Hetherington, 1972). In fact, in a study with disadvantaged black children, Santrock (1970a) found a tendency for father-absent girls to be more feminine on a doll-play sex-role measure than were father-present girls; a very high level of femininity may be a reaction formation that has the purpose of defending against the devaluation of males and masculine activities. Father absence seems to have more effect on the girl's ability to function in interpersonal and heterosexual relationships than it does on her development of an overt feminine sexual identity (Biller, 1974c; Hetherington et al., 1982).

In a clinical study, Heckel (1963) observed frequent school maladjustment, excessive sexual interest, and social acting out behavior in five fatherless preadolescent girls. Other investigators have also found a high incidence of delinquent behavior and sexual acting out among lower-class father-absent girls (Monahan, 1957; Toby, 1957). Such acting out may be a manifestation of a girl's yearning to find a meaningful relationship with an adult male.

In Jacobson and Ryder's (1969) interview study, many

women who had lost their fathers in early life complained of difficulties in achieving satisfactory sexual relationships with their husbands. The lack of opportunity to resolve the oedipal triangle in childhood can make it much more difficult for the father-absent female to develop the interpersonal skills necessary for adequate heterosexual functioning. Case studies of father-absent girls are often filled with details of problems concerning interactions with males, particularly in sexual relationships (Neubauer, 1960; Leonard, 1966; Cath et al., 1982).

Interactions with Males

The most comprehensive and well-controlled study concerning father absence and the girl's development was conducted by Hetherington (1972). Her subjects were lower middle-class girls (ages thirteen to seventeen) who regularly attended a community recreation center. Hetherington was particularly interested in the differential effects of father absence that were due to divorce or death of the father. She compared three groups of girls: girls whose fathers were absent because of divorce and who had no contact with their fathers since the divorce; girls whose fathers were absent because of death; and girls with both parents living at home. She was careful to control for sibling variables (all the girls were firstborns without brothers) and none of the father-absent children had any adult males living in their homes following the separation from the father.

The most striking finding was that both groups of father-absent girls had great difficulty in interacting comfortably with men and male peers. Hetherington discovered that the difficulties were manifested differently for the daughters of divorcées than for the daughters of widows. The daughters of divorcées tended to be very aggressive and flirtatious, while the daughters of widows tended to be very shy and timid in their interactions with males. Although their behavior was so different, most of the girls in both of the father-absent groups reported that they felt very insecure with males. In contrast, all three groups of girls generally appeared to have appropriate interactions with their mothers and with female adults and peers. One of the exceptions was that the father-absent girls seemed more dependent on women, and observation which is consistent with Lynn and Sawrey's (1959) findings of increased mother dependency among father-separated girls.

Hetherington generally found that girls had the most difficulty in their heterosexual interactions when their father absence began before the age of five. Early father separation was usually more associated with later inappropriate behavior with males than was father absence after the age of five, although differences were not significant for every measure. Early father absence was also associated with more maternal overprotection than was father absence after the age of five. There is other evidence indicating that early father absence is more associated with maternal overprotection than is father absence beginning later in the child's life (Biller, 1969b; Biller and Bahm, 1971). A more recent study has not replicated Hetherington's findings, but the subjects were college students and different in sociocultural background from those in her research (Hainline and Feig, 1978).

There were additional findings in Hetherington's study differentiating daughters who lost their fathers through death from daughters who lost their fathers through divorce. Daughters of widows recalled more positive relationships with the fathers and described them as warmer and more competent than did daughters of divorcées. The divorced mothers also painted a very negative picture of their marriages and ex-husbands. Daughters of divorcées were quite low in self-esteem, whereas daughters of widows did not differ significantly in their self-esteem from daughters of father-present families. Nevertheless, both groups of father-absent girls had less feeling of control over their lives and more anxiety than did father-present girls.

Other evidence also suggests the continuing influence of father absence on adult female development (Hetherington and Parke, 1986). Hetherington followed the development of daughters of divorcées, daughters of widows, and daughters from intact families for several years. The daughters of divorcées seem to have especially troubled heterosexual relationships. They were likely to marry at an earlier age than the other groups, but also to be pregnant at the time of marriage. Some of these women have already been separated or divorced from their husbands. A variety of data from interview, observational, and test measures indicated that the daughters of divorcées married less compatible men than did the women from other groups. The husband of the daughters of divorcées appeared to have a lower level of educational and vocational accomplishments, and more often had been involved in difficulties with the law. These men also had more negative feelings toward their wives and infants, and had more difficulty in controlling their impulses and behaving in an emotionally mature manner than did the husbands of the women in the other groups.

In contrast, there were findings that revealed that daughters of widows tended to marry vocationally successful and ambitious men who were overly controlled and inhibited in their social interactions. In general, the results of Hetherington's follow-up study suggested that women from intact families tended to make the most compatible marital choices. These women also reported more orgasmic satisfaction in the sexual relationships with their husbands than did the two groups of women who grew up in father-absent homes (Hetherington and Parke, 1986).

Inadequate Fathering

Clinical studies have revealed that difficulties in parental sexual adjustment, combined with overly restrictive parental attitudes, are often associated with sexual and acting-out behavior among adolescent females (Kaufman, Peck, and Tagiuri, 1954; Robey, Rosenwald, Snell, and Lee, 1964; Cath et al., 1982).

Perhaps the most devastating form of mistreatment by the father (or stepfather) is sexual abuse and incest. In a certain way, the daughter may suffer from father loss as a result of incest far more than she does if she loses him because of death or divorce. The trauma of manipulation, loss of protection and trust may be far more incapacitating and disillusioning for the daughter than any physical separation. By sexualizing the father–daughter relationship in inappropriate ways, the girl loses the ego boundaries necessary for developing a healthy sexual identity. Much research indicates that sexual abuse by the father puts daughters at high risk for severe depression, suicidal behavior, alcohol and drug abuse, as well as conflicts centered around sexuality (Biller and Solomon, 1986).

Although many of the studies examining the influence of paternal deprivation on childhood psychopathology reviewed earlier in this chapter did not include female children or did not take the sex of the child into account in the data analyses, paternal inadequacy can clearly be a factor in the development of severe psychopathology in the female child as well as in the male child. However, there is some research which focuses on or specifically includes females.

In their extensive studies, Lidz, Parker, and Cornelison (1956) reported a high incidence of inadequate fathering for female as well as male schizophrenics. The fathers of the schizophrenic females were frequently observed to be in severe conflict with their wives' decisions, and to degrade their wives in front of their daughters. These fathers made rigid and unrealistic demands on their wives. Similarly, such fathers were insensitive to their daughters' needs to develop an independent self-concept. The fathers of the schizophrenic females made attempts to manipulate and mold their daughters in terms of their own unrealistic needs. Females, who formed an allegiance with a disturbed father in reaction to rejection by an unloving mother, seemed most likely to become psychotic.

Hamilton and Wahl (1948) found that almost 75 percent of the hospitalized schizophrenic women they studied had experienced some major form of paternal inadequacy in childhood. Prolonged father absence, paternal rejection, and paternal abuse of daughters were very common among this population. Rosenfeld (1979) found that one-third of the adult female psychiatric inpatients in his sample had a history of father–daughter incest. A particularly devastating outcome appears to relate to the tendency of women incest victims to marry or live with men who, in turn, sexually abuse their children (Meiselman, 1978; Forward and Buck, 1979; Cooper and Cormier, 1982).

Many of the behavior patterns of incest victims can be viewed as masochistic and self-abusive; women who have had sexual relationships with their fathers are particularly prone to depressive symptomatology, low self-esteem, and a proclivity to be vulnerable to harsh manipulation by men. Drug addiction, sexual acting out, prostitution, and generally inadequate interpersonal relations have frequently been linked with a history of father–daughter incest (Kaufman et al., 1954; Benward and Denson-Gerber, 1975; Forward and Buck, 1978; Meiselman, 1978; James and Meyerding, 1977; Herman, 1981; deYoung, 1982).

Research Implications

At this juncture we will briefly highlight some of the major research avenues that are worthy of further exploration in the attempt to understand the complex impact of father loss on development. A longitudinal and multivariable perspective, one which takes account of conscious, preconscious, and unconscious levels of functioning, is necessary in order to better understand the influence of father absence and other forms of paternal deprivation upon a child. Obviously, carefully selected comparison groups are needed and any approach should take into account process variables and consider possible advantages as well as deficits that the father-absent child may encounter. In addition to the key role played by intrapsychic variables, researchers also must consider the potential impact of interrelationships between biological–constitutional contributions, and family and sociocultural factors (Biller, 1971, 1974c; Biller and Solomon, 1986; Martel and Biller, 1987).

A longitudinal-developmental approach may help give more attention to both genetic and prenatal environmental factors. Further scientific advances could lead to a clearer indication of the father's genetic contribution, even if he no longer plays a direct child-rearing role in the child's life. For instance, how are temperamental patterns in the child influenced by the father's genetic contribution?

There is also some evidence that father absence may be at least indirectly associated with maternal stress factors during the prenatal period which may, in turn, have negative effects on fetal development. For example, among poor expectant mothers, those without husbands seem particularly unlikely to receive adequate prenatal care. Even among unwed couples, the expectant father can give the expectant mother an emotional source of support and in a practical way may be a factor in her going to a physician (Biller and Salter, 1982, 1985). Some research evidence has indicated that the expectant father's death during the prenatal period is associated with a higher probability of behavior disorders in the child (Huttunen and Niskanen, 1978). A highly negative maternal stress reaction may damage the fetus and/or the lack of the father's support during pregnancy may lead a mother to be less likely to adequately nurture the newborn infant. Certainly these thoughts are speculative, but could provoke some exciting research projects.

We need more research which will carefully assess how sex and temperament differences, and level of intellectual and social functioning, may influence children's adaptation to father absence. Some of Biller's (1974c) research, for example, suggests that young children who are highly physically and intellectually competent at the onset of father absence are not as handicapped as are children who are average or below in their developmental level. We need more data on what are called "invulnerable children."

The child's temperament and behavior certainly can have a significant impact on the quality of the mother–child relationship and other adult–child relationships. Researchers need to be aware of various family structure and social system variables including the sibling composition of the family and availability of surrogate models. The child's characteristics and the parents' difficulty in coping with them may actually be a factor contributing to the father's unavailability and/or parental divorce.

The reason for the father's absence is another important variable. Divorce often seems to have a very different effect upon the child than the death of the father, or the father's absence because of employment. As has been stressed in this chapter, the mother's reaction to her husband's absence can be very influential. There needs to be more research focusing on how the perceptions of the reasons for divorce, at the conscious and unconscious levels, may relate to the child's adaptation. For example, how much difference does it make if the same-sex noncustodial parent is perceived by the child as the parent who initiated the divorce?

Researchers comparing father-absent families and intact families can more carefully analyze individual differences in family functioning among all types (and subtypes) of family patterns. For example, although studying the father-absent family may be of heuristic value in identifying the tremendous void left by father loss, such research is no substitute for direct analysis of the father's complex role in the intact family. We can profit from much more research on the family dynamics process in both father-present and father-absent homes, with particular emphasis on parent–child–sibling interactions. Other sources of significant interpersonal relationships, including extended family and peers, should also be considered.

An approach that takes into account the psychic functioning of various family members could shed light on the impact of the divorce process upon the child. For example, the reaction of different individuals (and sets of individuals) in the family at various times, pre- and postdivorce, may greatly influence the child's short- and/or long-term adaptation. A longitudinal perspective would help differentiate what may be short-term setbacks or spurts in development from what may be long-term deficits or gains in later functioning. A more limited cross-sectional approach can only consider the impact of divorce and father absence upon children at specific developmental periods.

It is very clear from data reviewed in this chapter that divorce does not necessarily mean that a child will be father absent. Many fathers are able to visit and be involved with their children, and still others have shared, joint, or full custody of their children. An analysis of different types of custody patterns can help us to learn more about how the father's availability and quality of functioning (along with the interaction of other factors) influences the child (Warshak, 1986).

Future research should also lead to a much clearer delineation of the kinds of maternal wishes, unconscious longings, behaviors, and the dimensions of the mother–child relationship that are relevant to certain aspects of the father-absent child's personality development. In an earlier section of this chapter some research concerning the effects of father absence on the girl's personality development is reviewed; it is important for investigators studying the impact of father absence to systematically examine the possible differential effects of the mother–child relationship as a function of the sex of a child. Data from such studies can be useful for programs designed to maximize the interpersonal and intellectual potential of father-absent children, and to help mothers in father-absent families to become more effective parents (Biller, 1974c; Biller and Solomon, 1986).

Although it is beyond the scope of the present chapter, there is much relevant information relating to the prevention and treatment of problems related to father loss. Various guidelines are available with respect to educational and therapeutic approaches that may be effective in helping fatherless and other types of paternally deprived children and their families overcome risks and disadvantages associated with father loss (Biller, 1974c; Biller and Meredith, 1974; Berlinsky and Biller, 1982; Biller and Solomon, 1986).

References

Aichhorn, A. (1925), *Wayward Youth.* New York: Viking, 1935.

Anderson, R. E. (1968), Where's Dad? Paternal deprivation and delinquency. *Arch. Gen. Psychiat.,* 18:641–649.

Andry, R. G. (1962), Paternal and maternal roles in delinquency. In: *Deprivation of Maternal Care.* Public Health Paper No. 14. Geneva: World Health Organization, pp. 31–43.

Apperson, L. B., & McAdoo, Jr., W. G. (1968), Parental factors in the childhood of homosexuals. *J. Abnorm. Psychol.,* 73:201–206.

Bandura, A., & Walters, R. H. (1959), *Adolescent Aggression: A Study of the Influence of Childrearing Practices and Family Inter-relationships.* New York: Ronald Press.

Barclay, A. G., & Cusumano, D. (1967), Father-absence, cross-sex identity and field-dependent behavior in male adolescents. *Child Develop.,* 38:243–250.

Bené, E. (1965), On the genesis of female homosexuality. *Brit. J. Psychiat.,* 3:815–821.

Benward, J., & Denson-Gerber, J. (1975), Incest as a causative factor in antisocial behavior: An exploratory study. *Comtemp. Drug Prob.,* 4:322–340.

Berlinsky, E. B., & Biller, H. B. (1982), *Parental Death and Psychological Development.* Lexington, MA: Lexington Books.

Berman, A., & Siegal, A. (1976a), Adaptive and learning skills in juvenile delinquents—A neuropsychological analysis. *J. Learn. Disab.*, 9:583–590.

———(1976b), A neuropsychological approach to the etiology, prevention and treatment of juvenile delinquency. In: *Child Personality and Psychopathology, Current Topics*, Vol. 3, ed. A Davids. New York: John Wiley & Sons.

Bieber, I. (1962), *Homosexuality: A Psychoanalytic Study*. New York: Basic Books.

Bieri, J. (1960), Parental identification, acceptability and authority, and within sex-differences in cognitive behavior. *J. Abnorm. & Soc. Psychol.*, 60:76–79.

Biller, H.B. (1968a), A multiaspect investigation of masculine development in kindergarten-age boys. *Genet. Psychol. Monog.*, 76:89–139.

———(1968b), A note on father-absence and masculine development in young lower-class negro and white boys. *Child Develop.*, 39:1003–1006.

———(1969a), Father dominance and sex-role development in kindergarten-age boys. *Development. Psychol.*, 1:87–94.

———(1969b), Father-absence, maternal encouragement and sex-role development in kindergarten-age boys. *Child Develop.*, 40:539–546.

———(1970), Father-absence and the personality development of the male child. *Development. Psychol.*, 2:181–201.

———(1971), *Father, Child and Sex Role*. Lexington, MA: Lexington Books.

———(1974a), Paternal and sex-role factors in cognitive and academic functioning. In: *Nebraska Symposium on Motivation 1973*, ed. L. J. K. Cole & R. Dienstbier. Lincoln: University of Nebraska Press, pp. 83–123.

———(1974b), Paternal deprivation, cognitive functioning and the feminized classroom. In: *Child Personality and Psychopathology: Current Topics*, ed. A. Davids. New York: John Wiley & Sons, pp. 11–52.

———(1974c), *Paternal Deprivation: Family, School, Sexuality and Society*. Lexington, MA: Lexington Books.

———(1974d), Syndromes of paternal deprivation in man. In: *Experimental Behavior: A Basis for the Study of Man*, ed. J. H. Cullen. Dublin: Irish University Press, pp. 147–171.

———(1981a), The father and sex role development. In: *The Role of the Father in Child Development*, 2nd ed., ed. M. E. Lamb. New York: John Wiley, & sons.

———(1981b), Father absence, divorce, and personality development. In: *The Role of the Father in Child Development*, 2nd ed., ed. M. E. Lamb. New York: John Wiley & Sons.

———(1982), Fatherhood: Implications for child and adult development. In: *Handbook of Developmental Psychology*, ed. B. Wolman. Englewood Cliffs, NJ: Prentice-Hall, pp. 702–725.

———Bahm, R. M. (1971), Father-absence, perceived maternal behavior and masculinity of self-concept among junior high school boys. *Development. Psychol.*, 4:178–181.

———Borstelman, L. J. (1967), Masculine development: An integrative review. *Merrill-Palmer Quart.*, 13:253–294.

———Davids, T. (1973), Parent–child relations, personality development and psychopathology. In: *Issues in Abnormal Child Psychology*, ed. T. Davids. Belmont CA: Brooks/Cole.

———Liebman, D. A. (1971), Body build, sex-role preference, and sex-role adoption in junior high school boys. *J. Genet. Psychol.*, 118:81–86.

———Meredith, D. L. (1972), The invisible American father. *Sex. Behav.*, 2(7):16–22.

——— ———(1974), *Father Power*. New York: David McKay, 1982.

———Salter, M., Adolescent unwed fathers. Unpublished study. The University of Rhode Island.

——— ———(1985), Fathers, mothers and infants growing together. *Lamaze Parents Mag.*, 4:56–64.

———Solomon, R. S. (1986), *Child Maltreatment and Paternal Deprivation: A Manifesto for Research, Treatment and Prevention*. Lexington, MA: Lexington Books.

———Weiss, S. (1970), The father–daughter relationship and the personality development of the female. *J. Genet. Psychol.*, 114:79–93.

Blanchard, R. W., & Biller, H. B. (1971), Father availability and academic performance among third-grade boys. *Development. Psychol.*, 4:301–305.

Block, J. (1971), *Lives Through Time*. Berkeley, CA: Bancroft Books.

———von der Lippe, A., & Block, J. H. (1973), Sex-role and socialization: Some personality concomitants and environmental antecedents. *J. Consult. & Clin. Psychol.*, 41:321–341.

Burton, J. V., & Whiting, J. W. M. (1961), The absent father and cross-sex identity. *Merrill-Palmer Quart.*, 7:85–95.

Burton, R. V. (1972), Cross-sex identity in Barbados. *Development. Psychol.*, 6:365–374.

Carlsmith, L. (1964), Effect of early father absence on scholastic aptitude. *Harv. Ed. Rev.*, 34:3–21.

Cath, S. H., Gurwitt, A. R., & Ross, J. M., eds. (1982), *Father and Child: Developmental and Clinical Perspectives*. Boston: Little, Brown.

Cooper, I., & Cormier, B. M. (1982), Inter-generational transmission of incest. *Can. J. Psychiat.*, 27:231–223.

Crandall, V. J., Dewey, R., Katkovsky, W., & Preston, A. (1964), Parents' attitudes and behaviors, and grade-school children's academic achievements. *J. Genet. Psychol.*, 104:53–66.

Deutsch, M., & Brown, B. (1964), Social influences in negro–white intelligence differences. *J. Soc. Iss.*, 20:24–35.

deYoung, M. (1982), Self-injurious behavior in incest victims: A research note. *Child Welf.*, 61:577–584.

Dyk, T. B., & Witkin, H. A. (1965), Family experience related to the development of differentiation in children. *Child Develop.*, 36:21–55.

Dyl, A. S., & Biller, H. B. (1973), Paternal absence, social class and reading achievement. Unpublished study. The University of Rhode Island.

Eisenstadt, J. M. (1978), Parental loss and genius. *Amer. Psycholog.*, 33:211–223.

Evans, R. B. (1969), Childhood parental relationships of homosexual men. *J. Consult. & Clin. Psychol.*, 33:129–135.

Fish, K. D., & Biller, H. B. (1973), Perceived childhood paternal relationships and college females' personal adjustment. *Adolescence*, 8:415–420.

Fisher, S. F. (1973), *The Female Orgasm: Psychology, Physiology, Fantasy*. New York: Basic Books.

Forward, S., & Buck, C. (1978), *Betrayal of Innocence: Incest and its Devastation.* New York: Penguin Books.

Freud, A., & Burlingham, D. T. (1944), *Infants Without Families.* New York: International Universities Press.

Freud, S. (1905), Three Essays on the Theory of Sexuality, *Standard Edition,* 7:125–245. London: Hogarth Press, 1953.

———(1933), New Introductory Lectures on Psycho-Analysis. *Standard Edition,* 22. London: Hogarth Press, 1964.

———(1939), Some Psychological Consequences of the Anatomical Distinction between the Sexes. *Standard Edition,* 5. London: Hogarth Press, 1950.

Green, R. (1974), *Sexual Identity Conflict in Children and Adults.* New York: Basic Books.

Greenstein, J. F. (1966), Father characteristics and sex-typing. *J. Personal. & Soc. Psychol.,* 3:271–277.

Grief, J. B. (1979), Fathers, children and joint custody. *Amer. J. Orthopsychiat.,* 49:311–319.

———(1985), *Single Fathers.* Lexington, MA: Lexington Books.

Guidubaldi, J. (1983), The impact of parental divorce on children: Report on nationwide NASP study. *School Psychol., Rev.,* 12:300–323.

———Perry, J. D. (1984), Divorce, socioeconomic status, and children's cognitive-social competence at school entry. *Amer. J. Orthopsychiat.,* 54:459–468.

Hainline, L., & Feig, E. (1978), The correlates of childhood father absence in college-aged women. *Child Develop.,* 49:37–42.

Hamilton, D. M., & Wahl, J. G. (1948), The hospital treatment of dementia praecox. *Amer. J. Psychiat.,* 104:346–352.

Heckel, R. V. (1963), The effects of fatherlessness on the preadolescent female. *Ment. Hyg.,* 47:69–73.

Heilbrun, A. B., Harrell, S. N., & Gillard, B. J. (1967), Perceived childrearing attitudes of fathers and cognitive control in daughters. *J. Genet. Psychol.,* 111:29–40.

Herman, J. L. (1981), *Father–Daughter Incest.* Cambridge, MA: Harvard University Press.

Herzog, E., & Sudia, C. E. (1973), *Children in Fatherless Families.* In: *Review of Child Development Research,* Vol. 3., eds. B. M. Caldwell & H. N. Ricciuti. Chicago: University of Chicago Press.

Hetherington, E. M. (1966), Effects of paternal absence on sex-typed behaviors in negro and white preadolescent males. *J. Personal. & Soc. Psychol.,* 4:87–91.

———(1972), Effects of father-absence on personality development in adolescent daughters. *Development. Psychol.,* 7:313–326.

———Cox, M., & Cox, R. (1978), Family interaction and the social, emotional and cognitive development of children following divorce. Paper presented at the Johnson & Johnson Conference on the Family, Washington, DC, May.

——— ——— ———(1982), Effects of divorce on parents and children. In: *Nontraditional Families,* ed. M. E. Lamb. Hillsdale, NJ: Lawrence Erlbaum Associates.

———Frankie, G. (1969), Effects of parental dominance, warmth, and conflict on imitation in children. *J. Personal. & Soc. Psychol.*, 6:119–125.

———Parke, R. D. (1986), *Child Psychology: A contemporary Viewpoint.* New York: McGraw-Hill.

Hoffman, M. L. (1971a), Father absence and conscience development. *Development. Psychol.*, 4:400–406.

———(1971b), Identification and conscience development. *Child Develop.*, 42:1071–1082.

———(1981), The role of the father in moral internalization. In: *The Role of the Father in Child Development*, 2nd ed., ed. M. E. Lamb. New York: John Wiley & Sons, pp. 359–378.

Holstein, C. E. (1972), The relation of children's moral judgement level to that of their parents and to communication patterns in the family. In: *Readings in Child Development and Relationships*, ed. R. C. Smart & M.S. Smart. New York: Macmillan, pp. 484–494.

Hurley, J. R. (1967), Parental malevolence and children's intelligence. *J. Consult. Psychol.*, 31:199–204.

Huttunen, M. O., & Niskanen, P. (1978), Prenatal loss of father and psychiatric disorders, *Arch. Gen. Psychiat.*, 35:429–436.

Jacobson, G., & Ryder, R. G. (1969), Parental loss and some characteristics of the early marriage relationship. *Amer. J. Orthopsychiat.*, 39:779–787.

James, J., & Meyerding, T. (1977), Early sexual experience and prostitution. *Amer. J. Psychiat.*, 134:1381–1388.

Kaufman, I., Peck, A. I., & Tagiuri, C. K. (1954), The family constellation and overt incestuous relations between father and daughter. *Amer. J. Orthopsychiat.*, 24:266–277.

Kelly, F. J., & Baer, D. J. (1969), Age of male delinquents when father left home and recidividism. *Psychol. Rep.*, 25:1010.

Keshet, J., & Rosenthal, R. (1978), Fathering after marital separation. *Soc. Work*, 25:14–18.

Lederer, W. (1964), Dragons, delinquents, and destiny. *Psychol. Rep.*, 10:43–53.

Lee, P. C., & Wolinsky, A. L. (1973), Male teachers of young children: A preliminary empirical study. *Young Children*, 28:342–352.

Leichty, M. M. (1960), The effect of father-absence during early childhood upon the Oedipal situation as reflected in young adults. *Merrill-Palmer Quart.*, 6:212–217.

Leonard, M. R. (1966), Fathers and daughters. *Internat. J. Psycho-Anal.*, 47:325–333.

Lessing, E. E., Zagorin, S. W., & Nelson, D. (1970), WISC Subtest and IQ score correlates of father-absence. *J. Genet. Psychol.*, 67:181–195.

Levy, D. M. (1943), *Maternal Overprotection.* New York: Columbia University Press.

Lidz, T., Parker, N., & Cornelison, A. R. (1956), The role of the father in the family environment of the schizophrenic patient. *Amer. J. Psychiat.*, 13:126–132.

Lozoff, M. M. (1974), Fathers and autonomy in women. In: *Women and Success*, ed. R. B. Kundsin. New York: William Morrow, pp. 103–109.

Lynn, D. B. (1974), *The Father: His Role in Development.* Belmont, CA: Brooks/Cole.

————Sawrey, W. L. (1959), The effects of father-absence on Norwegian boys and girls. *J. Abnorm. & Soc. Psychol.*, 59:258–262.

Machtlinger, V. T. (1976), Psychoanalytic theory: Preoedipal and oedipal phases with special reference to the father. In: *The Role of the Father in Child Development*, ed. M. E. Lamb. New York: John Wiley & Sons, pp. 277–306.

————(1981), The father in psychoanalytic theory. In: *The Role of the Father in Child Development*, 2nd ed., ed. M. E. Lamb. New York: John Wiley & Sons, pp. 113–153.

Martel, L. F., & Biller, H. B. (1987), *Stature and Stigma: The Biopsychosocial Development of Short Males*. Lexington, MA: Lexington Books.

McCord, J., McCord, W., & Thurber, E. (1962), Some effects of paternal absence on male children. *J. Abnorm. & Soc. Psychol.*, 64:631–639.

Meerloo, J. A. M. (1956), The father cuts the cord: The role of the father as initial transference figure. *Amer. J. Psychother.*, 10:471–480.

Meiselman, K. C. (1978), *Incest: A Psychological Study of Causes and Effects with Treatment Recommendations*. San Francisco: Jossey-Bass.

Miller, W. B. (1958), Lower-class culture as a generating milieu of gang delinquency. *J. Soc. Iss.*, 14:5–19.

Mischel, W. (1961a), Preference for delayed reward and social responsibility. *J. Abnorm. & Soc. Psychol.*, 62:1–7.

————(1961b), Father-absence and delay of gratification. *J. Abnorm. & Soc. Psychol.*, 62:116–124.

Mitchell, D., & Wilson W. (1967), Relationship of father-absence to masculinity and popularity of delinquent boys. *Psychol. Rep.*, 20:1173–1174.

Monahan, T. P. (1957), Family status and the delinquent child. *Soc. Forces*, 35:250–258.

Moulton, P. W., Burnstein, E., Liberty, D., & Altucher, N. (1966), The patterning of parental affection and dominance as a determinant of guilt and sex-typing. *J. Personal. & Soc. Psychol.*, 4:363–365.

Nash, J. (1965), The father in contemporary culture and current psychological literature. *Child Develop.*, 36:261–297.

Neubauer, P. B. (1960), The one-parent child and his oedipal development. *The Psychoanalytic Study of the Child*, 15:286–309. New York: International Universities Press.

Nye, F. I. (1957), Child adjustment in broken and unhappy unbroken homes. *Marr. & Fam. Living*, 19:356–361.

Parke, R. D. (1979), Perspectives on father–infant interaction. In: *The Handbook of Infant Development*, ed. J. D. Osofsky. New York: John Wiley & Sons.

Pedersen, F. A., Rubenstein, J., & Yarrow, L. J. (1979), Infant development in father-absent families. *J. Genet. Psychol.*, 135:51–61.

Plank, E. H., & Plank, R. (1954), Emotional components in arithmetic learning as seen through autobiographies. *The Psychoanalytic Study of the Child*, 9:274–293. New York: International Universities Press.

Radin, N. (1976), The role of the father in cognitive, academic and intellectual development. In: *The Role of the Father in Child Development*, ed. M. E. Lamb. New York: John Wiley & Sons, pp. 237–276.

————(1981), The role of the father in cognitive academic and intellectual development. In: *The Role of the Father in Child Development*, 2nd ed., ed. M. E. Lamb. New York: John Wiley & Sons, pp. 379–427.

Reuter, M. W., & Biller, H. B. (1973), Perceived paternal nurturance-availability and personality adjustment among college males. *J. Consult. & Clin. Psychol.*, 40:339–342.

Robey, A., Rosenwald, R. J., Snell, J. E., & Lee, R. E. (1964), The runaway girl: A reaction to family stress. *Amer. J. Orthopsychiat.*, 34:762–767.

Rogers, W. B., & Long, J. M. (1968), Male models and sexual identification: A case from the Out Island Bahamas. *Hum. Organ.*, 27:326–331.

Rosenfeld, A. A. (1979), Incidence of a history of incest among 18 female psychiatric patients. *Amer. J. Psychiat.*, 136:791–796.

Ross, J. M. (1977), Toward fatherhood: The epigenesis of paternal identity during a boy's first decade. *Internat. Rev. Psychoanal.*, 4:327–348.

——(1979), Fathering: A review of some psychoanalytic contributions on paternity. *Internat. J. Psycho-Anal.*, 60:317–327.

Saghir, M. T., & Robbins, F. (1973), *Male and Female Homosexuality*. Baltimore: Williams & Wilkins.

Santrock, J. W. (1970a), Paternal absence, sex-typing and identificaiton. *Develop. Psychol.*, 2:264–272.

——(1970b), Influence of onset and type of paternal absence on the first four Eriksonian developmental crises. *Development. Psychol.*, 3:273–274.

——(1972), Relation of type and onset of father-absence to cognitive development. *Child Develop.*, 43:455–469.

——(1975), Father absence, perceived maternal behavior, and moral development in boys. *Child Develop.*, 46:753–757.

Shinn, M. (1978), Father absence and children's cognitive development. *Psychol. Bull.*, 85:295–324.

Spelke, D., Zelazo, P., Kagan, J., & Kotelchuck, M. (1973), Father interaction and separation protest. *Development. Psychol.*, 9:83–90.

Stephens, W. N. (1962), *The Oedipus Complex: Cross Cultural Evidence*. Glencoe, IL: Free Press.

Sutton-Smith, B., Rosenberg, B.G., & Landy, F. (1968), Father-absence effects in families of different sibling compositions. *Child Develop.*, 38:1213–1221.

Thompson, N. L., Schwartz, D. M., McCandless, B. R., & Edwards, D. A. (1973), Parent–child relationships and sexual identity in male and female homosexuals and heterosexuals. *J. Consult. & Clin. Psychol.*, 41:12–127.

Tiller, P. O. (1961), *Father Separation and Adolescence*. Oslo, Norway: Institute for Social Research.

Toby, J. (1957), The differential impact of family disorganization. *Amer. Sociol. Rev.*, 22:505–512.

Wallerstein, J. S., & Kelly, J. B. (1974), The effects of parental divorce: The adolescent experience. In: *The Child in his Family: Children at Psychiatric Risk*, eds. E. J. Anthony & C. Koupernik. New York: John Wiley & Sons.

—— ——(1975), The effects of parental divorce: Experiences of the preschool child. *J. Amer. Acad. Child Psychiat.*, 14:600–616.

—— ——(1976), The effects of parental divorce: Experiences of the child in later latency. *Amer. J. Orthopsychiat.*, 46:256–269.

———— ————(1980a), California's children of divorce. *Psychol. Today*, 14:67–76.

———— ————(1980b), *Surviving the Breakup: How Children Actually Cope with Divorce*. New York: Basic Boks.

Warshak R. A. (1986), Father-custody and child development: A review and analysis of psychological research. *Behav. Sci. & Law*, 4:185–202.

West, D. J. (1967), *Homosexuality*. Chicago: Aldine.

Whiting, J. W. M., Kluckhohn, R., & Anthony, A. (1958), The function of male initiation ceremonies at puberty. In: *Readings in Social Psychology*, eds. E. E. Maccoby, T. M. Newcomb, & E. L. Hartley. New York: Holt, Rinehart, Winston, pp. 359–370.

Wohlford, P., & Liberman, D. (1970), Effects of father absence on personal time, field independence and anxiety. *Proceedings of the 78th Annual Convention of the American Psychological Association*, 5:263–264.

————Santrock, J. W., Berger, S. E., & Lieberman, D. (1971), Older brothers' influence on sex-typed, aggressive, and dependent behavior in father-absent children. *Development. Psychol.*, 4:124–134.

Yogman, M. W. (1982), Observations on the father–infant relationship. In: *Father and Child: Developmental and Clinical Perspectives*, eds. S. H. Cath, A. R. Gurwitt, & J. M. Ross. Boston: Little, Brown, pp. 101–122.

Part V

Loss, Mourning,
and the
Holocaust

14

Coping with Losses and Survival

JUDITH S. KESTENBERG, M.D.

The bereavement of children who have lost a parent has been most thoroughly investigated by E. Furman (1974) and her co-workers in Cleveland. A study of reactions to the loss of a significant person has been the subject of a group effort on the part of the Chicago Institute for Psychoanalysis. The contributions of Pollock (1961, 1977, 1978) are especially noteworthy. In the following first communication about reactions of children to losses in the Holocaust, I owe a debt of gratitude to these authors.

An account of an analysis by Fleming and Altschul (1963) deals with the lack of grief and denial of the loss in an adolescent who was sent to England while her parents remained in Germany and were killed by the Nazis. E. Furman (1974) drew our attention to other factors that were not discussed in the paper, but which contributed to this patient's difficulty in mourning: "No factual evidence of death, anxiety about its sadistic nature, survivor guilt, stress of adapting to a new country and language and lack of opportunity to share grief" (p. 291). Further factors are obscured by a lack of data about the patient's experience in England; it is not known whether she received loving care or struggled to make a place for herself without much help.

It is difficult to make general statements about children who suffered losses at different ages and under different circumstances as a result of the Holocaust. Some children did not know what happened to their parents until after the war, others witnessed the death of their parents through starvation, illness, or violence. Some children were taken care of by loving substitute families, others were left to fend for themselves or imprisoned in concentration camps.

In many cases, perhaps in the majority, the losses were catastrophic; they entailed a total loss of support from the family and from the community that generally is expected to protect children; they entailed the loss of identity, and not infrequently the loss of one's own self image, with meager links to the past remaining. Many of these children became creative, not at the end of their mourning period, but right from the start; they painted, they wrote stories and poems. Through identification with their lost objects and through the creation of linking objects they were able to reenact the role of caretakers and care for themselves (Greene, 1958; Volkan, 1972).

The autobiography of one such child will serve as a springboard for a discussion of the most salient factors of our main theme (Oliner, 1979).

Shmulek Oliner was seven when his mother was dying from tuberculosis. Lying in bed, "she said nothing but just looked at me—my mother dark and beautiful—she who soothed my aches and I wanted desperately to make her well" (p. 12). When she was taken away to another town, Shmulek waited for her return. He heard the grown-ups discussing the severity of her illness.

> We slept all together in this one room and I hid my face on the pillow so no one would hear me crying. I didn't know why I cried.

When his family came back from town and his mother did not come with them, he asked where she was and was told by his grandmother that she was dead.

> I simply couldn't believe such a thing. How could one's mother die? How could she bake special cookies and cakes (Kichelech

and rogelech) for Shabbat if she were not coming home again?

He asked:

My mother is dead. But that is only for a short time, isn't it?

His grandmother reassured him, and at night he wondered:

How short a time will death be? [p. 16].

Shmulek did not understand, or denied, the permanence of death, but the advent of the war in 1939 made the meaning of death very clear. By the time he was twelve he and his family had been exposed to persecution for some time. When there was a German razzia in the little ghetto where they lived, Shmulek had a dream about a gaping hole in the ground that seemed to draw him in; somehow he knew that it was his mother's grave. An explosion awakened him.[1] The Germans had surrounded the ghetto; they were shooting and shouting: "Juden heraus" (Jews out!). There was panic and helplessness. His stepmother clutching her little children told Shmulek to run away and save his life. He clung to her, but she pushed him away and her parting words, "Shmulek, I love you," gave him the courage to survive. He hid until the commotion was over and the ghetto was quiet like a ghost town. He felt that there was no one left for the breezes to touch.

> Like blood running through my veins, a feeling of great loneliness filled my body and I wondered whether I actually was dead [p. 7].

Keeping an eye on German, Polish, and Ukrainian looters, Shmulek went back to his father's house where he hoped to find photographs of his dead mother, but failed to do so.

The room was empty. They were gone. Only twisted bedding

[1]When the Nazis evacuated Jewish families, they either shot them en masse or deported them to concentration camps where death was imminent.

and wreckage of personal belongings was left. . . . Something rended and tore loose within me and I sank to the floor. The small childish sobs wouldn't come. Instead my chest felt crushed with the mature agony of an entire people [p. 9].

(See also Kestenberg and Brenner, 1986.) Hiding, he fell asleep, but sleep did not comfort him. It was "filled with the faces of my family staring at me." Not only his "just lost" family stared at him, but also his mother. All the while he remembered his stepmother's parting words: "Shmulek, I love you." Shmulek was shocked to hear from peasants that all the Jews from the ghetto had been taken to a meadow and shot. This was confirmed by Baldwina, a peasant woman he knew, who became his adviser during the time he had to pretend to be a Christian. Left all alone, with everybody dead, Shmulek thought:

The premature death of my mother had saved her much sorrow. In fact it seemed that her death was the only certainty there was . . . I tried to remember what my mother looked like. But there was just an impression, the smell of Shabbat baking. Even the face of my stepmother was sliding away, sliding away. . . . Also sliding away was Shmulek Oliner. He was a thing of the past buried in the memories of people now dead [p. 62].

Learning the Christian catechism and adjusting to a new life of deceit, Shmulek no longer cried.

Just to survive each day took a supreme effort and there was no time for tears.

He found a job as a farm worker at the home of a Christian couple who treated him kindly, but made anti-Semitic remarks, not knowing he was Jewish. Shmulek was beset with fears of being recognized and delivered to the tortures of the Germans. However, when the Russians drew near, fear was no longer necessary, and his "chest swelled with fresh and powerful hope" (p. 91). Yet a vague notion made his happiness incomplete. He had expected his life to return to the way it had been before the war when he had led a simple life. Life had robbed him of his family so quickly that he could not completely comprehend their death. He hoped to find them and knew they were dead. He went to the place of their execution, planning to exhume their bodies and bury them properly.

> Imagine the desolate loneliness I experienced while standing in a little wood looking at a small meadow knowing what lay underneath the grass. I cried out, I yelled to heaven. No one heard my yells except the tall trees [p. 102].

He thought of life after death. It was hopeless to retrieve the bodies. His family would have been indistinguishable in the mass of slaughtered people, and all he could be certain of was that he was a Jew. And yet he thought if he was a Jew why wasn't he buried with the rest of them? He had not yet justified his survival and had to live before he could do it. He began to say Kaddish (the prayer for the dead) and suddenly "felt good." The dead were at rest, probably because of the prayer, and "My family forgave me for not dying with them" (p.102).

Leaving Poland, the "graveyard" of his people, Shmulek joined a group of people who were smuggled out to Germany. Left in a displaced person's camp, he felt "forsaken and forlorn," greeting each day "as if it was an unfaithful friend." Unable to locate a living relative, he was sent on a children's transport to England, where he was very kindly received. Having lived in a state of uncertainty and darkness, in a void, England seemed like paradise (p. 103).

Support

Not all the children found their new countries a paradise. The new adjustment sapped all their resources and a great many had to change caretakers several times. These children were unable to receive support for mourning their parents (E. Furman, 1974). Even those who found loving care were enjoined to forget their past. Some described vividly how alone they felt. They had no one to "accompany" them in attempts to cope with their past (E. Furman, 1974; Miller, 1984). Many child survivors went to great lengths to retrieve photographs of the lost parents. While the memory of the parents' faces faded, the photographs remained alive and in some way supportive.

Children like Shmulek could find support in people their parents knew. Others, hidden by strangers or in convents, found solace in the Christian religion, with the holy family substituting for the lost one (Hogman and Wreschner-Rustow, 1985). Some children could create support systems for themselves, as did T.,[2] who had last seen her parents at an assembly point from afar when she was five years old. What remained from that parting scene was her mother's supportive look, which enjoined her to stay away and go with the Christian maid. T. created a mother out of a cow she tended and later, when the cow was taken away from her, she talked to the plants she had to water in a labor camp; she addressed them as mother and father and asked them not to die (Brenner, 1988).

The majority of the child survivors we interviewed did not receive support in their mourning. The "cure all" was to forget the past and to build the future. A prohibition against discussing the past (Krell, 1985) was for many survivors a continuation of the prohibition against divulging their Jewishness. One can even say that most of these children received countersupport. Some felt that allegiance to a dead parent would be looked upon as a crime against the present caretaker or adoptive parent (Moskovitz, 1983). As Shatan (1984) and Rosenfeld (1986) put it, the memory of parents was "encapsulated" and so to speak intrapsychically jailed, a mechanism different from denial of reality and repression which were also operative, as was denial of grief. As a result, these children seemed to progress developmentally, making rapid strides without integrating their grief and their memories into each prevailing developmental phase. We rarely saw arrested development as described by Fleming and Altschul (1963) but rather that the past was isolated from the present, which in itself constituted an adaptive measure.

---

[2]All material marked with initials we owe to reports of adults who told us about their childhood experiences.

Being Alone

Not all children were left all alone in the world, but among those who were stranded were children with no one to turn to, and no place to go. They had to rely entirely on themselves to cope and survive. Being alone is not only a question of survival without help, but also a loss of oneself ("sliding away was Schmulek Oliner. He was a thing of the past . . ."). This happened when the images of the dear ones were fading and only vague impressions and sensory remnants brought back the past. Shmulek remembered the smell of Shabbat cooking; T. remembered the taste and smell of her mother's soup. Some adults can be helped to recall early kinesthetic experiences like being rocked or touched on a part of their body. These are pieces of sensorimotor experiences which do not make for an image with clear boundaries. When memories fade, the coloring and the gestures of a person fade away as well and a kind of photographic, flat image remains. Remembering through smell, taste, touch, singing, and feeling does not necessarily mean the loss of the object's animate quality, but it is not conducive to the creation of a complete, tridimensional image.

When one feels utterly alone, others are experienced as dead whether their death is a reality or not, has been witnessed, or only heard about. Shmulek actually felt dead in his body, and this bodily sensation was then transposed into a metaphor. Shmulek said that the loneliness filled his body like blood fills veins. Seeing his house empty and ravaged, his mother's photograph not to be found, Schmulek felt that something rended in him and tore loose. Many years after he lost his parents in the Holocaust, K., a tough kid who survived the war by his wits, said sadly: "My parents are missing from me."

In such reminiscences and in the current feelings of survivors one detects the remnants of organ–objects imagery (Kestenberg, 1971), not the same as Kohut's (1971) self–objects, but similar. Out of the touch between the body part or organ and the early caretaker, there develops a unity that is a preamble to an object relationship. These early oral, anal, and urethral object–images and their subsequent editions in early and later genital phases evolve from one's own body connections to the body of others. When the intimacy of touch no longer exists, the child feels a bridge to the object–image via a variety of body contents like food, feces, and urine, the imaginary baby shared with mother, or a body part like the penis. Only after preoedipal object building is completed does the object representation gain the multidimensional quality that is not entirely based on sensorimotor experiences but on all of them combining with one another to form a unit "mother" or "father." When one gains an object one feels it in one's own body ("Schmulek's chest swelled"). Object loss becomes internalized via the same route. Something that belongs to the body breaks off, and this breaking off changes the wholeness of the subject as well. Something is missing. This is an experience connected with being left alone. Uhland (1813) expressed it in a poem about a good comrade who was shot before his friend's eyes. There was uncertainty for whom the bullet was meant. It got the friend who lay at his comrade's feet as if he were a part of the survivor.[3] Sometimes, the lesion to the self-image is more complete, for instance when a person feels crushed, not just in the chest as Shmulek felt, not just missing a piece, but broken into pieces. In a paper on amputees, Mahler and Silberpfennig (1938) found that the false image of the amputated leg, its phantom, disappeared when there was a concomitant loss of a loved person. The loss of the love object brought back the loss of the limb.

The physical pain of breaking, connected to object loss, is not only related to the origin of relationships in body sensation, but also to the fact that body pain is expected to be soothed by mother (Shmulek says: "she was the one who soothed my aches"). Szasz (1955) speaks of one of the principal meanings of pain as a call for help. When this help is not forthcoming, it leads to a loss of oneself. It depletes the narcissism that depends

---

[3]I am grateful to Mr. Dankwart Rustow for supplying me with his translation of Uhland's poem.

> A bullet came a-flying,
> Aimed at me or aimed at thee?
> It tore him right asunder,
> At my feet he went under,
> As if a piece of me.

on being loved, the primary narcissism that accounts for feeling alive and breathing (Kestenberg and Borowitz, 1983).

We do not know how many children gave up because they could not go on by themselves. Some children wanted to give themselves up to the Gestapo in order to join their parents or to put an end to their agony. Many children preferred to go with their parents to their death rather than grow up alone. Some survivors are still resentful that their parents abandoned them to life rather than taking them along so the family could die together. At the mass grave where his parents lay Shmulek asked himself how he came to be alive when all Jews were dead, why he wasn't buried with the others. He was no longer his parents' child, but what was left to him was his membership in the Jewish community. He, like many others, looked to survival as a way of perpetuating the lost Jews, a survival that had to be earned.

Parting Words

Not taking leave of a child constitutes a rejection. A lack of a memory of the parting scene feels like betrayal and makes one doubt the reality of the parent's disappearance. Halina*[4] remembered that the Germans took everything away from them when she was five years old. They shot her aunt in prison and sent her father to camp. "I think he died" she said, "but mommy cried alone and did not want to tell me the truth so I would not feel grief, but I felt it anyway." One day mother left her in the house of Polish people and told her to be good and to do what she was told, and she would come back for her, but "She never came back." She left in the morning when Halina was asleep. She did not even say good-bye and Halina never saw her mother again. This is a frequent description of object loss as it is experienced by Holocaust survivors. (See also Vegh [1979].)

[4]Names marked with an asterisk are taken from authentic reports of children who testified before the Jewish Historical Commission in Poland after liberation. We have obtained them courtesy of the Jewish Historical Society Director Dr. Epstein in Warsaw, and are especially grateful to Mr. Krupko for collecting them for us. The translation from Polish is the author's.

Having left without saying good-bye, Halina's mother lost her child's trust. This feeling was perpetuated when it was time, after the liberation, for Halina to leave her hosts. The foster mother could no longer keep her because she was poor and the Poles made fun of her as a Jew lover. Halina cried a lot and the family cried too because "They had gotten used to me." In contrast, Roma*, ten to eleven years old when she parted from her parents, though not allowed to cry so as not to arouse suspicion, was told by her father: "Remember that you had a father and a mother," and her mother added that she should always keep her courage up. After the war Roma said: "These words consoled me in times of apathy and total resignation." At first taken care of by a cousin, she soon remained "alone among strangers." After the war no one called for her and she was invited to stay with her Polish caretakers, who liked her. She felt comfortable with them, but was terrified at the prospect of remaining with them, and went willingly when a friend of her parents came to take her with him. Her allegiance to her parents and their group had remained intact throughout the separation; Schmulek's wholeness was restored when he recollected his stepmother's parting words (*I love you, Shmulek*). When one is loved there is sense in surviving. Many parents told their children to survive because they loved them. Then there were some who appealed to the child's conscience, telling him to survive in order to tell about the persecution and become a living witness. Others enjoined the children to promise that they would survive. This gave the children the right to survive rather than die with the parents. In a sense, the parting words became the child's companions, the living remnants of the parents' love and their desire for the child to survive, which were incorporated into the superego.

Links to the Past Through Transitional and Substitute Objects

A variety of links became safeguards against total forgetting and guidelines for living. Most of them had a transitional character. K., for instance, had two healing mechanisms at his disposal. One was the recurrence of a melody he sang, a melody the family, especially his mother, sang. The other was a magic verse his mother taught him that was to safeguard him against danger in dire emergencies. Shmulek, who grew up on a farm, felt that nature was part of his family life. Breezes, for instance, made him feel alive. More concrete was T.'s cow and her plants with which she consciously conversed as if they were her parents. Moreover, when she was in danger of amputation, she talked to her legs, treating them as if they were her sisters (she had none) and enjoining them to survive, which they did. After long tribulations, which will be described later, Abram* found a haven in a Polish peasant's house. He was around thirteen or fourteen years old. He reported:

> I became attached to a little horse, who filled my free time and gave me a great deal of joy. He was my best friend and my most beloved being. I called him "Siwek" (gray) and he too liked me and came only to me. The best part of my food, bread, I saved for Siwek. He was the speediest horse in the whole village. He jumped over ditches, over hedges and my Siwek was always first. I trained him that well. . . .

When buyers came for Siwek, Abram cried and threatened to leave if Siwek went. It is to be noted that this was a child who had been homeless for a long time. He found loving caretakers who tolerated other people's suspicions that Abram was Jewish. Yet, he wanted to leave if his beloved horse went. Levinson (1967) described how in normal conditions a pet can become a crutch that helps the child to hold onto life after a loss and "become whole again" (p. 200). Abram's caretakers could not comfort him and help him mourn. He could not reminisce with them or cry. But riding and taming the horse had two purposes. First, the rider felt one with the horse and the horse's feet became the rider's as well. This rebuilt Abram's self-esteem; he had been considered clumsy and funny and had fallen off the horse in the beginning. Second, the horse was his friend and loved him, and in this capacity was a substitute for his mother. The relationship to the pet in these cases becomes reciprocal. T. took care of the cow and found comfort in her; Abram took care of the horse and found comfort in him. Feeding and grooming became part of the caretaking activity the children missed, while at the same time it constituted an identification with the lost parents. To maintain a friend, to belong to a group, not to be alone, was an essential part of survival strategies which overshadowed grief and mourning.

Survival

Conditions of survival varied from place to place, from country to country. They ranged from being cared for by loving substitutes, to being imprisoned or in camps or being left all alone, subject to persecution, and in constant danger of discovery.

When Abram* was eight years old war broke out in Poland. He had spent a happy childhood in a little town where Monday was market day and the Jewish population was busy trading and working in their shops. Things continued to go fairly well after the Russians came, but when the Germans invaded in 1941 (Abram was then ten years old), they confiscated Jewish stores and robbed Jews' apartments. They rounded up people for labor. Those who failed to register were sent to a penal camp. A neighbor who failed to wear an armband, with a large "J" on it, was killed. A butcher who slaughtered a hen against German orders was tortured to death. A resettled woman who did not know that Jews had to give up furs was killed instantly because she had a fur collar. The town was crowded with people who had nothing to eat and no place to stay. Abram could no longer go to school, but he attended a cheder. In the beginning, Abram did not know "that the Germans were bad, I only heard how they talked," but he heard what they did. They caught children who smuggled food for their families, beat them, ridiculed them, and took their packages. Polish children teased their Jewish peers calling them "rotten Jews." Only at the end of his lengthy report did Abram admit that he and the other children from the cheder played "Germans." They ran in the courtyard screaming: "Juden heraus" (Jews out). They cursed "verfluchter Jude" (accursed Jews). The neighbors scolded them and they screamed "like madmen" and talked to them only in German. From this play, one can gather that children were witnesses to horrible cruelties and reenacted them in identification with the aggressors.

Abram's father was infected with typhus and died in the hospital. There were only a few people at the funeral because the Germans did not allow large gatherings. The home was sad and the family lived only from the sale of their belongings. Mother sent Abram to a peasant to work as a shepherd, but he could visit her on Saturday. She gave him his father's prayer-book and told him to pray every day, an order Abram could not fulfill because the other shepherds ridiculed him.

One day the Germans surrounded the town in an effort to deport all the Jews to the death camps. Neighbors built a shelter, but only one of Abram's family could squeeze in there. Instead of hiding there, as his mother suggested, he pushed her in and himself reported to the assembly place. (His brother had a work card and was not in danger.) The Germans chased people out of the houses and beat everybody, children, old people, and the sick. Abram saw how a German beat a hunchback, who could not stand up straight in the line, hitting him so hard with a truncheon that the man could no longer scream or moan. Abram said:

I shivered, that was the first time I saw that a man could be beaten like this.

He was frightened, but alert enough to see that a guard let a boy out to get a drink of water. So he went for water too, but escaped, ignoring the guard's admonitions to return. On the way out of town, Abram saw many corpses of people who had tried to escape. He hid in a field until it was dark, and then returned to his employer. Two weeks later, the Germans took all the remaining Jews to the cemetery and shot them.

Throughout this part of the report Abram hints that his mother and brother had been killed but he was still asking for them and did not acknowledge their deaths. He knew that Poles betrayed Jews who were in hiding. He himself was asked to leave the farm where he was working because the Germans had given orders that Jews must not be employed. It was getting dark and he was walking alone. For a while he joined a group of Jewish boys and girls, then he found a companion, and together they roamed around. All the children felt that "the cats and dogs had it better, a lot better, than they did." (This was a repeated theme of these children who were left alone. Z., for instance, hid in the hollow of a tree and wished to be a tree, a spider, a dog, or a German for the duration of the war.)

It was easier to wander, sleep in haystacks, and beg for food when Abram had a companion. Many peasants laughed at them and chased them away, threatening to denounce them. Some fed them, but could not let them stay. Eventually, Abram was deserted by his companion and was alone again. He returned to his former employer who fed him, but he could not remain there. Once, in his roamings, he got into an empty house belonging to Poles who had fled, and, as he was gorging himself on food, was caught by the Germans. Abram exhibited alertness and ingenuity and saved himself. He told a story about being a Polish boy who had come to visit his aunt. The Germans fed him and were nice to him, but when they found him again, they sent him to prison, and then to a detention camp. There, the Red Cross organized the adoption of Polish children or helped them find employment. Abram, who took on the name of his former employer, could not find a place. He was either suspected of being a gypsy or was recognized as a Jew. In one family the woman caught him naked and laughed at the Jewboy (in Poland only Jews were circumcised). Eventually, he went to work on a farm where he tended cows and horses. The employer was good to him even though there was a whispering campaign in the village that he was a Jew. Abram kept talking his way out of trouble, but his lack of knowledge about the Catholic religion betrayed him as did his poor knowledge of Polish grammar. Even the local partisans wanted to do away with him and the Russians who liberated the village called him a Jew (Yevrey). Abram was afraid to admit he was a Jew. His employer told him he would keep him if he were to be baptized. Abram worried. He thought there were no more Jews left, but still he refused to be baptized.

At last he was told that the Polish government was giving back expropriated houses to Jews and he was taken to town by the wife of his peasant employer, who directed him to the

Jewish Committee. As a result, he was placed in a residential school—this was two years after liberation. When he heard about Jews being in town, his heart "jumped for joy that I would meet Jews and be able to be *myself*." Study opened a new world for him. Even though still attached to his employer, he wanted to go to Palestine to be somewhere where there were many Jews and he would not be afraid to be one.

Now that he was relatively free of fear, he could begin to contemplate his past and speak of the future. He said that the greatest ordeal in his life was when he was separated from his mother, escaped from the square full of Germans, and lay in the field alone, waiting to die any minute. Several times he dreamed that the Germans chased, caught, and killed him. Once he dreamed about his brother being dead, but his mother alive.

> Now I think all the time what happened and life is not nice when I lost my whole family.

He was most unhappy in school because the other children had some relatives and he had none and was also behind in his studies. He felt he had been heroic throughout the war, but his great dream of finding someone who would care for him, a relative or even a stranger so he "would not be always alone," was not fulfilled. By himself he did not know what to do with things, how to behave, and needed "a living soul to talk to and get advice." Unlike many other children he did not make friends. He still felt segregated, surviving on his own.

Abram's story, greatly abbreviated, gives us only a glimpse into the massive, continuous, and life-threatening events that beset the lives of the children during Nazi occupation.[5] Other children in the ghettos were risking their lives smuggling food to help their families. Some were harbored by friendly Christians during the entire war and treated with great kindness, but

---

[5]Although most children were gassed in such camps as Auschwitz, quite a few survived their parents because they were tall enough or hidden by inmates. Many children's blocks were created in 1944. A certain number of children survived in them, especially after gassing ceased in the fall.

they were separated from their parents more often than not; still others, after a long period of deprivation in the ghettos were deported to camps where they were often torn away from their loved ones who "went up in smoke."[6]

Many children, especially those who were forced by the Rumanians to walk to Transistria (Gold, 1985; Rottenberg, 1985), witnessed the death of their parents by illness and starvation after long treks along muddy roads. Some of these children clutched onto their parents' bodies, especially the mother's, and did not want to let go of them for burial. Only a few saw their parents buried. Many had already encountered unburied corpses early in the war. These children understood very early what it meant to be dead, and some, like seven-year-old T., understood that death is inevitable. An inmate of a children's block in Auschwitz, she expected to be gassed with the other children because she knew this was due to take place sooner or later.

Is It Possible to Mourn in the Face of Impending Death?

Protected by a mother, children could endure a lot without too much fear. Wladyslaw* was eight years old at the beginning of the war. When mother heard terrible screams she knew the German murderers were nearby. She grabbed Wladyslaw and his four-year-old brother and ran away, hiding a night in a house and the next day in the fields. No one would let them hide in a barn. Wladyslaw reported:

> We were very cold, but we were not afraid because mother was with us.

The pain of discovery of a parent's or sibling's death was always overwhelming and sometimes cruelly convincing. Five children were hiding together wearing only sweaters and skirts or pants in the cold of the winter. Bronka's* mother and

---

[6]This death by gassing and the subsequent burning of bodies is commemorated in Jewish cemeteries in Poland by an inscription: "died between heaven and earth."

brother were killed by shots from German bandits. Still she and her younger brother went on, although his feet were frozen and they had to creep on their bellies. It was worse for Bronka when a boy brought a lock of her mother's bloody hair covered with pieces of her brain. Bronka lost her zest for life. It had no value for her. The rest of the children explained to her that she had to live for her brother. Eventually she obtained a job as a maid, but she changed jobs often because she could not listen to the frequent barbs against Jews.

Acute mourning and grief were common, but (as with Shmulek and Abram*) sadness had to give way to action or adaptation to new circumstances. In some children who were hidden and cared for, mourning did take place, but left the children vulnerable to future separation. Rezia* remembered her mother but faintly. In contrast, she had a clear memory of her little brother, who had to stay in bed because his legs were in a cast. She recalled that the Germans killed him. By the time she was four years old, her father took her away to a peasant's home. There she tended cows and horses and mothered little children younger than herself, whom she regarded as little sisters. She went to church with the rest of the family and did not know what a Jew was. Testifying at the age of twelve, she said:

> The first year I longed for mommy and then I got used to my caretakers. I was there for five years.

The caretakers treated the child like their own. After liberation she was afraid to go to Jews because other children told her that they were Christ-killers. She did not believe that the woman who came for her was really her aunt, and cried and screamed. Once more she got used to things, but she still longed for the children, and would like to have visited at least on vacations. The mourning for the absent mother, which gave way to an attachment to the foster parents, was now repeated. An undertone of resignation fills Rezia's report a year after she was separated from her Christian family.

As described by E. Furman (1974), mourning can give way to a new attachment to a parent substitute. The initial resignation when one's parents have died or left may be followed by a more intense reaction, with protest and screaming (Bowlby, 1960), followed by resignation and sadness at the time of separation from the substitute family.

Giving up one's identity as a Jew may come from being too young to have a Jewish identity or from such an identity not being important in the family. Once such an identity has been established, giving it up seems to be a sign of giving up one's parents and withdrawing libido from them. In cases where there is strong family loyalty, a child who has repressed his feeling of belonging to the Jewish community will reaccept it and reaccept the part of the self that has been lost. Many children pretended to be Christians to survive, but never lost their feeling of being Jewish. This was greatly reinforced by the continuous danger of being identified as a Jew by the enemy. By keeping their identity and caring for themselves in identification with their lost parents, these children engaged in what might be called a latent mourning. The link to parental Jewishness often constituted an internal memorial to them. Sometimes a return to Judaism in later life is a sign of a belated mourning mechanism, a reconciliation with the dead. Giving up one's belief in God was fraught with anger that He permitted the persecution. Reconciliation with God signifies forgiving the "abandoning" dead parent.

In time of danger there was rarely time for grief because grief immobilizes and removes active aggression from the fight for survival. It was not that the children did not feel guilty over their own survival and their parent's death. The guilt was there, but it was counterbalanced by conscious and unconscious resentment of the parents for abandoning them, for dying, for "giving up." Sometimes these feelings were well founded.

A. described how he was separated from his mother and sister when he arrived in Auschwitz. Mothers could save themselves by giving up their children to death, but from the long line of victims on their way to the gas chambers only three mothers chose this way to live. However, there were less obvious ways of abandonment. A mother whose son died in Transistria lost the desire to live and kept saying to her daughter that she had no one to live for. Another behaved this way when her husband died. These children felt rejected and resentful and still clung to their mothers even after the women had died. However, the children's anger contributed greatly to their own will to survive. In the case of one child, this will was enhanced by an intense loyalty to a surviving brother from whom she did not want to separate. Sometimes people felt angry *and* defied the "abandoning" parent by means of their own survival without her.

Until his placement in a residential school, Abram* hardly ever mentioned his mother and brother. He knew that he was proud of pushing his mother into the hiding place rather than saving himself. Yet, was he not also angry at her for allowing him to do so? Perhaps he felt that he was rewarded for his heroic deed and he felt that he must survive at all cost, even though he was repeatedly abandoned. One can speculate that his unexpressed anger at his mother and brother spurred him on and was an incentive for meeting the supreme challenge to his ego. The basic conditions of survival (food, warmth, shelter) took up all his remaining energy.[7] There was no time for grief or contemplation. He had to go on, relentlessly defending himself against the external enemy. A. at the age of thirteen could not think about the death of his beloved father, when his immediate task was for the remainder of his family to live one hour, one day longer.

It was as if all libido and aggression were concentrated in the ego to fulfill basic bodily needs. There was a moratorium on many demands on the superego. People experienced a feeling of triumph each time their narcissistic supplies were restored and their self-esteem was reconstituted. This happened to a greater or lesser degree when one had eaten enough food, had managed to wash oneself and one's clothes, or had escaped death. The final, almost intoxicating triumph came with liberation. The elation pertained not only to the individual's survival, but the survival of the group.

Fantasies of being reunited with the family or compensated

---

[7] In this connection, one wonders whether the German's inability to mourn after the war (Mitscherlich and Mitscherlich, 1967) was in part due to the then prevailing hunger, homelessness, and fear of retribution by the victors.

for all one's suffering either came in bursts or were put off until some unspecified future time. There was no room for grief, only for hope and for sustaining the ego's survival functions. When struggle was impossible and one was passive in the face of deprivation (as in the concentration camps), reminiscences had a healing quality (Hogman and Wreschner-Rustow, 1985). In a state of extreme hunger, concentration camp victims would reminisce together about the food their mothers had given them.

Children who had a good support system in terms of survival still did not have support for grieving because their origin had to be disguised and no one talked about their Jewishness. Their sadness gave way to attachments to substitutes. Sometimes a parent believed to be dead reappeared after the end of the war, and parents and children were estranged from one another. A bond was lost in the years of separation and yet there was an expectation that the past could be undone, and of finding a mother or a child of the same age and appearance as at the time of separation. It was difficult to accept each other, but it was no easier for the parent than for the child. The child's anger would flare up and the returned parent would be attacked directly or indirectly. V., who was happy in her orphanage, tore up the doll, her first doll, one her mother had given her as a reunion present. Her mother was angry and disappointed.

In normal development one gives up the current image of the mother at each new developmental phase and then accepts a new one. Children who lost their parents have a gap which they call "lost childhood." They not only mourn the lost parents but also the lost childhood during which the child and the parent grow together from one phase to another. There is a regret with each new change in one's life that the parent could not be there to share in the experience. The realization that one did not know one's mother or father during crucial years of childhood detracts from a fuller identification with the lost parent. People who lost their parents as very young children, and whose memories of their parents have faded long ago, react with a depressive core for which they cannot account until they can begin to mourn for those people they hardly knew.

After Liberation

After being exhilarated and feeling triumphant at the moment of freedom, there was a letdown for many. A., accompanied by a camp "colleague," walked out of a camp when he was fifteen. As they walked, he asked himself: "Where do I go now?" He knew his family was gone; there was no place to which he could return. Other people searched for lost relatives for many years. Many who did not accept the finality of their relatives' deaths suffered from a split between knowing and not knowing. It was not right to say Kaddish for them without being sure of their death. It was not right to mourn. Energies were concentrated on building a new life, on adjusting to a new country, on studies, and making a career, on adapting to a new family or creating a new one. Each child born to a survivor was a triumph of survival through the creation of a new generation, but it was also an occasion of sorrow if the grandparents were not there to enjoy the event.

In different cultures there are prescribed rules and rituals of mourning. In Israel the Yom Hashoah has provided an outlet for group mourning. With the emergence of gatherings of survivors, with the creation of Holocaust memorials, and the emphasis in recent years on remembering the past, a new venue was opened to mourn together, not only for lost relatives, but also for lost communities, lost cultures, and the loss of belonging and its continuity. This stands in contrast with the prohibition to talk and remember which counteracted attempts to mourn until thirty or forty years had elapsed from the time of the loss.

In closing, one must emphasize that this first attempt to describe the attitude to losses on the part of child survivors constitutes just a beginning. It must be followed by a more exhaustive study with consideration of ages, circumstances of loss, pre-Holocaust conditions, and the post-Holocaust vicissitudes. Greatly needed is an in-depth study of the child survivor's creativity that often led these children to write stories and poems, to paint and compose during persecution and after. The healing effect of these creative endeavors is attested to in many books (Hogman and Wreschner-Rustow, 1985). Furthermore, the inventiveness by which many children survived was a creative process in the service of survival and before adaptation through mourning could become manifest (Pollock, 1961, 1977). For a great many, mourning is still not completed, and this does not constitute pathology, but rather a lifetime response to massive losses, encompassing a whole world of objects and of one's own position in it. Perhaps the mourning of one generation is not enough and it has to continue for many generations to come.

References

Bowlby, J. (1960), Grief and mourning in infancy and early childhood. *The Psychoanalytic Study of the Child*, 15:9–52. New York: International Universities Press.

Brenner, I., (1988), Multisensory bridges in response to object loss during the Holocaust. *Psychoanal. Rev.*, 75(4):573–587.

Fleming, J., & Altschul, S. (1963), Activation of mourning and growth by psychoanalysis. *Internat. J. Psycho-Anal.*, 44:419–431.

Furman, E. (1974), *A Child's Parent Dies*. New Haven, CT: Yale University Press.

Gold, R. (Glasberg) (1985), A child in Transistria. *Newsletter of the Jerome Riker International Study of Organized Persecution of Children*, 2(1):2–3.

Greene, W. A.(1958), Role of a vicarious object in the adaptation to object loss. *Psychosom. Med.*, 20:344–350.

Hogman, F., & Wreschner-Rustow, M. (1985), Religion and child survivors of the Holocaust. Paper presented at the Psychohistory Forum, New York, March.

Kestenberg, J. S. (1971), From organ–object imagery to self and object representation. In: *Separation–Individuation*, eds. J. B. McDevitt & C. V. Settlage. New York: International Universities Press, pp. 75–99.

————Borowitz, E. (1983), Thoughts on the development of narcissism. Paper presented at the symposium on Narcissism: Clinical and Developmental Perspectives. Sponsored by the New England Psychoanalytic Society, New Haven, CT, April 16.

————Brenner, I. (1986), Children who survived the Holocaust. The role of rules and routines in the development of the superego. *Internat. J. Psycho-Anal.*, 67(3):309–316.

Kohut, H. (1971), *The Analysis of the Self*. New York: International Universities Press.

Krell, R. (1985), Therapeutic value of documenting child survivors. *J. Amer. Acad. Child Psychiat.*, 24(4):378–380.

Levinson, B. M. (1967), The pet and the child's bereavement. *Ment. Hyg.*, 51(April):197–200.

Mahler, M., & Silberpfenning (Kestenberg), J. S. (1938), Der Rorschachsche Formdeutversuch als Hilfsmittel zum Verstandniss der Psychologie

Hirnkranker (The Rorschach test as help for the understanding of the psychology of the brain-injured). *Schweitz Arch. Neur. & Psych.*, 40(2):302–327.

Miller, A. (1984), *Thou Shalt Not Be Aware*. New York: Farrar, Strauss & Giroux.

Mitscherlich, A., & Mitscherlich, M. (1975), *The Inability to Mourn*. New York: Grove Press.

Moskovitz, S. (1983), *Love Despite Hate: Child Survivors of the Holocaust and Their Adult Lives*. New York: Schocken Books.

Oliner, S. P. (1979), *Restless Memories. Recollections of the Holocaust Years*. Berkeley, CA: Judah I. Magnes Memorial Museum.

Pollock, G. H. (1961), Mourning and adaptation. *Internat. J. Psycho-Anal.*, 42:341–361.

———(1977), The mourning process and creative organizational change. *J. Amer. Psychoanal. Assn.*, 25:3–34.

———(1978), Process and affect mourning and grief. *Internat. J. Psycho-Anal.*, 59:255–276.

Rosenfeld, D. (1986), Identification and its vicissitudes in relation to the Nazi phenomenon. *Internat. J. Psycho-Anal.*, 67(1):53–64.

Rottenberg, L. (1985), A child-survivor's / psychiatrist's personal adaptation. *J. Amer. Acad. Child Psychiat.*, 24(4):385–389.

Shatan, C. F. (1984), Kinder und Krieg. In: *Jahrbuch der Kindheit*, eds. C. Buttnera & A. Ende. Laudenbach: Beltz Verlag, pp. 11–88.

Szasz, T. S. (1955), The nature of pain. *A.M.A. Arch. Neurol. & Psychiat.*, 74:174–181.

Uhland, H. (1813), Ich hatte einen kameraden (I had a comrade). In: *Der poetishe Almanach*, quoted in "Der grosse Brockhaus," Vol. 19, 1934.

Vegh, C. (1979), *Je Ne Lui Ai Pas Dit Au Revoir*. Paris: Gallimard.

Volkan, V. D. (1972), The linking objects of pathological mourning. *Arch. Gen. Psychiat.*, 27:215-222.

15

The Inability to Mourn—Today*

MARGARETE MITSCHERLICH-NIELSEN, M.D.

I should like here to pursue some of the thoughts which Alexander Mitscherlich and I dealt with in our book, *The Inability to Mourn* (1975). Originally published in 1967, our work served not only to elucidate the National Socialist past and its consequences; it grew out of our own distress, our sorrow, and our shame.

To start with, I shall summarize some of the views we set forth in that book and then consider whether mourning was or is possible at all for the majority of Germans, or whether it can be accomplished only by individuals.

Exchange of Identification Models

What does "mourning" mean? Mourning is a psychological process in which the individual, by repeated and painful remembering, slowly learns to bear and to work through a loss. The alternative to the sorrow and pain of mourning for a past heavy with loss is a rapid shift to new objects, new identifications, and new ideals. These then replace, without a break or a

---

*Translated from the German by Beverley R. Placzek.

405

thought, those that have been given up. A well-known instance of this—to move from the individual to a whole society—is the behavior of the Germans at the end of the last war. Abandoning their trust in the "Führer" and their Nazi ideals, their delusions of racial supremacy and power, their slogans of "seeing it through," a whole people rushed to identify with the victors and their leaders. With this exchange of identification models they chose the easiest way of avoiding the loss of national self-esteem that threatened them.

After the defeat there was first an abrupt derealization; the past simply faded away like a dream. The switch of identity through identification with the victors, accomplished as it was without particularly noticeable signs of injured pride, rein- forced the defense against any feelings of being implicated. The manic effort to undo, the enormous collective effort to rebuild, a kind of national occupational therapy, made perma- nent denial and repression possible for the majority of the Germans. But when denial, repression, and derealization of the past take the place of working through, a compulsion to repeat is unavoidable, even though it may be concealed. It is then not the content of a system but the structure of a society that is repeated. Nazi symbols and Nazi gatherings can be forbidden; but to purge the structures of Nazism from the realms of education, from attitudes, behavior and thought patterns, and from politics is impossible without the work of mourning. Hence we must recognize that today the younger generation, which feels itself to be without guilt, has inherited our past, not worked through but rather denied and repressed. One of the many indications of this is the naiveté with which a Helmut Kohl can speak—in Israel, in concentrations camps, or at the graves of SS men—of his generation being unaffected by the Nazi period. The so-called "Whites,"[1] and the generations that follow them, boast of their innocence: "We don't have to burden ourselves or think about things we didn't do." Psycho- logically and historically, that attitude is a dangerous one, both for the present and for the future.

---

[1] Those who were born during or just after the war and who could thus not have been "Brown"—the color of the Nazi uniform and so, by extension, the Nazis themselves, the "Browns."

Education for Mourning

In our work *The Inability to Mourn*, we proposed that the defense against shame, guilt, and mourning leads to emotional emptiness in the individual and, in consequence, to psychological and political immobility, to a lack of ideas and imagination in a society. In the past years, the German government seems intent on proving the truth of this thesis by its very obvious lack of imagination in dealing with the current situation, and this in spite of a clearly visible, urgent need to develop new and productive concepts in internal and foreign affairs. I shall return later to the issue of the past in the present.

A particular kind of memory work is needed to develop the ability to mourn. This is less a matter of recalling facts and events than of remembering ways of behaving, value judgments, feelings, and fantasies. The work of mourning involves mourning not only for the loss of persons, but also for ideals and narcissistic self-love; it also means confronting guilt and shame, defeats and disappointments. The ability to do this demands from the outset the right kind of upbringing, one in which parents and teachers relate to children and young people in a way that fosters it. Such an upbringing must not teach children to believe in success and endurance, neither should it teach them to repress pain and emotion, nor to adapt and obey, nor to foist their guilt onto scapegoats; all of which is to say that they must not be brought up to accept "the authoritarian thinking of servile minds." But in Germany there was hardly any of this kind of fostering upbringing, least of all where ideals of manliness and "manly" virtues predominated. This was surely one important reason why the mass of German men, and with them millions of women, had so little in the way of inner resources with which to counter the perverted ideals of supremacy, why they accepted the paranoid racism, the persecution and extermination of minorities without this generating any sense of guilt. For the Nazis and their precursors equality before the law and respect for minorities was nothing but mawkish sentimentality. There were, according to Hans Mayer (cited in Beuys et al., 1985) only supermen, men, and subhumans.

Mourning versus Suggestion

No one who had put that world view into practice would be able to shrug it off. No one brought up to believe in national self-glorification, success, the ability to "make it," to think in terms of authority and obedience, to search for scapegoats, to despise dissenters and the weak, is prepared to take a stand against that same mentality when raised to hallucinatory heights as it was during the time of the Nazis. Nor is he capable of a different, more empathic, and critical way of thinking, or of relinquishing dubious ideals; in short, he is unable to mourn. Only parents and educators who do not react defensively or by projection of guilt, shame, mental pain, and failure, and resentment of authority will share their efforts to understand and tolerate these things with their children. And only children brought up in this way will, as adults, question the origins of the values being offered, will remain unmoved by delusions of conquest and racial superiority, and will not be duped by appalling, lying ideologies such as those that were proclaimed and acted on in the Nazi state. A sadomasochistic upbringing and mind-set, a servile identification with the powerful, and contempt for the weak survive to this day in broad sectors of our society—as it does in the relation of the sexes to one another. Through character deformations of this sort and the mystifications and misinformation, the denials and repressions that go with them, the evil of the Hitler era is handed on indefinitely from generation to generation.

To repeat: the ability of an individual to mourn means that he is able to part with open eyes not only from lost human objects but also from lost attitudes and thought patterns that governed his life in important periods of his development. The work of mourning, a process of leave-taking, is the prerequisite for being able to think new thoughts, perceive new things, and alter one's behavior patterns. Without it, the unconscious motivations of one's actions and reactions cannot be unraveled, nor can other than sadomasochistic ways of relating and identifying be allowed to take hold. The process of mourning frees the individual from a neurotic compulsion to repeat the same thing over and over again.

The Zurich philosopher Hermann Lübbe dubbed the theory of repression a "pseudo theory." No one, he says, has repressed the "Thousand-Year Reich"; people have simply agreed to maintain a nationally supportive, constructive silence. Since most Germans were identified with the Nazi ideology and since, without them, the new state could not have been established, silence was the only possible way of arriving at a common national basis. According to Lübbe, the generation of 1968 and the "theorists of repression" had, with their theories, irresponsibly undermined the very foundations of the new, laboriously constituted state.

Commenting on this, Günther Rühle, the Frankfurt theater director, wrote:

> We are being made to feel that this old past will and should swallow up our present. This present was created laboriously and with an effort to atone, even though this made it necessary to put the political specter of those times at a distance. . . . What is now under way—for the most varied motives and reasons, and using the occasion of the Hitler half-century commemoration as a spur—is an effort to illumine, or even to achieve the still much touted "work of mourning," an effort which is only partially justified with rational arguments [1982].

Rühle, like Lübbe, is of the opinion that one can "relate freely and in a morally and politically appropriate manner to the reality of the Third Reich, without also being called upon to obliterate once and for all the roots of that Reich still purportedly surviving in our own successor state."

Michael Naumann called Lübbe's polemicizing against the "theorists of repression" an expression of repressed repression. Obviously, Rühle, too, wished to "relate freely and in a morally and politically appropriate manner to the reality of the Third Reich" with his intended staging of Werner Fassbinder's play, *Trash, the City, and Death* in Frankfurt. He forgot that there were people who had been affected, who could not repress, and that not everyone in Germany had repressed their repression. I shall later return to this problem.

But whatever one's attitude to Hermann Lübbe's views, they

will assuredly not jeopardize the theory of repression. Certainly, not many of the Germans who as children, young people, or adults lived through the war will have forgotten the facts of the Nazi time. Certainly, there can be a common agreement to keep silent on the national level about the horrors and falsehoods of that time. But the individual obeys different psychological mechanisms: he represses, denies, and derealizes emotions and ideals, actions, and attitudes. Looking back on these, and on the methods he used to adapt, endangers his self-esteem. Thus, here it is often a matter of psychological emergency mechanisms, seeking to ward off the risk of suicidal depression.

No Mourning for the Majority of Germans

For the majority of Germans there was, however, no mourning. The blanket of silence drawn over the past by the state and its institutions confirmed the individual in his repression and denial. When, every now and again, there is a call for reconciliation, for memory work, it is raised by single voices within the chorus of people fighting against the past. These latter adhere to the traditional political line, starting with Adenauer, which aims to render the image of the German again acceptable abroad. Asked whether he would like to be called "the conscience of the nation," the writer Heinrich Böll responded:

> The conscience of the nation consists of all the parliaments, all the political parties, of the churches, of the press, of every kind of public act or utterance. And these, that are actually called upon to be the conscience, gladly delegate this to someone who then must take over both roles: he becomes the scapegoat as well as the conscience. It's very simple.[2]

After the war, in addition to denial and repression, there was a manic effort to ward off depression by an enormous, unimaginative and often destructive rebuilding of the cities and the

[2]Although no reference was made available for this quote, we nevertheless decided to retain Böll's statement because it adds to and helps articulate one of the major themes of the chapter (Eds.).

economy. Germany once again came into money, but on the international scene she remained without power or intellectual influence.

But aside from upbringing and childhood experiences, when is an individual—when is a society—actually capable of mourning? When can the painful loss of persons or ideals, the misery of self-devaluation be borne? What are the conditions under which a person can admit to his sorrow, his guilt, and his feelings of shame? A society, if it wishes to preserve a nationally viable continuity ("No experiments," was the pronouncement under Adenauer), has apparently no choice but to remain silent, thereby encouraging the individual to continue the building of his own defenses undisturbed.

After 1945, "we merely followed," replaced the First World War legend of the "knife in the back" as a collective defense against working through the past. After World War II it was hard to find a scapegoat; it was clear that only we Germans ourselves were guilty. But who can actually bear that? In order to escape from it, we defined ourselves in great numbers as having "merely followed," which implied that the guilt could be assigned to the system into whose power we had purportedly been helplessly delivered, and which in this way could be turned into the guilty party. Over 6 million Jews bestially slaughtered; the Gypsies have, to date, been virtually annihilated; 20 million Russians dead, all of them, "Bolshevik subhumans"; 3 1/2 million Russian prisoners of war, and millions of our own people dead and murdered; such were the consequences of our having "merely followed." Could we, and can we, confront this without defenses, without derealization, without a renewed search for a scapegoat?

I quote here the Latin-American writer Alejo Carpentier, long resident in France (1977):

Here was a new thing, a thing that had never been before, a modern thing, this den of horror into which we had stumbled in our advance! A house of terror where everything spoke of torture, of mass carnage, of cremations between blood-spattered, filth-spattered walls in front of which mountains of bones and human dentures had been shovelled into piles. Not to speak of those worse ones brought coldly to death by rubber-gloved hands in clean, bright, antiseptic, shiny-white operating rooms. And only a few steps from here sensitive, cultivated people, untroubled by the gruesome smoke from certain smokestacks or—beforehand—by the shrieking Jewish prayers, went on collecting their stamps, studying the glorious history of their race, performed Mozart's "Kleine Nachtmusik" and read Andersen's fairy-tale of the "Little Mermaid" aloud to their children. That too was new, in an appalling way modern, dreadful in a way that had never been before . . . never had I been able to imagine a bankruptcy of Western man so absolute as that which was revealed by the leftovers of horror.

Death becomes a "Master from Germany" (Celan, 1952).

In a murderous history of this sort what lost love objects can be mourned for? What possible purpose can the work of mourning still have? Mourning may be seen as a process in which an evil deed is recognized as such and "reparation" is attempted. Mourning over evil actions can then lead to good actions. But what does a people, a whole society, do when confronted with crimes of such magnitude and the incalculable scope of its own part in them, crimes that are irreversible, for which there can never be "appropriate" reparation? Is it then possible, as Rühle thought, to relate "freely" in a morally and politically appropriate way to such a reality? Do people then not have to forget and remain silent, do they not have to throw themselves into a maniacal whirl of reconstruction if they are unwilling, as the only alternative, to commit suicide? Indeed, is mourning even possible for a whole society? Is it not a matter only for individuals? But what about the deluded individual who has lost all his ideals or, worse still, what about the person who actually committed the murderous acts, how should he face his past? Because it is undeniable that making clear to an ex-Nazi that all his virtues were actually vices, all his values false and corrupt, is to destroy him. What makes the Nazi time so incomprehensible, so monstrous, and so unfathomable remains the fact that we, the majority of the Germans, members of an ancient and cultivated people could, for twelve years, live and act in it with conviction. The truly ungraspable, unencompassable quality of the Nazi crimes is what blocks the work of mourning and its aim: to be a learning process through which an evil deed can be recognized as such and made good.

Is Atonement Utopian?

Is the ability to mourn over the Nazi period, with its goal of atonement, ultimately a utopian aim that must be buried? If what is meant is atonement for the massive human and spiritual destruction, the question has to be answered affirmatively. But there is not only mourning for evil deeds for which no atonement is possible; there is also mourning for good deeds left undone. Might mourning not be possible for those who failed to act? There are those, for instance, who prevented the removal of Hitler from office, and those who gave too little help to the resistance fighters, and those others who failed to succor the persecuted for fear of themselves being destroyed, those who made compromises or, too, those who in great numbers remained silent or who, either from fear or expediency, were guilty of passive complicity. Should not some of them be able to mourn without being overwhelmed by fear of losing themselves in mourning forever? For people such as these, the work of mourning could be linked to a goal, that of preventing such crimes and delusional thought-processes from ever being repeated. Committing oneself to lifelong efforts of memory and self-examination does not mean remaining passively caught in the past, nor does it entail losing the ability to live and act. The kind of mourning I mean should enable one to identify with the role of critic and observer, of self-critic and self-observer, a role, that is, which should enable one to maintain contact with oneself, one's behavior, feelings, and ways of thinking. This is a role which is also acceptable because, humanly and historically, it is the role that most nearly apprehends the truth and so helps to recognize and break through repetitions of brutality and meanness—even in everyday life. This is the very thing that, for instance, psychoanalysts should be able to achieve, since their profession defines them a priori as outsiders, not as conformists. A psychoanalyst who does not accept himself as an outsider has, in my opinion, missed his calling. It is not by accident that we have a Jew and outsider to thank for the science of psychoanalysis.

Psychoanalysts: Experts in the Work of Mourning

In this connection, allow me to digress to a discussion of the ability to mourn of my colleagues, male and female, a discussion, that is, of my own fraternity. Evidently, even psychoanalysts, though by profession themselves memory workers, find it hard to confront their own adaptive mechanisms, their own opportunism, and their fear of being outsiders. This was borne out by an exchange of letters that became known beyond the confines of our profession. The letters were in reaction to some articles on the subject of "Psychoanalysis and National-Socialism," and were published by the journal *Psyche (Psychoanalyze unter Hitler*, 1984). As psychoanalysts, our professional obligation is "remembering, repeating and working through."

As all of us who concern ourselves with the human psyche know, without mourning there can be no development in the inner life of the individual. To confront one's own shame, to question whether there might not have been some other way than by accommodation, to free oneself from self-idealization, is evidently no less problematic for psychoanalysts than it is for any other of our fellow countrymen. As soon as their own fraternity was involved, violent defense movements emerged among German psychoanalysts against any critical examination of the past or present. The predominant reaction was either of anger and rage at the very idea of questioning our colleagues' ideals or behavior during the Hitler time, or there was an attempt to gloss things over with a fraternal spirit and false conciliation at the expense of remembering and working through the past. Those Germans who had conformed but who were not of the psychoanalytic fraternity—here there was virtually no disagreement among our colleagues—had to be persuaded of the need to face and deal with their guilt, shame, and mourning. Indeed, specifically through psychoanalysis, they were to be enlightened as to what had allowed them to become followers of a criminal system. However, we, as psychoanalysts, did not wish to be disturbed in our self-idealization, nor to see ourselves as having any share in the general bankruptcy of values. When that was no longer possible, when we had to demand shame, mourning, and memory work of ourselves, the aforementioned conflicts arose, with their angry or whitewashing defensive reactions.

In addition to their reluctance to confront their own or their colleagues' accommodation or conformism during the time of the Nazis, the psychoanalysts also mostly warded off any work of mourning in the sense of critical working through and gaining distance from long-held psychoanalytic ideals and training criteria. To work through experiences, to rethink and critically to examine previously held values and concepts and thereupon laboriously and painfully to break free of them when their constricting power over development and thought has been recognized is the aim and purpose of psychoanalysis. To be virtually forbidden to do this contradicts the very essence of psychoanalytic thinking. There exists an extensive psychoanalytic literature about the inner emptiness, the creative incapacity and stagnation, that result from the absence of the work of mourning. Thus psychoanalysts contradict their innermost convictions when they take criticism of their own past or of their existing institutions as "betrayal" and "fouling of the nest," or, when at all possible, blanket any criticism, any slip, any misdirection of psychoanalysis and the organization of its institutions in—to paraphrase Hermann Lübbe—"institutionally supportive constructive silence."

Rethinking a thing, thinking it anew and differently, goes hand in hand with the work of mourning. One might even say that "betrayal" is the unavoidable consequence of an ongoing process of learning to relinquish, to let go. Anyone who succumbs to his fear of being an outsider is in danger of becoming a conformist. Insofar as the critics of psychoanalytic institutions and memory workers were not of the fraternity, or worse still, were tagged as Marxists, they could safely be consigned to oblivion by psychoanalysts, since they were not worthy opponents and most certainly were not in possession of the "truth." "The journal *Psyche* is no longer acceptable," resounded from the lips of leading psychoanalysts after that journal had attempted to stimulate the aforementioned sorrowing memory work among German psychoanalysts themselves. The reason alleged was that "Of course you know, one of their editors is a Marxist."

How accurate this may be is not under discussion here. But to return to postwar German society: it is typical that here the label "Marxist" puts a negative stamp on a man or a woman from the start.

Emotional Anti-Communism as a Defense against Mourning

After the war, as most people quickly realized, it was not expedient to maintain one's anti-Semitism publicly; although no one had any illusions as to what was being said under their breath by many average German citizens. Conversely, anti-Communism soon became again socially acceptable. The "Bolshevik subhumans" of yesterday are also more or less the "Bolshevik subhumans" of today. Thanks to the Cold War and the opportunities so eagerly espoused for identification with the Western victors, little has changed in the thinking of the West German.

As a result of emotional anti-Communism, there has occurred a historical misrepresentation and distortion of the resistance movement during the time of the Nazis. As everyone knows, the last "free" election, called by Hitler in March, 1933, soon after he came to power, gave only 44 percent of the vote to the National Socialists, in spite of extreme pressure from the Party. After 1945, the resistance offered by Communists, Social Democrats, undogmatic Leftists, and Liberals was scarcely mentioned, although once Hitler had seized power these people were persecuted by the thousands, thrown into prison and killed, or were forced to emigrate. Surprisingly, this "other Germany" has been lost to view. As late as the 1970s in German schools the resistance of only a few Prussian officers and conservative politicians was mentioned; only the young idealistic students of the "White Rose" were remembered. In fact, however, only after innumerable Communists, Social Democrats, intellectuals, and pacifists who tried to resist had been murdered, imprisoned, or driven out, did further German resistance of any consequence against National Socialism cease to exist.

As we all know, identification with the victor, the Cold War, and anti-Communism went hand in hand. The outbreak of the Korean war was used as a welcome excuse to ban the German Communist Party, and once again to imprison many former resistance fighters, people who had already been cruelly mistreated during the time of the Nazis. Once again the climate prevailing in the German Federal Republic was such that opposition was in danger of being made a crime. The *Spiegel* affair[3] of the 1960s was a striking instance of this.

Perhaps the first slogan of Nazi ideology to be resurrected in a different form in postwar Germany was the one calling for a "Crusade against the Bolsheviks." The gulf that existed between the West and the Soviet Union was not the fault of the ex-Nazis but neither were they discouraged from making it wider and deeper. The aggressive–projective component in Nazi ideology lived on, abetted by an emotional anti-Communism that blocked any differentiated perception of the East and thus any Eastern policy worthy of the name. And where there is no real will to come to an understanding nor any attempt at a perception free of projection, the danger grows ever greater that both sides will retreat more and more into the paranoid madness of the armament race.

Guilt, Shame, and Mourning Are Today Still Being Warded Off

After Hitler's Germany was defeated, the infatuation with Hitler vanished like a will-o-the-wisp, although until then millions of people had replaced their own ego ideal with his image, and his followers had been ready to sacrifice everything for him. Through twelve long years, whatever the Führer decreed became ipso facto the truth, the law. "Conscience has

[3]In 1962 the offices of the opposition news magazine, *Der Spiegel*, were raided and members of the magazine's personnel arrested on orders of the Defense Minister, Franz Josef Strauss.

no application to anything that is done for the sake of the object; in the blindness of love remorselessness is carried to the pitch of crime" (Freud, 1921, p. 113). The German virtues, command and obedience, became vices which led to unimaginable crimes. After the defeat, had guilt and shame not been repressed, self-hatred and self-doubt, depression and disorientation would necessarily have dominated the scene. Aided by identification with the victors and emotional anti-Communism, old enemy images and ideals could be kept alive or revived. In this way too, aggressions could be redirected from the inside outward, or be changed into submissiveness toward the conquerors. "The Western protective powers have turned our country into the most important atomic arsenal, and therefore into the most important target of nuclear war for the Soviet Union. And yet most of our people continue to delude themselves about this reality by means of defense mechanisms that proved serviceable in the 'Holocaust!'" (Dahmer, 1982, p. 1072). The irrationality of the armament politicians, concealed behind pseudoreasonable arguments, is shared by the German population. Anti-Communism, sycophantic Americanism, lack of imagination, and repression of reality here constitute a dangerous mixture.

Depression was warded off, helped by the hectic reconstruction and the "economic miracle." Consumerism took the place of love for the Führer, and national humiliation was pushed aside by the gratification of material needs. If love for Hitler was a pseudo-love grounded in narcissism, so the all-dominating consumer orientation of our society—"my car, that's me"— seems to be a sort of substitute gratification for the narcissistic love affair with the Führer and for our badly battered self-love. For Hitler's sake the majority of the German people became criminals "with no remorse"; today the same people turn to consumption with all its consequences and again with no remorse, even if with less ecstasy than was communicated by Leni Riefenstahl's films—*The Victory of Faith* (1933), *The Triumph of Will* (1935)—of the time of the Nuremberg Party Rallies.

The libido being channeled toward consumerism fails when, to vary a phrase from *The Inability to Mourn*, it comes to working on the experiences of the past. Even after the "values" that led to Auschwitz were lost, the mentality characterized by remorse-less self-aggrandizement remained more or less unmourned. It has been preserved over time in the indifference to the destruction of the environment, and in the paranoid arms race mentality, imbued as it is with emotional anti-Communism.

There is an incapacity to establish priorities in dealing with the destruction of the environment, with the reconstruction of our cities, with social legislation and old age assistance, and, last but not least, when it comes to abolishing the sadomasochistic dominance–submission relations between the sexes. The "authoritarian thinking of servile minds" which permeates our whole society must be recognized as a result of the inability to mourn, in the sense of the inability to depart from the mentality and attitudes of mind that led to Hitler and held sway during the Nazi period.

In our work on the inability of the Germans to mourn, our principal concern was to examine the daily reality of National Socialism; to examine, that is, the sociopsychological situation of the great number of Germans who could not properly be counted either as victims or as culprits, who were neither free of guilt nor, to any particular extent, actively and directly guilty. Without these great numbers of Germans, generally of the lower or middle levels of society to which more or less all of us belong, Hitler's rise to power would not have been possible. Many of them were the people who continued to collect their stamps, to make music, to read fairy-tales to their children, to discuss philosophy, worry about the German national health service, and none of them took any notice of the smoke from the chimneys nor heard the piercing Jewish prayers. This majority of the Germans did not mourn, so ran our argument, although seen from the viewpoint of psychological prerequisites and possibilities, many of them, as I have tried to show, would have been in a position to do so.

Identification with the Victims

Among the patients we described in our book, many belonged to this group. At least some of them could have learned to mourn over good deeds left undone and, through the work of remembering, achieved atonement; or if not atonement, they could at least have worked to prevent a repetition of the brutality. That is, they could, through the work of mourning, have prevented paranoid defensiveness or also deep-seated depression. But even in these people, who had loaded themselves with no direct guilt, repression and denial or identification with the victims was uppermost in their way of coping psychologically with the past: at bottom, most of them felt that the victims of National Socialism and its consequences, who were most to be pitied, were they themselves. They mourned only over their own unhappy experiences and over the loss of their narcissistic self-worth as Germans. But anyone who mourns ultimately only for himself, for his own loss of worth, and national ideals—anyone, that is, who does not mourn for others, for love objects or for the victims of his opportunism or fear—cannot be interested in atoning. And here the only sense in which atoning is still possible is in preventing similar future crimes and in shedding light on the mental attitudes that may lead to such crimes.

Recently, Heiner Geissler, Secretary General of the Christian Democratic Union (the party presently leading the coalition government in West Germany), inveighed against awarding the Nobel prize to the Russian doctor, Chasov, the advocate on the Russian side for the peace organization International Physicians for the Prevention of Nuclear War. More than anything else, this polemic demonstrates the urge to prevent understanding between large sections of the populations of East and West. His purpose was at all costs to sustain the emotional anti-Communism with its fundamentally Manichean attitude of "I am good, you are bad," and its egocentric and paranoid arms race mentality. Geissler fosters this stance although he knows that the monies expended on armaments could prevent millions of people in the Third World from starving to death. It is clear to me that by thus hardening the line, Geissler is trying to win votes; but I do not think it is clear to Geissler that with this kind of election campaign, he is reviving old slogans that grew up "on the dung-heap of Nazi ideology." Only the work of remembering, constantly renewed, can free us from this sort of catastrophe-promoting mentality.

Interest in the Recent German Past Is Decreasing

When I think over experiences with my countrymen and my patients, I cannot fail to recognize that interest in the past and in working it through has decreased since the generation of 1968. Not one of the so-called "Whites," or of the following generations, feels any guilt, and only a few even feel concern. The result is that they also have little internal incentive or external cause to grapple with the horrors of the past and the mental attitudes that made them possible. Only the victims of the Nazi period and their children are still intensely concerned about the past and the past in the present. Their German countrymen were more or less oblivious to the feelings of these Holocaust survivors, but with the plan to stage Fassbinder's play, *Trash, the City, and Death* in Frankfurt, these feelings became impossible to overlook. It is clear that in the conflicts and controversies set off, or that came to public attention because of the plan to perform Fassbinder's play, more fundamental issues were at stake than merely to establish whether the play was in fact anti-Semitic or not. Himself a member of a minority that has long been persecuted, Fassbinder certainly identified himself to a great extent with the Jews and their fate. Self-destructive as he was, he could turn his aggression outward to only a limited degree and by means of scapegoats. He was probably representing himself in the "rich Jew," in the prostitute Roma B., and in her husband and pimp Franz B., who discovers his own homosexuality. Just as the prostitute Roma B. begs her lover, the "rich Jew," for death, so too, Franz B., in a masochistic homosexual passion, begs to be destroyed. Because the major figures in Fassbinder's play are virtually all "self-objects," representing facets of his own personality, he lacks empathy for other people whose experience of suffering and whose problems he cannot equate with his own. Consequently, he overlooks the psychological situation of the Holocaust survivors. He does not understand that in the Holocaust they and their children lost everything that gave their lives content and meaning, and that it unleashes unbearable fear, rage, and despair when in public, on a stage in Germany, a Jew is spoken of as a bloodsucker whom they forgot to gas. The vile language of humiliation, calumny, and persecution, the kind of language used by *Der Stürmer*,[4] reawakens terrible memories and deadly fear. This was surely not Fassbinder's intention. But what he was trying to represent could not fail, by the language he used, to touch upon incurable wounds, wounds which will not heal within measurable time. This is what Jews, in Germany and throughout the world, must live with as best they can. This is what we as Germans must live with; if possible with empathy and without repression. For the sufferers, who had felt "racial supremacy" acted out in practice on their very bodies, the past is in fact not a "ghost of yesterday's politics" from which one should distance oneself, as Günther Rühle put it and as he evidently tried to do with the production of the Fassbinder play. But nothing can be taken back. Hans Mayer speaks of the so-called German–Jewish symbiosis which was canceled on the Germans' part "in a way till now unprecedented among all the crimes of our present day. It also implies the inclusion of stages of cancellation on the part of the Jews. Only then does it become clear that all the catastrophic happenings of today remain linked, as they have always been, to the catastrophe of German Jewry" (Beuys et al., 1985). Günther Rühle's "ghost of yesterday's politics" is, in fact, not simply a ghost from which one can distance oneself, as he believes, but rather a wound that does not close. To demand that the relation between Germans and Jews be finally normalized is naive, bearing witness to a lack of empathy and to the fact that repression of the past and its consequences still persists.

The German Follower-Conformist Generation and Their Children

I now return to my experience with patients: belonging to no minority, almost all of them are children of the generation that followed and conformed. In them, one not infrequently senses a veiled depression in which accusation alternates with self-accusation. These patients are almost exclusively of the small

[4]The most offensively anti-Semitic of the Nazi newspapers, the editor of which was the notorious Julius Streicher.

and middle bourgeoisie. Their parents conformed more or less critically, more or less passively; the thought that it might have been possible to resist never crossed their minds. But, once the National Socialist system was established, could one offer resistance without exposing oneself to mortal danger? This, at least, is doubted by many of our contemporaries; also by many of those who actually did resist and even by some who were in concentration camps. But resistance is not limited only to action in situations where it has become almost hopeless; resistance is also a way of thinking, a way of behaving. There are critical moments when, at the outset of a criminal and paranoid system, there is a chance to use one's head. Or, if not at its outset, then at least, as it ends. This is just as valid for the "Whites" as for the following generations who, through memory work, could prevent repetitions. The patients I have in mind were the offspring of parents who, by character and in their thinking, were able to offer little resistance, even though not themselves actual "perpetrators." And these parents have handed their denial and repression down to their children. Evidently, they have also handed down their repressed depression, with its underlying aggression reinforced by narcissistic injury. And now, with the end of the "economic miracle," this comes to full expression in the passive–accusatory work inhibition of this next generation. The depression that originally was warded off by manic reconstruction, the narcissistic love-disappointment that sought substitute gratification in consumerism, is today no longer readily dealt with in this way. Substitute gratification has become dull and stale. Reconstruction is ended and has destroyed cities and the environment and so has not achieved any reparation, but instead has added a further burden of "guilt." Socialism, as a possible way to shape a humane concern for each other, has been buried under emotional anti-Communism. This, be it said, does not mean that the sort of bureaucratic socialism prevailing in the Eastern block could serve as a model for the West.

In keeping with these developments and with the unworked-through past, fewer outsiders are to be found today who as observers of the situation have freed themselves from "follow-erism," and who, with the help of memory work, are able to achieve some partial atonement. These few have become aware of the general indifference to the destruction of the natural environment and the disastrous effects of rearmament. And it is they who seek actively to bring about changes, as opposed to the dropouts who refuse to take any further responsibility for the course of history, whose only desire is that none of it be their fault.

Women and the Ability to Mourn

The manic reconstruction is over. Now fear of unemployment rules great numbers of the young, and not only them. The foreign workers needed for the reconstruction have become superfluous. Xenophobia, often heartless or paranoid, has more or less replaced anti-Semitism, which has now become embarrassing and which people dare express only in whispers. Many members of the Green party and the Peace Movement— although these associations are made up of extremely disparate groups from within the population and have correspondingly massive internal political problems—are trying to combat the ruin caused by indifference and repression both regarding the environmental destruction and the insane, apocalypse-gravid armament race. The rebellion of the 1968 generation has virtually caved in. Only the women's movement has emerged from the student revolt stronger than before. In spite of all the differences in their aims and goals, most of these women share a wish to learn from the past and so discover and realize new, less self-destructive and destructive ways of being and thinking. Such women seem willing, more often than are men, to grapple with the past. Their lives, more than those of men, are ruled by separations and loneliness: separation from children who grow up, separation from sexual attractiveness that determines important interpersonal relationships; loneliness that can only rarely be filled or masked by professional work or by success. All this fosters a more intense acquaintance with the process of mourning. Learning to part with, to let go, to take leave, is an art women must master in wide areas of their lives if they are to avoid bitterness or the acceptance of hurts and loneliness as something to be passively endured. Taking leave of outdated role-patterns has taught a woman to control her own fate better than heretofore and has enabled her to free herself increasingly from the "value world" of men, of which much is corrupt and dangerous: because in fact, throughout the centuries, paranoia combined with physical violence was and is the affair of men.

Freud traced the urgent need of men to discharge their internalized violent aggression outward onto scapegoats to the fact that this aggression would otherwise destroy them themselves. According to him, a man's aggression is originally aimed at his father as the rival, and is internalized for fear of the father's retaliation, that is, above all, for fear of castration. Among women who, it is true, also suffer from castration fantasies, although much more rarely, the fear of retaliation in the sense of physical destruction—a fear that so easily changes into violence—plays a much smaller role. A woman's central fear is the fear of loss of love. Hence women convert their aggressions into a masochistic need for self-sacrifice, guilt feelings, or into reproachful attitudes, rather than into a search for scapegoats through which violent rivalrous aggression can be lived out without fear or guilt. The upbringing and sex-specific development of a woman does not, in the same way, predestine her to developing a character structure in which paranoia and violence are intertwined. Nevertheless, for fear of loss of love, she is still inclined to adopt the role-patterns, prejudices, and value judgments preassigned to her by a society shaped by men. The way both sexes are brought up is naturally dependent on these "values." In other words, the search for enemies, anti-Communism, anti-Semitism, the armament mentality, all those lamentable linkages of paranoia and violence, are etched more deeply into a man's bones than a woman's. The advice one would want above all to give a woman is to deepen her critique of the "value world" of men and to face her need for love as well as the concomitant inclination to false feelings of guilt with greater distance and with a more critical attitude.

To avoid any misunderstanding: women are certainly no less aggressive as far as their basic psychological makeup is concerned than are men. But they learn, or have been forced to learn, to deal with their aggression differently. Their societal as well as their individual situation confronts them with many losses which they can ward off less easily than men. For this reason, they seem more capable of mourning, or at any rate, they are constantly confronted with the necessity of parting.

True, the German men and women of the postwar generation have frequently inherited the defense against memory work from their parents and grandparents, a defense that is bound up with guilt, shame, outrage, and sorrow over our most recent past. True, societal structures are repeated or, in other words, the past colors the present to a greater and more dangerous extent than is realized by the general population of the German Federal Republic. Nevertheless, some sectors of the postwar generation—among which are the women who take a critical stance toward the patriarchal "value world"— seem to be grappling more intensively than before with the past and with the past in the present. This, of course, does not mean that the danger of paranoid inhumanity or destructiveness has been banished, nor that Fascism has ceased to be within the realm of human possibility.

References

Beuys, J., Mayer, H., et al. (1985), *Reden über das eigene Land: Deutschland* (Talks about One's Own Country: Germany), Vol. 3. Gütersloh: Bertelsmann Verlag.

Carpentier, A. (1977), *Krieg der Zeit* (Stories from the Spanish by Anneliese Bolond). Frankfurt am Main: Suhrkamp Verlag.

Celan, P. (1952), Todesfuge. In: *Mohn und Gedächtnis*. Stuttgart: Deutsche Verlags-Anstalt, p. 38.

Dahmer, H. (1982), *Psyche*. Stuttgart: Klett-Cotta Verlag, p. 1072.

Freud, S. (1921), Group psychology and the analysis of the ego. *Standard Edition*, 18:67–143. London: Hogarth Press, 1955.

Mitscherlich, A., & Mitscherlich, M. (1975), *The Inability to Mourn*, trans. B. R. Placzek. New York: Grove Press.

Psychoanalyse unter Hitler (1984), Dokumentation einer Kontroverse. Herausgegeben von der Zeitschrift *Psyche*. Frankfurt am Main: April, together with *Nachtrag zur DPV-Dokumentation*. Zum Briefwechsel Ehebald/Dahmer. Redaktion der Zeitschrift *Psyche*.

Riefenstahl, L. (1933), Film: *The Triumph of Will*.

———(1935), Film: *The Victory of Faith*.

Rühle, G. (1982), Newspaper Interview, *Frankfurter Allgemeine Zeitung*, December 28.

16

Mourning in Survivors and Children of Survivors of the Nazi Holocaust: The Role of Group and Community Modalities

YAEL DANIELI, PH.D.

The sun made a desperate effort to shine on the last day of May in 1944. The sun is warm in May. It heals. But even the heavens were helpless on that day. A force so evil ruled heaven and earth that it altered the natural order of the universe, and the heart of my mother was floating in the smoke-filled sky of Auschwitz. I have tried to rub the smoke out of my vision for forty years now, but my eyes are still burning, Mother.

[Leitner, 1985, p. vii]

After liberation, upon leaving Europe on her way to America, Isabella Leitner tells us:

I search the sky to see if I can conjure up my mother and my little sister, Potyo. I look in desperate sorrow but can discern no human form. The smoke has vanished. There is not a trace. No grave. Nothing. Absolutely nothing.

My mother lived for just a while—Potyo for less than fourteen years. In a way they didn't really die. They simply became smoke.

How does one bury smoke?

How does one place headstones in the sky?

427

How does one bring flowers to the clouds?
Mother, Potyo . . . I am *trying* to say good-bye to you. I am *trying* to say good-bye [Leitner, 1985, p. 77; emphasis added].

Her poignant questions articulate but a few of the numerous obstacles confronting survivors and children of survivors of the Nazi Holocaust in their attempts at mourning.

In his seminal paper "Delayed Mourning in Victims of Extermination Camps" Meerloo (1963) reported with "amazement" and "surprise" his observation that "having gone through the horror of concentration camps," the survivors' "greatest complaint" was "not torture, not the famine, not the humiliation," but that "they had not been permitted to mourn over those they had lost." What "kept them down now" was "this lack of cathartic ceremonial" (p. 97). As a result, "years later when some acquaintance or relative died . . . they *had* to go through an outburst of increased mourning and (often suicidal) depression . . . through . . . which . . . they tried to purify themselves of [guilt over] past death wishes" (p. 98) (see also Krystal, 1968, p. 28), and could participate in the "mourning rituals they were forbidden to perform during the camp years" (p. 98). Some survivors, indeed, have become "funeral addicts": they attend *every* funeral in their community, even of people they know only superficially.

Insisting on acknowledging individual differences among survivors, Terry (1984) concurs that "Actually, it is the trauma of the libidinal object losses and inability to mourn them during and following the Holocaust that has the highest pathogenic potential." Like Krystal (1968) and Sigal (1971) he states that: "It is the disturbance in the work of mourning that interferes with the individual's subsequent human relations" (p. 147).

During the war, mourning endangered victims' lives. As with any prisoner's behavior which might have even slightly deviated from that of the totally obedient automaton the Nazis expected, grieving-related behavior, like the open expression of any emotion, had to be suppressed in order to prevent Nazi retaliation. Morever, even the inner experience of grief and other mourning-related emotions endangered the fragile psychological balance of the physically starved, abused, and overworked captives during the Holocaust. The latter is also true for those in hiding and those living in ghettos. As one survivor, F.T., put it, "Everyone knew that for very very little each one could be the next to die and whole ghettos would have had to sit shivah around the clock. That could not be done. We had to limit our emotions to those necessary for survival. We were too weak and numb."

Formation of Survivor Families

One way that survivors coped with the prolonged horrors of the Holocaust was to imagine and sustain the hope of being reunited with their families (Frankl, 1959). This led many of them, when physically able, to return immediately to their hometowns, only to find their property destroyed or taken over, their prewar "friends" indifferent or hostile ("why did you survive?"; "aren't all Jews supposed to be dead?"), and their communities obliterated. Waiting for family members "to come back home" proved futile for most. Some continued their search in displaced persons camps and elsewhere in Europe over the next three to five years. A fortunate few found surviving relatives, but most of them discovered not only that their family members had perished, but also, sometimes, the horrible circumstances surrounding their death. Some responded to their shattered sense of feeling at home in the world by committing suicide (Levi, 1986a).[1] While some learned that every single Jewish person they had ever known before the war

---

[1]Primo Levi, an Auschwitz survivor, a chemist, and a winner of several literary prizes, opened both *Moments of Reprive* (1986b) and *The Drowned and the Saved* (1988) with
> Since then, at an uncertain hour,
> That agony returns,
> And till my ghastly tale is told
> This heart within me burns.
>   Samuel Taylor Coleridge
>   *The Rime of the Ancient Mariner*
Indeed, it did burn out. On April 11, 1987, he committed suicide in his home in Turin, Italy, forty-two years after he wrote that "Only when April came, when the last snows had melted and the mild sun had dried the Polish mud, did we begin to feel ourselves truly free" (Levi, 1986b, p. 243).

had been murdered, others, despite intense searching, never discovered what had happened to their loved ones after their separation during the war.

Bettelheim (1984, p. 172) suggests that in the absence of evidence of death, and without a "definite point in time when mourning could have started, and with it no date at which it could be expected to end (according to Jewish custom) . . . mourning seemed impossible to complete, and one is apt to suffer all one's life from its continuation" (see also discussions in Krystal [1968]; Trautman's description of "the grief syndrome" [1971, pp. 127–130]). Rare stories of reunion, sometimes years after survivors seemingly "accepted" their losses, tended to revive hopes, yearnings, and searching behaviors. Having just heard of such a reunion, a seventy-six-year-old survivor reported feeling sure that he "spotted" his mother in the street. Momentarily feeling "very young and happy," he was startled by the realization that his mother could not possibly have been alive today "even if the Holocaust never happened. I froze the passage of time all these years so I wouldn't let her die. Oh, my God, I mean so *they* wouldn't kill her." Weeping, he suddenly felt "very tired and old, ready to die now." (Thus, he was still holding on to the fantasy of reuniting with his mother—this time after both their deaths.) An extreme example of continued denial of loss can be found in Levi (1986a).

Some could never even recover any "evidence"— photographs or other mementos—of their past, their lives and heritage before the war. This loss of "transitional objects" exacerbated their sense of rupture, of total destruction, and that their "*entire* people and civilization perished" (Krystal, himself a survivor [1981], emphasis added; Bychowski [1968]). Wiesel's (1965) search for his Bar Mitzvah watch twenty years after the war and Spiegelman's (1986) calling his father a "murderer" for burning his dead mother's war diaries are poignant examples of survivors' and children of survivors' need to connect with and resurrect their lost past. Survivors' and offsprings' pilgrimages to their hometowns, to concentration camps, and to Holocaust monuments are informed both by their search for roots and by their need to mourn.

Consciously and unconsciously, many had to grieve for the

loss of youth, of educational, economic, communal, and socio-cultural opportunities and hopes, of innocence and the capacity for joy, and faith in humankind and in God. The lack of any prescribed ways to meaningfully mourn the Holocaust is often experienced by survivors and their children as a source of further bewilderment.

Unable to fully comprehend their tragedy or to express their grief and rage, they were nonetheless confronted with the task of rebuilding their lives: "I am lonely and I have nothing; you are lonely and have lost everything and everybody; let's get married" was a proposal made by the majority of adult survivors after a short acquaintance (from as little as a week to three months). Even a remote connection of the chosen spouse to the survivor's past was sufficient for this decision. These marriages of despair disregarded differences in prewar socioeconomic and educational status, life-style, age, or other ordinary criteria for marriage. Re-creating a family was a concrete act to compensate for their losses, to counter the massive disruption in the order and continuity of life, and to undo the dehuman-ization and loneliness they had experienced. These marriages, burdened by the inevitably unrealizable unconscious expectations of both spouses to substitute for lost loved ones and ways of being, particularly in the "victims families" category (Danieli, 1981a,c), frequently turned into interminable, lifelong exchanges of complaints about their mutual disappointments: "I would have never married you had it not been for the war." However, since survivors experience breaking up families as tantamount to perpetuating Nazi deeds, these marriages rarely end in physical separation or divorce (for the implications to their future offspring's lives, see Danieli [1981a,c]).

Many survivors gave birth in DP camps as soon as it was physically possible. For some who had lost spouses and children during the war, these were second families. Almost without exception, the newborn children were named after those who had perished. In survivors' eyes, these children were a replacement for the agonizing losses of the past and were to realize the lost war years and opportunities of their parents. The children, often viewed as a blessing, miracle, gift, or symbol of victory over the Nazis, were to be the future—secure, normal, capable, happy, proud members of the human race. Their world would be free of oppression and equal to or even better than the now idealized prewar world of their parents. Their disasterwise parents would prepare them for any eventuality in life. They would never be caught off-guard or be passively helpless, defenseless, or incompetent in any way. Some chose to never marry or have children for fear of further loss.

The survivor's actual conditions of living continued to be extremely difficult. Uprooted, dislocated, and robbed, they were still residing in the same countries that had permitted the destruction of European Jewry. Given the responsibility of a new life to care for, most survivors decided to leave Europe and find a safer place in which to settle and build. Most of those who had survived the war adhering to Zionism went to Palestine, then struggling to be Israel. Others who had relatives in America went there with the hope of re-creating an extended family. Immigration to the United States engendered a new set of challenges for survivors (Koenig, 1964; Rappaport, 1968; Rabinowitz, 1976). Most arrived as penniless refugees and received initial financial aid and help in finding housing; some obtained jobs from relatives and Jewish organizations. However, the survivors were provided with very little or no help in emotional rehabilitation, despite the fact that as early as 1948, Friedman (for example, had clearly stated the need to "heal the *psychological* scars of Nazism." Terry (1984) also describes some adolescent survivors who, for a variety of reasons, fared much better.

The Conspiracy of Silence

In truth, after liberation, as during the war, the survivors were victims of a pervasive societal reaction comprised of obtuseness, indifference, avoidance, repression, and denial of their Holocaust experiences. Survivors' war accounts were too horrifying for most people to listen to or believe. Survivors were faced with the pervasively held myth that they had actively or passively participated in their own destiny by "going like sheep to the slaughter." This myth implied not only that they could have fought back and that they should have been prepared for the Holocaust—as if anyone could have been—but it also assumes that Holocaust victims had somewhere to go had they chosen to escape, and that the rest of the world wanted them. This was clearly not the case. Additionally, bystander guilt led many to regard survivors as pointing an accusing finger at them and to project onto the survivors the suspicion that they had performed immoral acts in order to survive. They were also told to "let bygones be bygones," to "look at the positive side of things," and to get on with their lives.

Such reactions ensured the survivors' silence about their Holocaust experiences. They were forced to conclude that nobody cared to listen and that "nobody could really understand" them unless they had gone through the same experiences. The resulting conspiracy of silence between Holocaust survivors and society proved detrimental to the survivors' familial and sociocultural reintegration by intensifying their already profound sense of isolation, loneliness, and mistrust of society. Moreover, those who reunited with their American relatives in the hope of sharing with them their sense of loss, grief, and rage and of reestablishing some semblance of familial continuity felt embittered and betrayed when their relatives also participated in the conspiracy. This further impeded the possibility of their intrapsychic integration and healing, and made the task of mourning their massive losses impossible (Danieli, 1985a).

Survivors were left with two major options. One was to seek out and cling to fellow survivors. Thus, some established their own societies and organizations with membership based either on common war experiences or on a common place of residence before the war while others chose to live in the same neighborhoods. Pairing and maintaining bonds of loyalty and mutual help proved of utmost importance for survival during the war and immediately afterward (Luchterhand, 1967, 1971; Eitinger, 1972; Matussek, 1971; Des Pres, 1976; Moskovitz, 1983; Davidson, 1984). Many survivors kept these interpersonal ties intact even when dispersed in different countries. However, as one survivor explained, with regard to mourning, "being one of a handful of survivors each of whom lost so many people, was such a common shared experience that to make a fuss about it was out of place. You always found somebody who instead of 72 lost 150 people, so who am I to make such a big thing of it?"

The second option for survivors was to withdraw completely into their newly established family, using their children as a captive audience. Children of such families, although remembering their parents' and lost families' war histories "only in bits and pieces," attested to the constant psychological presence of the Holocaust at home, verbally and nonverbally. In some cases they reported having absorbed the omnipresent experience of the Holocaust through "osmosis." It has been the author's observation that the survivor-parent who suffered the greater loss did not do the talking. His or her account either was related by the other spouse or remained for the children an awesome mystery fraught with myths and fantasies, and therefore unavailable for mourning. As Bettelheim (1984) comments, "what cannot be talked about can also not be put to rest; and if it is not, the wounds continue to fester from generation to generation" (p. 166).

In contrast, other survivor-parents welcomed the conspiracy of silence because of their fear that their memories would corrode their own lives and prevent their children from becoming healthy, "normal" Americans. The parents' denial and avoidance often resulted in a false family atmosphere in which "everything was all right." But the children grew up in painful bewilderment; they understood neither the inexplicable torment within the family nor their own sense of guilt.

To this day, most of these families are extremely small. The Holocaust deprived them of the normal cycle of the generations and ages, and of natural death (Eitinger, 1980). Each family tree is laden with murderous deaths and losses. Indeed, the *genuine impossibility of mourning* is the most painful and intolerable struggle underlying all attempts at coping with and integrating the impact of the Holocaust into the lives of these families. As one seventy-four-year-old, recently rewidowed and the sole survivor of a family of seventy-two people, put it: "Even if it takes one year to mourn each loss, and even if I live to be 107 [and mourn all members of my family], what do I do about the rest of the 6 million?"

Some excellent reviews of the psychiatric literature on the long-term effects of the massive traumata experienced by survivors of European Jewry and of their treatment can be found in articles by Krystal (1968), Krystal and Niederland (1971), Chodoff (1975), Israel Netherlands Symposium (1979), and Dimsdale (1980), among others.

Literature on the integenerational transmission and treatment of the psychological effects of the Holocaust on survivors' offspring (children born after the war) began with Rakoff's article (1966). A review of this literature and an up-to-date bibliography can be found in Wanderman (1979), Danieli (1981c, 1982a, 1985b), Bergman and Jucovy (1982), and Steinberg (1986). Recently, concern has also been voiced about the transmission of pathological intergenerational processes to the third and succeeding generations (Rosenthal and Rosenthal, 1980). The findings of Danieli (1981a) and Rich (1982) of a heterogeneity of responses to the Holocaust and post-Holocaust life experience in families of survivors caution against the simple grouping of individuals as "survivors" who are expected to exhibit the same "survivor syndrome" (Krystal and Niederland, 1968), and the expectation that children of survivors will manifest a singly transmitted "children of survivors syndrome" (Phillips, 1978).

Psychotherapists have also typically participated in the conspiracy of silence when survivors or their offspring mentioned or recounted Holocaust experiences. In a previous paper (Danieli, 1984), I have identified and systematically examined forty-nine psychotherapists' "countertransference reactions" and attitudes. My research (Danieli, 1982a) strongly suggests that the source of these reactions is the Holocaust itself, horrific loss, rather than the actual encounter with its survivors and their offspring.

The Group Project for Holocaust Survivors and their Children was established to counteract the profound sense of isolation and alienation among Holocaust survivors and their children and compensate for their neglect by the mental health profession. Begun in 1975 by volunteer psychotherapists in the New York City area, the Project recognized the vital importance of mutual and self-help toward reaching this goal and has capitalized on group and community therapeutic modalities from its inception. By participating in groups, survivors and children of survivors could at last talk about their memories and experiences. They are also able to explore with each other and comprehend the long-term consequences in their lives of the Holocaust and the conspiracy of silence that followed it, and share their feelings and current concerns (Danieli, 1982a).

Its goals, which are preventive as well as reparative, are predicated on two major assumptions: (1) that integration of Holocaust experiences into the *totality* of the survivors' and their children's lives, and awareness of the meaning of post-Holocaust adaptational styles (Danieli, 1981a, 1981c) will liberate one from the trauma and facilitate mental health and self-actualization for both; and (2) that awareness of transmitted intergenerational processes will inhibit transmission of pathology to succeeding generations.

Thus, it is critical to consider pre-Holocaust background to understand postwar adjustment. This includes the characteristics and dynamics of the survivor's family of origin in the pre-World War II European Jewish life in its heterogeneity; and such demographic factors as the nationality, age, education, occupation, and marital and social status of the survivor at the onset of the Holocaust. These should be explored in psychotherapy with survivors and their children in order to (re)establish the sense of integration, rootedness, and continuity so damaged by their traumata. Therapy should also allow these individuals to discuss the meaning of being a Jew and the belief in God before and after the Holocaust (Danieli, 1981b, 1984).

Children of survivors seem to have consciously and unconsciously absorbed their parents' Holocaust experiences into their lives. Holocaust parents, in the attempt to give children their best, taught them how to survive and in the process transmitted to them the life conditions under which they had survived the war. Thus, one finds children of survivors, who psychologically, and sometimes literally, live in hiding. Others are always ready to escape or continuously run from relationships with people, from commitment to a career, or from one place of residence or country to another. Some keep split or double (fake) identities. Yet others adopt a resigned, "Mussel-man" passivity as their mode of being in the world camp. We see tireless manipulators and those who, in whatever they do, are resistance fighters. These modes of being are manifested in their language, behavior, fantasy life, and dreams.

Like their parents, many children of survivors manifest these Holocaust-derived behaviors particularly on the anniversaries of their parents' traumata. Moreover, some have internalized as parts of their identity the images of those who perished and hence live in different places (Europe and America) and different time zones (1942 and the present) simultaneously. The individual survivor's family tree and (war) history are crucial to understanding the survivor's offspring, and should be explored in detail in their psychotherapies to help them separate and find their own identities.

But, Holocaust experiences render the normal process of separation a highly complex and arduous struggle in survivor families. During the war, being separated meant total and permanent loss. This meaning still pervades anything that may, realistically or symbolically, consciously or unconsciously, represent a threat to the intactness of the family. In a recent paper (Danieli, 1988), I reported a case of a survivor, Mrs. B., that illustrates issues related to separation. A thirty-year-old married daughter, reflecting on her difficulties in separating psychologically from her parents, stated poignantly, "When my mother separated from her mother (in Auschwitz), her mother went to the left (to the gas chambers) and my mother went to the right. How could I possibly do anything like that?" Another constantly prevented or destroyed his success because, "surpassing [his] parents means leaving them behind, to die." Steinberg (1986) cites ample clinical and empirical evidence of separation–individuation difficulties among survivors' children in her review of the literature as well as in her own study. Goodman's (1978) findings, across all dimensions of his study, suggest that when the survivor's child was better able to mourn the death and loss of family members who perished in the Holocaust, his or her chances for more positive life adjustment in general and for growth and autonomy in particular were increased. The latter was true for both clinical and nonclinical samples. Therapists, often viewed as encouraging separation, must confront the family's perception of them as Nazis and be able to contain both the family's and their own emotional reactions.

Psychological/internal liberation from the trauma of victimization and its effects is the ultimate goal of treatment for survivors and their children, and *integration* is its central and guiding dynamic principle. Such integration can only be achieved through a full longitudinal perspective of the victimization experiences and their impact upon one's life space at any point in time. An essential aspect of the establishment of such perspective is that when we speak of integration for severely victimized people we speak of integrating rupture and the *extraordinary* into one's life—that is, confronting and incorporating aspects of human experiences that are not normally encountered. The massive catastrophe of the Nazi Holocaust not only ruptured continuity but also destroyed all the individual's existing supports. The conspiracy of silence exacerbated the situation by further depriving survivors of *potential* supports.

In fact, the hope of resurrecting their (now often idealized) previous lives is unrealizable. Moreover, clinging to such a hope attests to attempted denial of their Holocaust and postvictimization experiences and their significance. Some survivors are solely preoccupied with their Holocaust experiences: "I can't think of anything else. There is nothing to live for after what happened to us." Still others compulsively cling to current concerns, live vicariously through their children, and strongly refuse to talk about the Holocaust.

The therapist's compliance with survivor-parents' original stated refusal to talk about the Holocaust may reinforce their fears that, to this day, it still has the power and the destructive force to do to the family what it did during the war, and that there is no way to contain and work through the feelings associated with this part of their history.

Family members report relief and a sense of liberation upon comprehending the parallels of their behavior and feelings with the parents' victimization experiences and with their history and family tree. This is especially true after those phases of treatment which allow "exorcism" of the Nazis out of the family, and "invited" and "introduced" murdered family members through gestalt and psychodrama techniques, which began the process of mourning and successful integration.

Therapists who comply with survivors' reluctance to talk about their pre-Holocaust life ("It was all destroyed") participate in depriving them of the prolife forces and sense of rootedness and belongingness originating from that period of their lives.

The task of therapy then is to help survivors and children of survivors achieve integration of an experience that has halted the normal flow of life. Indeed, when psychotherapy dwells on certain periods in the survivors' lives and neglects others, it hinders survivors and their offspring from meaningfully recreating the flow within the totality of their lives, and may perpetuate their sense of disruption, discontinuity and rootlessness (see also de Wind, 1972; Lifton, 1973, 1979; Danieli, 1982b).

Integration and recovery involve the survivor's ability to develop a realistic perspective of what happened, by whom, to whom, and to accept the reality that it happened the way it did; what was and was not under his or her control, what could not be and why. Accepting the impersonality of the events also removes the need to attribute personal causality with the consequent guilt and false responsibility. Elsewhere (Danieli, 1988), I have described the therapeutic transformation in Mrs. K.'s case, from survivor's guilt through mourning, to healing.

The therapist's full understanding and acceptance of the meaning of survivor's guilt within the therapeutic process is crucial in aiding the survivor in constructively transcending it. The same principles hold for helping the survivor in constructively transcending the crippling effects of identification with the aggressor.

The distortion caused by insufficient understanding of the meaning and functions of the experience of *survivor guilt* is one of the most poignant instances of how extraordinary human experience challenges and exposes the limits of traditional psychological theories of ordinary life. Elsewhere (Danieli, 1984), I stated that the pervasiveness of *bystander guilt* among psychotherapists and researchers may account for what I feel is their overuse, stereotypic attribution, and reductionistic misinterpretation of concepts such as "survivor's guilt," which Niederland (1961, 1964) and Krystal and Niederland (1968) described as a major feature of the "survivor's syndrome."

In the process of therapy, therapists often misconstrue the functions and meanings of their patients' experience and expression of survivor's guilt as a manifestation of resistance or negative therapeutic reaction. As a result, they tend to become intolerant of their patients' apparent "stubborn" suffering, which often leads to therapeutic impasses, or worse, to termination of treatment. I will, therefore, point to some of the central meanings and functions of guilt in the survivors or their offspring that are most related to issues of mourning.

Guilt as a defense against the experience of utter helplessness (Danieli, 1981b) links both generations to the Holocaust. The children are helpless in their mission to undo the Holocaust both for their survivor parents and for themselves. This sense of failure often generalizes to "No matter what I do or how far I go, nothing will be good enough."

In addition, survivor's guilt is a way of working through late mourning and bereavement for loss of beloved people. According to Klein (1968): "It also seems to serve as means of survival in a chaotic world where all objects of love have been lost and where there are no people with whom to cry and to share one's grief" (pp. 234–235). Survivors fear that successful mourning may lead to letting go, thereby to forgetting the dead, and committing them to oblivion, which for many of them amounts to perpetuating Nazi crime. Thus, guilt also serves a commemorative function and as a vehicle of loyalty to the dead (Sterba, 1968). In Elie Wiesel's words (1979), "they have no cemetery; we are their cemetery." Many children of survivors also share this sentiment and, like their parents, hold on to the anhedonia, guilt, shame, and pain related to their family history during the Holocaust and its consequences: "I feel the pain that my mother and father went through. If I don't, I am a disloyal son."

Counteracting psychological aloneness and reestablishing and maintaining a sense of belongingness and (familial/social and cultural) continuity are two additional crucially important functions of survivor's guilt. One survivor stated, "How can I be happy, knowing that they (family) are not here to celebrate with us." And another survivor commented, "If we accept the ashes, then we have no past." (For a fuller discussion of the functions of survivor guilt, see Danieli, 1988.)

Although the diagnostic and therapeutic use of constructing a three-generational family tree with survivors and their offspring triggers an acute sense of pain and loss, it serves to recreate a sense of continuity, so damaged by their Holocaust and post-Holocaust experience. Regardless of whether family therapy is feasible or not, viewing the individual within the dynamics of his or her family system and culture is of great therapeutic value. Further, combining therapeutic modalities is especially helpful in working through long-term and intergenerational effects of victimization.

An educated and contained image of the events of one's life before, during, and after victimization can free one from constructing a view of self and humanity based solely on victimization events. For example, having been helpless does not mean one is a helpless person; having witnessed or experienced evil does not mean that the world as a whole is evil; having been betrayed does not mean that betrayal is an overriding human behavior; having been violated does not necessarily mean that one has to live one's life in constant readiness for its reenactment; having been treated as dispensable does not mean that one is worthless; and taking the painful risk of bearing witness does not mean that the world will listen, learn, change, or become a better place.

Certain features of the survivor and his or her past should be fostered in the course of therapy. These involve general cognitive abilities, and elements of one's active control and mastery in the act of survival and the rebuilding of life, such as hope, determination, courage, loyalty, humor; and sources of support and love in one's memories and current life. These features nurture one's ability for self-soothing, trusting, experiencing, accepting and giving love and help; and attaining a sense of wholeness, healing, and recovery. These must develop if the survivor is to gain perspective, integrate other elements of his or her Holocaust or other victimization experiences, such as evil, hate, murder, brutality, destruction, injustice, indifference, chaos, helplessness, degradation, and humiliation, shame, rage, loss, shattered trust, and unbearable grief.

Our work has shown that allowing survivors to express themselves in the language primary to the (pre)victimization experience is helpful even if the therapist does not understand it and must await a translation. In determining placement of treatment, therapists should also be aware of the symbolic meanings of the therapeutic setting and/or the symbolic function of medication for the survivor in order not to trigger reenactments of victimization experiences, and in order to understand the survivor's response to them. For example, hospitalization may be experienced as incarceration and medication as a return to helplessness. For issues and concerns specific to aging survivors, see Danieli (1981d) in the special issue of *The Journal of Geriatric Psychiatry*, 1981, "The Aging Survivor of the Holocaust" (Blau and Kahana, 1981).

Some of the pessimism voiced in the literature about helping survivors (Chodoff, 1975, 1980; Krystal, 1981) may be due to its primarily intrapsychically biased, psychoanalytic orientation. This perspective largely ignores acknowledging the Holocaust as a group phenomenon and the central role of "we-ness" in the survival and the identity of its survivors, a characteristic that should be considered in treatment goals, techniques, and modalities.

Group and Community Therapeutic Modalities

The unique reparative and preventive value of the group modality in meeting the needs of survivors and their offspring cannot be overemphasized. First and foremost, as mentioned earlier in this paper, group and community therapeutic modalities counteract their sense of alienation and isolation, and affirm the central role of "we-ness" and the need for a collective search for meaningful response (Danieli, 1985c). These modalities also help rebuild a sense of extended family and community which were lost during the Holocaust.

Group modalities have also helped psychotherapists compensate for and modulate their own difficulties in treating survivors and children of survivors. Whereas a therapist alone may feel unable to contain or provide a "holding environment" (Winnicott, 1965) for his or her patient's feelings, the group as a unit is able to. While any particular intense interaction invoked by Holocaust memories may prove too overwhelming to some people present, others invariably come forth with a variety of helpful "holding" reactions. Thus, the group functions as an ideal absorptive entity for abreaction and catharsis of emotions, especially negative ones, that are otherwise experienced as uncontainable (Krystal, 1975, 1978; Wilson, 1985).

The group offers a multiplicity of options for expressing, naming, verbalizing, and modulating feelings (Krystal, 1979, 1982). It is a safe place for exploring fantasies, for imagining, "inviting," and taking on the roles of murdered relatives or victimizers, and for examining their significance to the identity of group members. Group members learn to observe and identify victimization-derived behaviors in themselves and others and use peer clarification, confrontation, and interpretation for change. They can also safely test out new behaviors and receive feedback about their impact on others. The group also encourages and demonstrates mutual caring which ultimately enhances self-care in survivors and their families.

Survivor and children of survivors' groups uniformly begin with a dramatic sense of immediate cohesion, which I have called the "me-too" stage. Members feel "at home" with each other and often experience a sense of "otherness" from the rest of the world. They express a great sense of exhilaration, relief, and reassurance not only at being confirmed as "perfectly normal" by the commonality of their experiences, but also at discovering that their experiences are comprehensible in the context of their or their parents' victimization history.

Following the "me-too" stage in the life of the group, members discover, through the exchange of mutual experiences, their *differing* postvictimization adaptational styles which I have elaborated in detail elsewhere (Danieli, 1981a,c). This awareness begins the process of integration and liberation. Realizing the heterogeneity beyond their commonality helps develop respect and tolerance for the particularity of the individual which paves the way for self-actualization unique to each group member.

The Group Project offers opportunities to participate in six types of therapy as well as "self-help" groups. It is important to note that members of the latter groups are deprived of a leader, and therefore are unable to work through issues of power versus helplessness so central to victim/survivors. For an evaluative description of the six types of groups offered by the Group Project for Holocaust Survivors and their Children, see Danieli (1981e, 1985b, 1985c).

Intergenerational Community Meetings

Every two months, the Project invites all group participants, their families, and newcomers, free of charge, to share mutual past and present concerns. To actively encourage and substantiate the sense of community established by the Project, meetings usually begin with announcements of "bad" and "good" news: wishing well and assigning volunteers to visit the ill and comfort the troubled; mourning and commemorating members who recently died; congratulating, celebrating, and sharing members' marriages, births, and professional and career accomplishments. This encourages members to use each other's resources informally in their daily lives. The time span between meetings gives members a perspective on each other's growth and reinforces hope. Newcomers gain hope by seeing the potential and possibility for their own growth.

At these meetings, families and generations often open lines of communication and mutual understanding for the first time. Family members have the opportunity to see themselves as they behave in the larger context of the community, to change rigid perceptions of one another, and better experience each other's humanity. This is particularly true when members of one generation observe the interaction between peers of the other generation. Insights gained at the Intergenerational meetings are more easily generalizable to life than are those gained in individual, family, or even group therapy.

Compared to the smaller group formats, these large meetings more easily allow participants to take their time until they are ready to open up, to listen, learn from others, and quietly experience their own reactions. These meetings also offer a safe opportunity for social learning for extremely isolated individuals and open up for them the possibility of belonging to the human world. The structure of these meetings allows some to rationalize their participation by "coming for the children," "coming for the parents," or coming "strictly out of intellectual curiosity."

J.L., a fifty-six-year-old survivor, opened a May 1984 Inter-generational meeting compelled to ensure that his being single would not exclude him from "having a place" in the Project. His concern over not being accepted stemmed from numerous encounters with indifference and rejection by a variety of organizations he had applied to for help for his "deep, deep depression." In the group interaction that ensued he described severe nightmares, panic attacks, and "bad thoughts come to you . . . your experiences . . . your family . . . why you are here, why you are by yourself, what is the sense to go on." These feelings, according to him, worsened after a heart attack.

Other survivors responded that for "outsiders" (nonsurvivors), Holocaust experiences "seemed to be a very hidden subject," and that "nobody was interested"; that "it seemed so painful for people to listen that they just couldn't bear it. Therefore our pain is always inside. It cannot be brought out in the open because nobody would understand." They added that on their part, too, they "would suffer too much and would try to get away from it, because like you say, you get depressed, you get mental breakdowns." All of these, they said, led them to "close up completely."

Following a complex and intense discussion between parents and children about the many reasons for miscommunication between the generations, it was J.L. who concluded: "we deny our feelings. That's the most important point. I have a very tough time dealing with my own feelings. It's a very painful thing." His comment paved the way for the children to share with their parents and the community that they feel they are "walking on dangerous territory" when they attempt to explore their parents' experiences and feelings, and fear hurting their parents when they have "bad news" of their own or when they feel, for example, angry with them.

During the interactions that followed, fellow survivors encouraged J.L. to tell his story. Born in Hungary, he was the sole survivor of his family, was in Auschwitz, and was liberated at seventeen from Buchenwald. After a short stay in France, he came to the United States. Six months later he was drafted into the United States army and sent to Korea where he was wounded. He described his life:

> I pushed my emotion, my feelings, to the side so I never get in touch with myself. Working hard [successfully] I was earning money. I belonged to a group of survivors, all single men. We could communicate, could feel a little better, went back home, and that's it. This continues day after day, month after month, and year after year. It's just the way Bashevis Singer describes. Now most of them are dying out. These other people come out of the past. You get more depressed, more agitated. It takes you over, your feelings and thoughts, and you have no control over it.

His heart attack intensified the situation: "In the hospital you lay in bed. Nobody is coming so all your thoughts and feelings come to you. It becomes very painful. You missed your life and you don't have nothing to show for it."

In answer to the leader's question of whether not having a child was part of what he missed out on, J.L. explained that he did not want to have children: "they shouldn't have the same thing that happened to my sisters and brothers." Responding to a strong sense of urgency generated during the meeting, the leader then suggested that L.O., a child of a survivor, record J.L.'s life story. The leader's suggestion was informed both by the severity of J.L.'s health condition and his need for familial continuity and communal belongingness, as well as by L.O.'s need for caring communication with a father figure and to further explore the history of her survivor/father's family.

J.L. was discovered dead by a maid in his residential hotel room a few months later. The Project held a memorial for him at the November 1984 Intergenerational meeting. Project members and some of his lifelong friends (who have since joined the Project, also feeling "as if [they] fell into a big family . . . [where they receive] love and moral and spiritual support") spoke of the May meeting as a turning point in J.L.'s life. He felt complete and content following the many hours of recording his family history, despite his initial protest that he had "nothing to say." The leader's promise to deposit his tapes at Yad Vashem in Jerusalem further reassured him. He became a very active member of the community, involving himself primarily with Project members who are children of survivors, and participating in every informal and artistic activity until his death. His involvement directly benefited not only him but also L.O. who had recorded his oral history.

It is L.O.'s immersion in all aspects of the Project that seems to account for the profound gains she has made in treatment, which she experienced as a "coming back to life process." When she first joined the Project at age thirty, L.O., the oldest of four children born in the United States to a survivor father, was extremely thin, inaudible, and afraid to speak up, and appeared lost and forlorn. Her most striking characteristics were her intense frozenness and deadness. She maintained a corpse-like facial expression, and a stonelike posture. An underachiever at work, she was earning very low wages. "Not feeling close" to her family (who lived in the Midwest) and having "very few friends," she described "suffering extreme isolation and loneliness" and feeling that life was passing her by.

Her initial response to joining a therapy group was of "finding a home." Despite this, both her individual and group treatment began with months of total silence and proceeded with periods of chronic lateness.

The only child of German-Jewish assimilated parents, L.O.'s father had been sent by his parents to Switzerland for safety in 1938 at the age of seventeen. His parents, however, stayed in Germany "until it was too late" for them to leave. In 1942, ten days after his mother died of cancer, his father was deported to Theresienstadt and was last seen by a survivor from his town awaiting a transport to Auschwitz in the Fall. While still in Germany, L.O.'s father converted to Christianity, in Switzerland he married a Christian woman, and later raised his children as Christians.

L.O. carries her paternal grandmother's name as her middle name. Except for this link to her father's past, however, there was no mention at home of either the Holocaust or their Jewish heritage. Father was "German." In fact, it was only at age fourteen (upon moving to the East Coast) that her mother, "in order to prepare [her], because of [their] Jewish name, for possible anti-Semitism by her classmates," told her of the Jewish part of her history. She reported "not being surprised." Instead, "It made sense." It explained the "dim, shrouded, dark" side of herself, and her father's "pregnant silences," which were sometimes "dangerous, sometimes soft and sad," but always "a vacuum that needed to be filled." It also later explained to her her father's "howling screams" in the middle of the night. "Darkness filled with inarticulate howling. . . . Father can't put feelings into words, only howling."

As a young teenager, she unconsciously responded to the information her mother volunteered by becoming preoccupied with raising rabbits, creating "families of bunnies," tracing their lineages, and keeping a notebook with a full record of "past and future generations." It was not until L.O. was separated from her family at seventeen—which, significantly, was the same age as her father had been when he separated from his parents[2]— that she noted a marked change in her personality: "Deadness and disorientation to the world began to set in."

Her identification with being dead began to fade when she brought in an "old man dream" she had had years earlier, the first dream she reported in her "analysis" in Switzerland, marking the age (21) in her father's life when he lost his parents:

> . . . The parents didn't know that I was secretly arranging to move out into a place of my own. . . . I was sorry for hiding it from them. . . . I was just taking a walk in Zurich . . . I came to a gravel road going up hill gently. At the top of the hill I met an old man under a bridge.

[2]This is an example of an intergenerational anniversary reaction, commonly seen in clinical work with children of survivors of the Nazi Holocaust.

The old man looked sick and tired and lost. He was standing under the bridge teetering, bent crooked, with a sunken face and white hair. But he looked like he had once been handsome like Papa maybe. I took his arm and wanted to help, even though I felt disgusted by him. He really seemed to be in trouble. He didn't know where he was and couldn't hardly stand up. I tried to support him and talk with him. But he began to cling to me and hang on to me and staggered crazily, pushing me almost over. I became frightened as he became more aggressive, and bore down on me more and more. He became hysterical, frantic, spastic. We struggled and staggered down the hill again, in the direction where I'd come from, to the side of the road. I frantically tried to get loose of him but he clung to me insanely.

Some young women came up the road and I called them for help. But they seemed helpless and just stood there, watching. . . . The old man collapsed on the grass by the side of the road totally finished and sad. . . . One of the girls suggested we all donate some money to the man, since there seemed to be no other way to help him. He didn't know where he was going to and seemed to have no home. I thought it was a pretty superficial solution but grateful to be rid of him. It was a simple enough way to help. I hesitated over how much to give him. . . . I found a $1\frac{1}{2}$ franc piece in my purse and gave him that.

His presence of mind returned and the old man was so pleased and so happy, his face became all red and tears were in his eyes. He thanked us over and over and over. He sort of got up and stood stooped. I walked away, back down the road where I'd come from, to the city. I glanced back at the groveling, prideless old man with his red face and thought he was a greedy, old, disgusting man, thoughtless, stupid. I thought: he is only a drunkard probably. He is just going to drink the money away. What a waste of my time he'd been.

The analyst who treated L.O. in Zurich, though Jewish-American, interpreted the repeated old man image as a "dirty old man" and as a "negative father complex." Only eight years later, upon interpreting and associating this old man with her murdered grandfather, did she begin the process of "coming back to life." [This was the first of many "grandfather" dreams].

This image became a central theme in her newly (re)awakened creative activities, and she developed it through a series of short stories that wove history with dream and fantasy into a character in a theatrical piece. At the same time, she actively, almost obsessively, began to research her family history, read on all aspects of the Nazi Holocaust, and contacted any distant relative she could find in the United States, Europe, and Israel. An important aspect of this search was her pilgrimage to her father's hometown, an abbreviated version of which follows below. She also began recording oral history with her parents, which included reading and translating, and with her father, read, translated, and recorded his correspondence with his own father during the war.

In addition to her identification with her murdered grandfather, and pivotal in her therapy, was the issue of her almost totally hidden Jewish identity. Despite the fact that her youngest sibling is a male, he was not named after their paternal grandfather. After five years of therapy, when L.O. made a formal decision to convert "back" to Judaism and "out of the family's conspiracy of silence," she chose a Hebrew name that started with the same letter as her murdered grandfather's name. Experiencing herself as the "vehicle for bringing his memory back to life," she began, for the first time, to be able to separate from her identification with his "deadness": "Now there was somebody to mourn. By being (unconsciously) identified with him, I avoided mourning. Instead, I mourned my own life without knowing why."

She concluded her conversion speech by stating that it is "one way in which I can establish a concrete link to my paternal grandparents . . . I feel my conversion is a kind of triumph over Hitler, and in a small way heals the rupture and the wound that Hitler inflicted upon my family, and upon our larger Jewish family. This is my way to make public my commitment and to express my loyalty to my people. . . ."

Group members became a strong support network for L.O. during her therapy. When she returned to school for an advanced degree, in order to pursue a new career commensurate with her actual talents and abilities, she engaged them as partners in creative projects which focused on their experiences as children of survivors. Many group and community members attended her conversion ceremony and celebrated with her. The Intergenerational meetings, larger than the group, but still within the context of the Project, provided her with "a world to move around in." She adopted a family that invited her on holidays. She also adopted "siblings" and "grandfather substitutes" with whom she did oral histories and attended Holocaust-related and Jewish lectures, movies, theater pieces, and whom she encouraged to speak to schoolchildren, for example, about their Holocaust and Holocaust-related experiences. By being able to use people in the group and in the community, L.O. helped both others and herself. From a gravestonelike mode of being began to emerge a resourceful, outspoken, and articulate leader in the Project's community, and a budding young woman, eager to experience a full relationship with a man and have children of her own.

Before L.O. began therapy, she had lived alone and felt quite cut off from her family, but soon after, she sought roommates and felt comforted when her sisters joined her for extended periods of time. Her search for a heritage and an identity spurred them "to reexamine past events and open up a new dialogue in the family—dead and living . . . [so that] they can also 'touch' the subject and begin a healing process in themselves as well."

The following is an example of one of the creative attempts inspired by the Project, L.O.'s abbreviated account of her visit to her father's prewar hometown:

> In March 1983, fifty years after Hitler came to power in Germany, I was on a train to visit the city that was my father's former home. Years of silence slid by as I watched the gray countryside outside the window. Once I had had family here. Family I never knew.
>
> On March 20th of 1942, a memo went out to the District President:
>
>> RE: 1000 Jews will be evacuated to the East from the district of the Hannover Main Police Station. The evacuation of 325 Jews from the former district of the Bielefeld Main Police Station . . . is to be arranged. The names of Jews to be evacuated from the individual police sub-districts are entered on the attached list. . . .
>
> My grandparents were on that list. My grandmother died one week before the deportation. "Guiding principles" had been spelled out in six steps:
>
>> *Step 1*: The Jews for deportation are to be fetched from their homes on 30.3.42 and by noon of the same day *at the latest* are to be conveyed to Bielefeld to the Large Hall of the Kyffaueser.

> The executive officers acting as escort are to undertake the transportation in civilian clothes. As far as possible, the transports are to take place by train.

I got off at the little train station. My head swiveled. People thronged. Traffic moved. Window displays and sausage stands. Electronic equipment, thermal underwear, running shoes, cameras, and jewelry. I stopped and stared.

A shoebox of jewelry and some photographs are all that had survived. The only tangible proof I had of my grandmother was a necklace, a round gold piece with a tiny pearl in the center. That and my middle name.

> *Step 2*: Before the Jews leave the premises, an official must collect all ready cash, valuables (jewelry, gold, and silver articles, including gold watches)—excluding wedding rings. On the premises of the Jew concerned, one of the enclosed receipts is then to be made out by an official, and signed by two officials and the Jew concerned whose belongings have been taken into safe keeping. The cash and valuables are then to be *sealed* with the receipt under the same cover and handed over to the police officer supervising at the reception depot in Bielefeld.

I found the street corner where my grandparents' home had once stood. It had been bombed during the war, and now there was a parking lot that served the city jail.

> *Step 3*: Before leaving the Jewish premises, it must be made sure that the gas and water are turned off and that the light is switched off (black out!).

I searched the walls of the remaining buildings for some piece of rubble that might stand as a reminder of the house that had once been attached. Did these neighbors remember? Were they here the day my family was forced out?

> *Step 4*: Immediately after leaving the premises, they are to be sealed. Sealing stamps are to be used for this purpose. The keys to the premises are to be collected by the local police and deposited at the station. They are to be tied together and attached to a label on which the name and address of the Jew is written.

Somewhere nearby was the site of the former synagogue. I walked the length of the narrow street and turned the corner. In front of an ugly, square, concrete municipal building sat a tiny plaque among the bushes:

> Here stood since 1905 the Synagogue of the Jewish community. It was burnt down on the night of the 9th and 10th of November 1938 by the National Socialists.

I wished I hadn't come alone to stand and mourn a community of 1,000 of my people by myself. It was impossible.

Across the street was a municipal parking lot where there had once been a park. At the far end, where a row of semi-high-rises stood, had once been a hall that served as "reception depot" where Jews were detained before deportation. I clutched my bag, money, passport, and limited-period airplane ticket with return date set. It was important to me that I came here knowing exactly when I would be leaving again.

> *Step* 5: Upon delivery at the reception depot, the Jews must be in possession of their identity cards. All other papers are to be left behind in their dwellings. Ration cards are to be withdrawn and sent to the appropriate food office. Employment record books and pension cards are likewise to be withdrawn and sent to the appropriate labour exchange or pension insurance office.

It began to rain and I was drenched. I needed a change of clothes. I needed to eat. And I needed to call Frau D. She had survived to return to her former home. She would remember a world I never knew.

> *Step* 6: The Jews due for evacuation are instructed to take 25 kg. of baggage. In addition, food for two days may be taken. The local police authorities have to collect the baggage of the Jews . . . and keep it until departure. Before the evacuation starts, the baggage is to be *reweighed and examined meticulously.* The baggage may not contain any weapons (firearms, explosives, knives, scissors, poison, medicine, etc.). If the baggage is heavier than 25 kg. it is to be reduced accordingly. The Jews are also to be instructed that they may take with them up to two blankets which, however, must be included in the 25 kg.

When I finally met Frau D. she served me tea and Scottish shortbread. I was grateful for her warm rush of quaint English. Adding a generous shot of rum to the tea, she nudged me to help myself. "I remember quite well your grandma Meta. She was a bit hard of hearing and unusual looking. Very . . ." she made a wave of the hand, "attractive. Your grandpa, he was stout." I smiled. She looked at me pointedly, judging how much I really wanted to hear. I wanted to hear it all. "He was sent by the same transport to Theresienstadt as my mother, who was sent to Auschwitz in October 1942." Frau D. sat straight in her chair and adjusted the silk bow of her blouse. When she stood, her back was bent, her body wiry and intense, and she moved agilely around her modest kitchen. She was eighty-three.

The Nazis had chosen her to stay and help with deportations. She had seen her whole community board trains for the east.

"The day I was deported, was my birthday," she recalled. "I had received many flowers and I was damned if I was going to leave them behind. So I arrived on the station with an armful of flowers. The officer in charge, he knew me. 'Frau D., you have so many flowers,' he said. I told him it's my birthday and he replied, 'What bad luck it should fall on this day.' I answered, 'Herr officer, this day should be bad luck in any case!'" She laughed and showed me how she had held her head haughtily.

And then she offered to take me to the Jewish cemetery. I tried to protest, knowing this was a long trip for her to make. But she insisted. Then I realized that she was afraid of the cemetery and welcomed the opportunity to go with a young person.

We traveled on the streetcar. And she pointed out the former Gestapo building with its flag pole still sticking out. She knew this town inside out and had lived to tell the tale. I was proud. The younger housewives seated next to us couldn't help but overhear and I felt a surge of victory at making them remember too, in a town that I was sure would rather forget.

Frau D. explained there was no sign identifying the Jewish cemetery tucked away behind the Christian one. It would only invite more vandalism, like the time the new Jewish Community Center had had a swastika painted on it. The mayor himself had rushed over to supervise cleaning it off but there had been no mention of it in the paper. This town wanted to forget.

"Only twenty-four Jews live here today, almost all of them not originally from here," Frau D. continued. "There are not even ten men for the Minyan so we cannot hold services." A path sloped down toward a grove of tall fir trees that leaned dark in the wet air. An empty fountain stood dry with memories. It had been ten years since she had last come here.

This was not an active cemetery except for the few who had

memories attached to it. Once it had been part of a living community. Now it haunted me with a world that had been severed. The stones were all from another time, many inscribed in Yiddish. Occasionally a green sticker warned, "Do not stand close—beware of falling stone." Empty beer and wine bottles lay in heaps under the bushes. Frau D. feared running into adolescents who used the isolated spot as a hang-out. She pointed to the far side.

My family's stone was wide, decorated with sandstone roses, the dirt eroded around its base, and a bush growing over its sides. It was inscribed with the names of my grandparents and great grandparents. I was bewildered and felt awkward in front of this sudden, tangible connection to the generations before me. I knelt closer to touch it, with the strange feeling of eroding stone and dirt in my mouth.

"Meta R., born W., died 1942" on one side. "Otto R., died Fall 1942, Auschwitz," on the other. My father had returned, like many others, to inscribe my grandfather's name as testimony on the stone where he should have rightfully been after his death. I knew his body was not buried here.

I looked around and read the next headstone as well, and then another and another: Marta Leffman, died 1944, Auschwitz. Hugo Leffman, died 1944, Auschwitz. Hermann Hirschfeld, died 7/20/1944, Auschwitz. Friederike Greve, died Theresienstadt. Beate Kugelman, born Netheim, died December 26, 1942, Theresienstadt. Gustav Bornheim, died 12/23/1942, in K.Z. Theresienstadt. Rosa Grunewald, killed Auschwitz, 1944. Regina Kohane Dr. Med., died 3/27/1948, victim of torture experienced in K.Z. Auschwitz. Richard Hennig, died April 23, 1943, in Auschwitz. Eduard Wertheimer, died 7/21/1942. The silence of the cemetery filled with the memory of my people. The dark years came alive with names of the graveless.

In the distance Frau D. was puttering among the graves. I remembered her words. "The next time you come visit, I hope you'll stay overnight. That way we'll have plenty of time talking, TV-ing, walking in the near pinewood, die Fichten." And I imagined my grandfather as he might have been, taking me for a walk in the squishy woods after a spring rain. He would tell me stories and take care that I should become pretty and healthy and strong. He might wear a simple but distinguished overcoat, dark green perhaps, with a hat and walking stick. He would be warm and comfortable to be with, not saying too much but easy to talk to.

From the little I knew, my grandfather had been a mild mannered, quiet person, a businessman, trustworthy, and believing in the goodness of people. He had firm sense of himself as being an important part of his community and a strong sense of family. He was just a bit stuffy perhaps, but easy going and quick to give a warm smile and a kiss. He wanted so much to believe that everything would turn out okay.

I imagined he would have wanted that I, my sisters, and brother should be alive in this world today. He would have wanted that his memory be a cozy, warm spot in our hearts. If he could, he would have written a long letter in his squiggly handwriting, enclosing a check to buy a nice sweater and telling me how best to apply to a school, who might offer me a job, to be sure and visit a good friend of his, and not forget the thank you letter afterwards. And all the while, he would be leading up to asking if I had met some nice man yet or whether I was learning my tennis, a social sport. He would be telling me that it is okay for the fist in my stomach to melt and uncurl long enough for me to sing inside and that life should go on at all cost.

The "Fourth Narcissistic Blow"

Elsewhere (Danieli, 1984), I wrote:

Perhaps the deepest aspect of shame is what I have called the *fourth narcissistic blow*. When Freud (1917) speculated about the reasons people rejected and avoided psychoanalysis, he said that Copernicus gave the first blow to humanity's naive self-love or narcissism, the cosmological blow, when humankind learned that it was not the center of the universe. Darwin gave the second, the biological blow, when he said that humanity's separation from and superiority to the animal kingdom is questionable. Freud claimed that he gave the third, the psychological blow, by showing that "the ego is not [even] master in its own house" and that, indeed, we have limits to our consciousness. I believe that Nazi Germany gave humanity the fourth, the *ethical blow*, by shattering our naive belief that the world we live in is a just place in which human life is of value, to be protected and respected.

A country considered the most civilized and cultured in the Western World committed the greatest evils that humans have

Western World committed the greatest evils that humans have inflicted on humans, and thereby challenged the structure of morality, human dignity, and human rights, as well as the values that define civilization. Not only psychotherapists, but all of us, in various degrees of awareness, share this sense of shame. Indeed, this fourth narcissistic blow may have caused many in society to avoid confronting the Holocaust by refusing to listen to survivors and their offspring, those who bear witness to it and to its consequences.

Although all four "blows" forced confrontation with essential truths about human existence, the ethical blow distinguishes itself by massively and mercilessly exposing the potential boundlessness of human evil and ugliness. Unless humanity is willing to integrate this most recent narcissistic blow, . . .

as I have commented elsewhere (Danieli, 1985a), we, all of us, will experience an enormous loss: the memory of the Holocaust and the indispensable lessons we must learn from it.

References

Bergman, M. S., & Jucovy, M. E., eds. (1982), *Generations of the Holocaust*. New York: Basic Books.

Bettelheim, B. (1984), Afterword to C. Vegh, *I Didn't Say Goodbye*, trans. R. Schwartz. New York: E. P. Dutton.

Blau, D., & Kahana, J., eds. (1981), The aging survivor of the Holocaust [Special Issue]. *J. Geriat. Psychiat.*,14(2):191–210.

Bychowski, G. (1968), Permanent character changes as an aftereffect of persecution. In: *Massive Psychic Trauma*, ed. H. Krystal. New York: International Universities Press.

Chodoff, P. (1975), Psychiatric aspects of the Nazi persecution. In: *American Handbook of Psychiatry*, Vol. 6, 2nd ed., ed. S. Arieti. New York: Basic Books.

———(1980), Psychotherapy of the survivor. In: *Survivors, Victims and Perpetrators: Essays on the Nazi Holocaust*, ed. J. E. Dimsdale. New York: Hemisphere.

———(1981), Survivors of the Nazi Holocaust. *Children Today*, 10(5):2–5.

Danieli, Y. (1981a), Differing adaptational styles in families of survivors of the Nazi Holocaust: Some implications for treatment. *Children Today*, 10(5):6–10, 34–35.

———(1981b), Exploring the factors in Jewish identity formation (in children of survivors). In: *Consultation on the Psycho-dynamics of Jewish Identity: Summary of Proceedings*. American Jewish Committee and the Central Conference of American Rabbis, March 15–16, 1981, pp. 22–25.

———(1981c), Families of survivors of the Nazi Holocaust: Some short- and long-term effects. In: *Stress and anxiety*, Vol. 8, eds. C.D. Speilberger, I. G. Sarason, & N. Milgam. New York: McGraw-Hill/Hemisphere.

————(1981d), On the achievement of integration in aging survivors of the Nazi Holocaust. *J. Geriat. Psychiat.*, 14(2):191– 210.

————(1981e), The group project for Holocaust survivors and their children. *Children Today*, 10(5):11, 33.

————(1982a), *Therapists' Difficulties in Treating Survivors of the Nazi Holocaust and Their Children*. Doctoral dissertation. New York University, 1981. University Microfilms Internat., #949–904.

————(1982b), Group project for Holocaust survivors and their children. Prepared for National Institute of Mental Health, Mental Health Services Branch. Contract #092424762. Washington, DC.

————(1984), Psychotherapists' participation in the conspiracy of silence about the Holocaust. *Psychoanal. Psychol.*, 1(1):23–42.

————(1985a), Separation and loss in families of survivors of the Nazi Holocaust. *Acad. Forum*, 29(2):7–10.

————(1985b), The treatment and prevention of long-term effects and intergenerational transmission of victimization: A lesson from Holocaust survivors and their children. In: *Trauma and its Wake*, ed. C. R. Figley. New York: Brunner/Mazel.

————(1985c), The use of mutual support approaches in the treatment of victims. Paper presented at a Services Research and Evaluation Colloquium, "The Aftermath of Crime: A Mental Health Crisis," NIMH/NOVA. Washington, DC, February–March 3, 1985.

————(1988), Treating survivors and children of survivors of the Nazi Holocaust. In: *Post-Traumatic Therapy and Victims of Violence*, ed. F. M. Ochberg. New York: Brunner/Mazel.

Davidson, S. (1984), Human reciprocity among the Jewish prisoners in the Nazi concentration camps. In: *The Nazi Concentration Camps: Proceedings of the Fourth Yad Vashem International Historical Conference*, eds. Y. Gutman & A. Sat. Jersusalem: Yad Vashem, pp. 555–572.

Des Pres, T. (1976), *The Survivor: An Anatomy of Life in the Death Camps*. New York: Oxford University Press.

Dimsdale, J. E., ed. (1980), *Survivors, Victims and Perpetrators: Essays on the Nazi Holocaust*. New York: Hemisphere.

Eitinger, L. (1972), *Concentration Camp Survivors in Norway and Israel*. The Hague: Martinus Nijhoff.

————(1980), The concentration camp syndrome and its late sequelae. In: *Survivors, Victims, and Perpetrators: Essays on the Nazi Holocaust*, ed. J. E. Dimsdale. New York: Hemisphere.

Frankl, V. E. (1959), *Man's Search for Meaning*. Boston: Beacon Press.

Freud, S. (1917), A difficulty in the path of psycho-analysis. *Standard Edition*, 17:135–144. London: Hogarth Press, 1955.

Friedman, P. (1948), The road back for the DP's: Healing the psychological scars of Nazism. *Commentary*, 6(6):502–510.

Goodman, J. S. (1978), *The Transmission of Parental Trauma: Second Generation Effects of Nazi Concentration Camp Survival*. Doctoral dissertation, California School of Professional Psychology, Fresno. University Microfilms Internat., #7901805.

Israel-Netherlands Symposium on the Impact of Persecution, October 1977

(1979), Rijswijk (Z.H.), The Netherlands: Ministry of Cultural Affairs, Recreation and Social Welfare.

Klein, H. (1968), Problems in the psychotherapeutic treatment of Israeli survivors of the Holocaust. In: *Massive Psychic Trauma*, ed. H. Krystal. New York: International Universities Press.

Koenig, W. (1964), Chronic or persisting identity diffusion. *Amer. J. Psychiat.*, 120:1081–1084.

Krystal, H., ed. (1968), *Massive Psychic Trauma*. New York: International Universities Press.

———(1975), Affect tolerance. *The Annual of Psychoanalysis*, 3:179–219. New York: International Universities Press.

———(1978), Trauma and affect. *The Psychoanalytic Study of the Child*, 33:81–116. New Haven, CT: Yale University Press.

———(1979), Alexithymia and psychotherapy. *Amer. J. Psychother.* 33(1):17–31.

———(1981), Integration and self-healing in posttraumatic states. *J. Geriat. Psychiat.* 14(2):165–189.

———(1982), Alexithymia and effectiveness of psychoanalytic treatment. *Internat. J. Psychoanal. Psychother.*, 9:353–378.

———Niederland, W. G. (1968), Clinical observations on the survivor syndrome. In: *Massive Psychic Trauma*, ed. H. Krystal. New York: International Universities Press.

———Niederland, W. G., eds. (1971), *Psychic Traumatization: Aftereffects in Individuals and Communities*. Boston: Little, Brown.

Leitner, I. (1985), *Saving the Fragments*. New York: New American Library.

Levi, P. (1986a), The memory of offense. In: *Bitburg in Moral and Political Perspective*, ed. G. H. Hartman. Bloomington: Indiana University Press, pp. 130–137.

———(1986b), *Moments of Reprieve*, trans. R. Feldman. New York: Summit Books.

———(1988), *The Drowned and the Saved*, trans. R. Rosenthal. New York: Summit Books.

Lifton, R. J. (1973), The sense of immortality: On death and the continuity of life. *Amer. J. Psychoanal.*, 33:3–15.

———(1979), *The Broken Connection*. New York: Simon & Schuster.

Luchterhand, E. (1967), Prisoner behavior and social system in the Nazi concentration camps. *Internat. J. Soc. Psychiat.*, 13(4):245–264.

———(1971), Sociological approaches to massive stress in natural and man-made disasters. In: *Psychic Traumatization: Aftereffects in Individuals and Communities*, eds. H. Krystal & W. G. Niederland. New York: Little, Brown.

Matussek, P. (1971), *Internment in Concentration Camps and its Consequences*, trans. D. Jordan & I. Jordan. New York: Springer Verlag, 1975.

Meerlo, J. A. M. (1963), Delayed mourning in victims of extermination camps. *J. Hillside Hosp.*, 12(2):96–98.

Moskovitz, S. (1983), *Love Despite Hate*. New York: Schoken.

Niederland, W. G. (1961), The problem of the survivor: Some remarks on the psychiatric evaluation of emotional disorders in survivors of the Nazi persecution. *J. Hillside Hosp.*, 10(3)–4:233–247.

———(1964), Psychiatric disorders among persecution victims: A contribution to the understanding of concentration camp pathology and its aftereffects. *J. Nerv. Ment. Dis.*, 139:458–474.

Phillips, R. D. (1978), Impact of Nazi Holocaust on children of survivors. *Amer. J. Psychother.*, 32:370–378.

Rabinowitz, D. (1976), *New Lives: Survivors of the Holocaust Living in America.* New York: Alfred A. Knopf.

Rakoff, V. A. (1966), A long-term effect of the concentration camp experience. *Viewpoints*, 1:17–22.

Rappaport, E. A. (1968), Beyond traumatic neurosis: A psychoanalytic study of late reactions to the concentration camp trauma. *Internat. J. Psycho-Anal.*, 49:719–731.

Rich, M. S. (1982), *Children of Holocaust Survivors: A Concurrent Validity Study of a Survivor Family Typology.* Unpublished doctoral dissertation. California School of Professional Psychology, Berkeley.

Rosenthal, P. A., & Rosenthal, S. (1980), Holocaust effect in the third generation: Child of another time. *Amer. J. Psychother.*, 34(4):572–580.

Sigal, J. J. (1971), Second-generation effects of massive psychic trauma. In: *Psychic Traumatization: Aftereffects in Individuals and Communities*, eds. H. Krystal & W. G. Niederland. Boston: Little, Brown, pp. 67–92.

Spiegelman, A. (1981), *Maus.* New York: Pantheon Books.

Steinberg, A. J. (1986), *Separation–Individuation Issues Among Children of Holocaust Survivors.* Unpublished doctoral dissertation. Ferkauf Graduate School of Psychology, Yeshiva University.

Sterba, E. (1968), The effect of persecution on adolescents. In: *Massive Psychic Trauma*, ed. H. Krystal. New York: International Universities Press.

Terry, J. (1984), The damaging effects of the "survivor syndrome." In: *Psychoanalytic Reflections on the Holocaust: Selected Essays*, eds. S. A. Luel & P. Marcus. New York: Holocaust Awareness Institute Center for Judaic Studies, University of Denver and Ktav Publishing House, pp. 135–148.

Trautman, E. C. (1971), Violence and victims in Nazi concentration camps and the psychopathology of the survivors. In: *Psychic Traumatization: Aftereffects in Individuals and Communities*, eds. H. Krystal & W. G. Niederland. New York: Little, Brown.

Wanderman, E. (1979), *Separation Problems, Depressive Experiences and Conception of Parents in Children of Concentration Camp Survivors.* Unpublished doctoral dissertation. New York University.

Wiesel, E. (1965), The watch. In: *One Generation After.* New York: Avon Books, 1972, pp. 79–86.

———(1979), Listen to the wind. Statement made at Auschwitz, Poland, August 1, 1979. In: *Against Silence: The Voice and Vision of Elie Wiesel*, Vol. 1, ed. I. Abrahamson. New York: Holocaust Library, 1985, pp. 166–168.

Wilson, A. (1985), On silence and the Holocaust: A contribution to clinical theory. *Psychoanal. Inquiry*, 5(1):63–84.

Wind, de, E. (1972), Persecution, aggression and therapy. *Internat. J. Psycho-Anal.*, 53:173–177.

Winnicott, D. W. (1965), *The Maturational Processes and the Facilitating Environment.* London: Hogarth Press.

EPILOGUE

Reflections on Loss, Mourning, and the Unconscious Process of Regeneration

PETER C. SHABAD, PH.D.
DAVID R. DIETRICH, PH.D.

In selecting *The Problem of Loss and Mourning* as a title for this book, we wanted to specifically highlight our belief that while there has been seventy years of psychoanalytic clinical findings and scholarship, there is still much to learn about the psychological aspects of loss and mourning. We might also add that there remains more to be understood about not only what is lost, but also—and this is too often overlooked—how and in what particular ways loss experiences are restituted, repaired, and restored by an unconscious process of regeneration. Inasmuch as restitution, restoration, reparation, and adaptation are all major themes that emerge from the various chapters of this volume, we believe this book can significantly contribute to the further clarification of this regenerative process. Indeed, in clinical practice we continually observe how individuals attempt to compensate for experiences of loss by resurrecting a range of fantasies, images, memories, representations, and thoughts of who or what had been lost. As Freud (1908) said: "Really we

463

never can relinquish anything; we only exchange one thing for something else. When we appear to give something up, all we really do is adopt a substitute" (p. 145). Loss and the process of regeneration are pervasively and intricately linked within the realm of the unconscious.

Freud (1915) pointed out that "in the unconscious every one of us is convinced of his own immortality" (p. 289). We would add that not only is our own death in one sense inconceivable at an unconscious level, but so are the deaths of others; loss, specifically enduring loss, is alien to the unconscious. Thus, the continual resurrection of replacements in one form or another for the most important ties that we lose reflects an unconscious process of regenerating and immortalizing attachments to valued people, places, ideas, or institutions. The mythological phoenix rising from its own ashes is an apt metaphor for psychic life unconsciously and spontaneously regenerating from the loss experience.

Inasmuch as we must recognize and appreciate, clinically and theoretically, this unconscious process of regeneration, and in a sense, re-creation, it is important that we keep in mind the well-known but important distinction made by Dr. Viederman between the actual physical world of love objects and their corresponding intrapsychic representations. In maintaining this distinction, we are able to differentiate loss as a physically verifiable event from loss as an intrapsychic experience. Dr. Shabad, for example, describes a type of inner experience of loss occurring while in the physical presence of another, whereas Dr. Krueger likens the loss experience to early empathic failures. Dr. Viederman observes what is frequently seen clinically—that the death of a parent can be experienced as a "release from bondage" by its survivor.

Clearly, the traumatic devastation and pathological effects often engendered by physical loss have been evocatively documented in this volume. The case material vividly presented by Erna Furman and Dr. Robert Furman, the empirical and clinical studies and conceptual contributions made by Dr. Dietrich, the father-loss research data comprehensively reviewed by Drs. Biller and Salter, the biographical and dynamic material insightfully unearthed about James Barrie by Dr.

Kulish, and the acute pain of parental divorce carefully observed and reported by Rebecca Lohr and Morton Chethik all point to the traumatic and distorting effects that actual physical object loss has upon personality development. Additionally, Dr. Kestenberg and Dr. Danieli poignantly document the great suffering and numbing forlornness left in the wake of the horrendous losses of the Holocaust.

Loved ones die, and all but the very youngest inevitably experience some unique type of loss or sense of loss, but we may ask then: "What is the intrapsychic impact of such losses upon the survivor's representational world?"

We know, for example, that the ego employs denial as one means of accommodating to the timelessness of the unconscious. Becker (1973) suggested that denial is necessary in order to ward off the crippling anxiety and excessive obsessions and compulsions that an illusion-free confrontation with death might entail. By removing the potentially paralyzing danger of loss from awareness, the use of denial enables one to safekeep an element of self-confidence in everyday life.

To some extent, this protective-maintenance function of denial may also have the adaptive purpose of buffering a bereaved individual in the immediate aftermath of loss and trauma. Drs. Grunes and Wasson show in their chapter how the older adult sometimes makes use of denial and fantasy in particular ways as a means of coping with loss. Time, so to speak, is put on hold as the ego gradually acclimates to the reality and shock of the trauma of loss. Under certain disadvantageous conditions, however, this adaptive protective-maintenance function of denial may be used extensively, and sometimes indefinitely. At these times, excessive denial may only further the moratorium upon mourning work. And as clinicians, we are well aware there is a heavy price to be paid for the unconscious conflicts and symptoms resulting from pathological or distorted mourning.

The irrelevance of time within the realm of the unconscious seems to be one major factor that places a fundamental limit upon the manner and intrapsychic degree to which the finality of loss can be realized, and therefore mourned. Thus, we are speaking of relative degrees of mourning, or the ego's need to balance the primary process, unconscious tendency of remaining blind to the finality of loss with the realistic requirements of recognizing and mourning that finality. In this regard, as many of the present book's chapters demonstrate, the relative acceptance or denial of the finality of loss and death will significantly influence the capacity to eventually work through and resolve the loss experience.

It is worth noting that the untimeliness of many losses, occurring before a child is able to emotionally tolerate and assimilate the full meaning of the trauma, may often be one important factor contributing to the development of psychopathology. Very young children, for example, often equate death with sleep, or view it as a separation. Dr. Dietrich has shown how in the lost-immortal parent complex, those who as children lost a parent by death create a specific constellation comprised in part of fantasies and representations of the dead parent. Where the finality and inexorability of loss is denied or largely denied, the imagination is often characterized by fantasies of reunification.

Such fantasies of reunification may result, in part, from a defensive warding off of the mourning process and, as such, may be a manifestation of the repetition compulsion. In those individuals where the repetition compulsion appears to have influenced personality development to a relatively greater extent, we might conclude that a stunting of ego growth may replace the more adaptive and creative activity of mourning work.

Often, the compulsion to repeat and seek mastery over the loss experience becomes evident in one form of restitution or another. In their chapter, Drs. Zuckerman and Volkan report the fascinating clinical case of a woman's desperate unconscious attempt to restore a defective spine. And Dr. Mitscherlich-Nielsen has passionately and eloquently shown how an unconscious quest for restitutive ideals (Nazism, consumerism) can take the place of genuine mourning work, and lead to destructive and, at times, self-destructive ends.

Despite these pathogenic aspects of loss and its accompanying unconscious regenerative components, loss may have other creative, more constructive, long-term ramifications that are not always evident in its immediate aftermath. Not infrequently, the death of the old gives way to the birth of the new in ways that are sometimes not apparent in the midst of grief. We shall quote from Melanie Klein, and while it is the same passage quoted by Dr. Pollock in his chapter, we feel it is worth repeating once more. She writes that in acute mourning:

> Suffering can be productive. We know that painful experiences of all kinds sometimes stimulate sublimations, or even bring out quite new gifts in some people, who may take to painting, writing or other productive activities under the stress of frustrations and hardships. Others become more productive in a different way—more capable of appreciating people and things, more tolerant in their relationships to others—they become wiser [Klein, 1940, p. 143].

Indeed, if the finality of loss can be accepted, integrated, and assimilated, at least to some significant degree, then the ego may be able to draw upon the unconscious internal process of regeneration as a source of creative strength in coping with loss. Out of the ashes, at times literal ashes of loss and death, as the Holocaust section of our book starkly and dramatically reveals, a phoenixlike process of internal restructuring may be set in motion which can have a liberating, regenerative effect upon the survivor.

E. James Anthony (1973) has noted, for example, that when a child loses a parent, an essential core of good feeling is magnified, with the consequence that an idealized picture emerges of the parent. Perhaps this illusory parental representation—undisturbed by the return of the flesh-and-blood parent—is, in instances of parent loss, a necessary prerequisite to the internalization of the parental image at "deeper levels of the ego system" as suggested by Loewald (1962). Loewald observes that when a parent dies, what were originally ego ideal or superego elements while the parent is living become progressively internalized upon the parent's death. Such a process of increasing internalization of the representation of the dead parent may, in turn, set the stage for what Pollock (1982) refers to as the mourning–liberation process.

In this way, with time, slowly and painfully, via the work of mourning, the uncertainty of whether a parent will return or not, or whether long-held wishes in relation to the living parent will be fulfilled or not is gradually replaced by the relative psychological freedom brought about by an acceptance that a parent's loss is final. A person may then lend his or her creative capacities toward reconstituting a replacement for what was lost.

Dr. Niederland delineates in his important chapter how loss and body defect may culminate in successful artistic attempts of creatively restoring that which is missing. And Dr. Pollock demonstrates in his scholarly chapter how Gustav Mahler's musical compositions were directly and profoundly influenced by his many early losses. In his noteworthy chapter on object loss in normal development, Dr. Pine points out that loss is typically accompanied by various forms of restitution when it occurs according to a normal developmental timetable.

In some respects, such considerations of the constructive, regenerative, and, at times, even advantageous aspects of loss can be disturbing for the clinician, theorist, and nonprofessional alike. Here, there is a potential for countertransference reactions, as well as ideological and ethical considerations to skew a fuller understanding of loss. It may be both intellectually tidier and more ethically comforting to believe that nothing advantageous should arise out of the loss of a loved one. It may sometimes be intolerable to realize that a loved one's death has sown the seeds for one's own psychic growth or creativity. The use of isolation, repression, and other defenses may then enable one to deny that the loss of a valued other could eventually become a spur to creative work, or even an impetus to the further maturation of character.

Dr. Danieli emphasizes in her chapter how certain Holocaust survivors use guilt as a safeguard against forgetting the dead. She points out that for these survivors to completely decathect and successfully mourn their loved ones would mean the equivalent of psychically killing them off and becoming, in a sense, like the Nazis themselves. Although this sense of guilt often is clearly highlighted in the Holocaust survivor, we may be able to apply some of the insights gained from them to survivors of loved ones in general.

For many survivors, who often feel responsible for the death of their loved ones, the retention of guilt with its nostalgic ruminations and idealized reminiscences of the dead person may function as a partial atonement to the dead for their own survival. By thinking about, occupying oneself with, and commemorating the dead person, the survivor, through guilt and its vicissitudes, sacrificially gives back eternal life to the loved one in fantasy.

Such thoughts concerning the survivor's guilt and reparative aims in mourning loss lead us also to consider the special mourning tasks encountered by aggressors in coming to terms with their transgressions. Although some attention has been focused on the mourning requirements of victims, the need of aggressors to mourn their crimes has been a largely ignored area, with the notable exception of *The Inability to Mourn* by Drs. Alexander and Margarete Mitscherlich (1975). Dr. Mitscherlich-Nielsen further examines this critically important topic in her chapter and suggests that the German people must begin to make reparations in some way in order to begin mourning their crimes. It is clear that the need to make amends—whether derived from the survivor's guilt for the fantasied crime of survival or the aggressor's guilt for an actual crime—exacts a powerful influence upon mourning work. Indeed, if one takes seriously the assertion of Dr. Danieli, and we do, that the Holocaust may be seen as a fourth narcissistic blow to mankind, "the ethical blow," we will realize that the mourning problems of survivors and aggressors have, in many ways, become universal and contemporary ones.

In closing, we believe this book goes a long way toward furthering our understanding, advancing our knowledge, and clarifying some of the problems and questions concerned with loss and mourning. Moreover, it is also our hope that this volume will stimulate efforts on the part of the reader toward helping his or her patients or students to better find their own constructive resolutions of their inevitable losses and mourning reactions.

References

Anthony, E. J. (1973), Mourning and psychic loss of a parent. In: *The Child in His Family*, ed. E. J. Anthony, New York: John Wiley & Sons.

Becker, E. (1973), *The Denial of Death*. New York: Free Press.

Freud, S. (1908), Creative people and day-dreaming. *Standard Edition*, 9:143–153. London: Hogarth Press, 1955.

———(1915), Thoughts for the times on war and death. *Standard Edition*, 14:275–300. London: Hogarth Press, 1957.

Klein, M. (1940), Mourning and its relation to manic-depressive states. *Internat. J. Psycho-Anal.*, 21:125–153.

Loewald, H. (1962), Internalization, separation, mourning and superego. *Psychoanal. Quart.*, 31:483–504.

Mitscherlich, A., & Mitscherlich, M. (1975), *The Inability to Mourn*. New York: Grove Press.

Pollock, G. (1982), The mourning–liberation process and creativity: The case of Käthe Kollwitz. *The Annual of Psychoanalysis*, 10:333–354. New York: International Universities Press.

NAME INDEX

471

SUBJECT INDEX

481